Dual Diagnosis

An introduction to the mental health needs of persons with developmental disabilities

These 2 illustrations from one of our clients, illustrate that a biopsychosocial approach is the "**KEY** " to providing optimal service to individuals with dual diagnosis

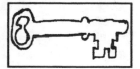

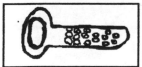

**We wish to
dedicate this book to
all the clients who have made it possible**

Dual Diagnosis: An introduction to the mental health needs of persons with developmental disabilities

**Published by: Habilitative Mental Health Resource Network
First Printing, March 2002**

**Copyright © 2002 by
Habilitative Mental Health Resource Network
PLAZA 69 POSTAL OUTLET
1935 PARIS STREET
BOX 21020, SUDBURY
ONTARIO, CANADA P3E 6G6**

Canadian Cataloguing in Publication Data

Dual Diagnosis: An introduction to the mental health needs of persons with developmental disabilities
/ edited by Griffiths, Dorothy ; Chrissoula Stavrakaki ; and Jane Summers.

Includes references and index.
ISBN 0-9688694-0-8

**1. Developmental Disability   2. Mental Health Problems
3. Dual Diagnosis**

Cover design : Usha Meister, Hamilton, Canada

Key drawing on facing page : Terry Bastarache

Printed in Canada by :   Webcom Limited

About our authors:

Judy Adamson, R.N., clinical psychiatric nurse
is with the Area Resource Team at the Hamilton Health Sciences, with many years experience as a clinical psychiatric nurse for individuals with dual diagnosis. Her areas of interest include community mental health programs and crisis intervention models.

Ruxandra Antochi, H.B.Sc., M.D.
received her B.Sc. in Biology (Honors program) from the University of Guelph, followed by medical training at the University of Western Ontario. She published on basic science research. Dr. Antochi is currently a third year resident in Psychiatry at the University of Ottawa.

Kerry Boyd, M.D., FRCP (C)
completed her medical training, at the University of Western Ontario in London, Ontario, and specialty training in psychiatry at McMaster University in Hamilton, Ontario. She now sub-specializes in the realm of dual diagnosis and is a consulting psychiatrist with the Area Resource Team at the Hamilton Health Sciences.

Elspeth Bradley, Ph.D. MBBS, FRCP(C), FRC.Psych.
completed her Ph.D. in neurobiology and behaviour and medical studies at the University of London, UK. She trained in psychiatry, specializing in developmental disabilities at the Maudsley and Bethlem Royal Hospitals and at the Institute of Psychiatry, London, UK. Currently, Dr. Bradley is Psychiatrist-in-Chief at Surrey Place Centre, Toronto, and Associate Professor in the Department of Psychiatry, University of Toronto. Her research interests include mental health disturbances in persons developmental disability and autism, and self-psychological approaches to therapy.

Lillian Burke, Ph.D., C.Psych.
specializes in Clinical/Developmental psychology. She is presently at Surrey Place Centre, Toronto in the Adult Services Division. She has worked in community and facility settings with children and adults with developmental disabilities and also in private consultation. Her focus is in both clinical and research activities on dual diagnosis, autistic spectrum disorders, aging, sexual assault and women's issues.

Robert Carey, Ph.D., C. Psych.
is in full time private practice at Carey & Associates. He is the former Director of the Community Support Team with Oxford Regional Centre. He continues to be a Consultant to Regional Support Associates and many Associations for Community Living.

Thomas Cheetham, M.D.
is Director of the Developmental Disabilities Program at the University of Western Ontario. He is medical co-leader of the Dual Diagnosis Developmental Behaviour Management Unit at Regional Mental Care, St.Thomas and provides primary medical care at Southwestern Regional Centre. For the past 25 years, he has worked with persons with developmental disability.

Laurie Dart, M.S.W., R.S.W.
been the Executive Director of the Griffen Centre since 1987; an agency with expertise in the delivery of mental health services to individuals with complex needs. She has extensive clinical, program development and management experience in the young offenders, children's mental health and developmental service sectors.

Len Dykstra, M.S.W.
is Education Co-ordinator with Brain Injury Community Re-Entry of Niagara, a counselor with the Personal Counselling Centre and Brock University, and does private
counseling in St.Catharines. He has extensive experience supporting persons with a
dual diagnosis. He is a former Adult Protective Service Worker and coordinator/social
worker with the Niagara Dual Diagnosis Team based in St. Catharines, Ontario.

Paul Fedoroff, B.A. (dist), M.D., DABPN(P)
is Associate Professor of Psychiatry at the University of Toronto and Co-Director of the
Sexual Disorder Program of the Royal Ottawa Hospital. He is former chair of the Clinical Ethics Committee of the Centre for Addiction and Mental Health. His research interests include neuropsychiatric influences on sexual behaviors.

Keith Fidler, M.D.
holds a M.D. degree from the University of Western Ontario. He spent time in India
and returned to do Family Medicine in the Smiths Falls area. He has worked with persons with developmental disabilities for over 20 years and has been assistant professor
at Queen's University, Department of Family Medicine, since 1985 with duties at
Rideau Regional Centre, a facility for persons with developmental disability.

Sandra Gahan, M.S.W.
has previously worked as an Adult Protective Service Worker and Family Service
worker with Family and Children's Services Niagara. Currently Sandra is the Clinical
Social Worker with Brain Injury Community Re-Entry of Niagara.

William R. Gapen (Bill), B.A., B.S.W., M.S.W., C.S.W.
is the Clinical Facilitator for the Griffen Community Support Network. He is also a
faculty member with the Human Services Counsellor Program at George Brown, and an
adjunct faculty member with the School of Social Work at York University and the
Centre of Addiction and Mental Health. In addition, he is an active member in the social services community for 15 years assisting persons who are dually-diagnosed in
Toronto.

William I. Gardner, Ph.D.
is a Professor Emeritus, Rehabilitation Psychology Program, University of Wisconsin-
Madison. He is a long-term board member of NADD and currently serves as Vice-
President. He has over 150 publications in the area of mental health issues with persons
with developmental disabilities.

Val Gignac, D.S.W.
is a behaviour therapist with the Area Resource Team, Hamilton Health Sciences Corporation. She has completed her DHSW and ABA certificates. She has worked in
Developmental Services for 30 years and as a behaviour therapist for thirteen years.

Dorothy Griffiths, Ph.D.
is an Associate Professor in the Child and Youth Studies Department at Brock University, St. Catharines. She has been on the Executive Board of NADD for 15 years and is
a member of the Habilitative Mental Health Resource Network of Ontario. Her research, writing and lectures focus on persons with dual diagnosis and challenging behaviours.

Brenda Habjan, E.C.E.
is a communication assistant with the Area Resource Team, Hamilton Health Sciences,
and has a diploma in Early Childhood Education and is trained as a Resource Teacher.

Her interest include teaching, sign language and working with individuals with autism.

Robert King (Bob), M.D., FRCP(C)
is consultant psychiatrist to the Developmental Disabilities Program of the North Bay Psychiatric Hospital. He was the recipient of the Robert Sovner Memorial Essay Award in 1998 and continues to publish and lecture frequently in the field of Dual Diagnosis.

Yona Lunsky, Ph.D., C.Psych.
is currently working on post-doctoral research in dual diagnosis. Her clinical and research interests are in the psychosocial risk factors for dual diagnosis. She was trained at Ohio State University.

William J. Mahoney, M.D., FRCP(C)
is director and Clinical Leader of the Developmental Pediatric Programs at the Chedoke Child & Family Center, part of the Children's Hospital at the Hamilton Health Sciences that supports children with Developmental Disabilities and their families. He is involved in research on the genetics of Autism and other Pervasive Developmental Disorders.

Bruce D. McCreary, M.D., FRCP(C)
is Professor of Psychiatry and Chairman of the Division of Developmental Disabilities at Queen's University. He has worked in the field of developmental disabilities for over 30 years and has a special interest in the association between Down's Syndrome and Alzheimer's disease. He provides "outreach" consulting services in southeastern Ontario including a regular clinic at Rideau Regional Centre in Smith Falls.

Jacqueline McFarland, Ph.D.
is an Assistant Professor of Education at Niagara University. Dr. McFarland specializes in Special Education, especially in the area of inclusion of students with special needs in the regular classroom and students with severe and profound disabilities. Other topics of interest and research include dual diagnosis and multiple/physical disabilities.

Chuck Meister, M.A., C.Psych.Assoc.
is Co-ordinator of the Behaviour Therapy Consultation Service and the Area Resource Team at the Hamilton Health Sciences. His areas of expertise include socio-sexual education and training, anger management and applied behaviour analysis.

Susan Morris, B.S.W., M.S.W., R.S.W.
is the Clinical and Administrative Director of the Dual Diagnosis Program at the Centre for Addiction and Mental Health. She also holds a cross appointment as a lecturer with Department of Psychiatry, University of Toronto. Susan has worked in the hospital and children's sectors and has extensive experience in clinical, program and system development for individuals with dual diagnosis. Susan is Editor of the Habilitative Mental Health Resource Network Newsletter.

JoAnne Nugent, M.S.W.P.
is professor at Humber College, Toronto, and a private consultant/trainer working extensively in the area of dual diagnosis. She is a board member of the National Association on Dual Diagnosis, chairperson of the Habilitative Mental Health Resource Network and chairperson of the Peel Region Dual Diagnosis Committee. JoAnne is the author of several books.

Frances Owen, Ph.D., C. Psych.
is Associate Professor of Child and Youth Studies at Brock University, and was for-

merly a counsellor educator in the graduate program of Niagara University's College of Education. She has worked as a psychologist in schools and community service agencies, and has been a supervisor in various human service organizations.

Patricia Peppin, B.A.(Hons.), M.A., LL.B.
is Associate Professor in the Faculty of Law and Assistant Professor in the School of Medicine at Queen's University. She teaches and does research in the field of health law, and has a particular interest in women's health, mental disability law and drug liability and regulation. She has chaired the Developmental Consulting Program and has worked with the Ministry of Community and Social Services.

Julie Reid, M.A., CCC-SLP
is the Speech Language Pathologist with the Area Resource Team at the Hamilton Health Sciences Corporation. Her research interest is in the area of dysphagia.

Debbie Richards, D.S.W.
is the supervisor of the sexuality programme / clinic for the Welland District Association for Community Living and other local agencies. She has lectured in the area of sexuality and most recently co-developed a protocol for reporting sexual assaults for individuals who have developmental disabilities.

Debra L. Smith, C.C.W.
is a graduate of the Law and Security Administration program and the Ontario Police College. She has been with the Niagara Regional Police Service for several years in the Child Abuse Unit investigating sexual and physical assaults against children under the age of sixteen as well as persons with developmental disabilities. Prior to this she was behaviour therapist for persons with developmental disabilities.

Jane Summers, Ph.D., C.Psych.
is Clinical Leader of Area Resource Team and Behaviour Therapy Consultation Service, Chedoke Child & Family Center, Hamilton Health Sciences. She is also an Assistant professor in the Department of Psychiatry and Behavioural Neurosciences, McMaster University. She was Director of Outpatient Services in the Department of Behavioural Psychology at the Kennedy Krieger Institute, Baltimore, Maryland.

Chrissoula Stavrakaki, M.D., Ph.D., MRCPsych., FRSM, FRCP(C)
is Director of the Dual Diagnosis Program at the Children's Hospital of Eastern Ontario, and an Associate Professor and Coordinator of Dual Diagnosis Services for the Department of Psychiatry at the University of Ottawa. She has written books and publications on topics pertaining to Child Psychiatry and Developmental Disabilities and has done numerous presentations locally, nationally and internationally.

Peggy Taillon-Wasmund, B.S.W., B.A. Hons Law, DPA
is the Co-ordinator of the Champlain Mental Health Task Force. She has been an advocate and community developer for most of her professional career. She has published many articles and written various reports relating to human service development and reform.

Shelley Watson, M.Ed.
currently works at the Welland District Association for Community Living where she conducts social skills and sexuality training, as well as research and assessments of socio-sexual skills. Shelley has co-authored several articles and chapters on sexuality and disability issues.

An Introduction to the Mental Health Needs of Persons with Developmental Disabilities

Edited by: Dorothy M. Griffiths, Brock University
Chrissoula Stavrakaki, Children's Hospital of
Eastern Ontario and University of Ottawa
Jane Summers, Chedoke Child and Family Centre
and McMaster University

Page

Page

Page

How to Use this Book for Training and Personal Referencing

Jill Saldanha

Dual Diagnosis can be a complicated, multi-faceted issue. And finding theory, science and practice in one resource has not been easy. Whatever your role – parent, advocate, family member, clinician, student or worker – you may not know how to get started, what is required in a certain area, what resources are available or what considerations you may need to think about.

This book can help – it's like having an array of experts at your side to give you advice, theoretical background and practical solutions. There are two versions of this book: one for trainers and one for general use. No matter what your situation, you can use this book in a number of ways. For example:

- To update your knowledge and understanding of the field
- To find practical solutions to assist in supporting persons with dual diagnosis
- To expand your understanding of current issues involving service delivery
- To increase your awareness of the importance of early intervention and proactive support
- To provide information to allow you to advocate a holistic approach to support and intervention
- As a self-study guide to enhance your learning

- If you have the trainer's version of this book, you will also use it as your guide to delivering effective, interactive training workshops

Overview of the book

This book is divided into chapters. Each chapter attempts to answer the following questions:

- Why are we interested in this?
- What light does theory shed on this?
- What are the practical implications of this theory?
- How can this information be used?

You will notice that the chapters are divided into several broad topic areas:

A. Overview and Background Information.
Including Chapters 1, 2 and 4, these provide foundation information about the nature and mental health needs of person with developmental disabilities.

B. Supporting Individuals
Chapters 3, 6, and 11 detail a variety of approaches useful in supporting individuals.

C. Assessing Needs
Chapter 5 outlines screening and assessment processes and tools.

D. Treatment
Chapters 7 and 8 deal with pharmacological and non-pharmacological treatments and approaches.

E. Systemic Approaches

Chapters 9, 10, 11 and 18 address systemic approaches for individuals who have a dual diagnosis.

F. Distinct Circumstances

In chapters 12, 13, 14,15, 16, and 17 you will find discussion of distinct or specific situations, including offenders, sexuality, substance disorders, children, aging, and communication impairments.

How to use this Book

Do not attempt to read this book as you would a novel. Rather, when you use this book, it is helpful to:

- Review the Table of Contents to identify the key areas that interest you or are applicable to your situation;
- Within the chapters of most interest and relevance to you, read the Learning Objectives to pinpoint relevant areas of content;
- Tailor the learning objectives to your own needs. For example, stop and consider the current state of your knowledge and understanding on each learning objective. Is there a particular area or emphasis that you wish to consider?
- Skim the chapter and highlight areas of specific interest;
- Read the case studies, and consider their application to the material you are reading. How does the case study illustrate the learning objectives of the chapter? What lessons can you draw from the case study?
- Deepen your learning by evaluating your understanding, using the "Do you know?" questions at the end of

       each chapter;
- °   Supplement your learning by referring to the recom-
       mended resources in the bibliography at the end of
       each chapter.

The authors' intent is to make this book as useful and practical as possible. The learning objectives at the beginning of each chapter and the "Do you know?" at the end serve as a guide to your learning. You can elect to complete them as a way of measuring your progress and understanding. Adapt and use these tools as you wish.

If you will be delivering training workshops, you will also have specific materials designed to make this job easier. Overheads, lesson plans and learning objectives are provided for your use.

Learning and understanding can often be enhanced through discussing and comparing notes with others in similar situations. If you are able, finding a "study buddy" as you go through this book can be invaluable. One approach may be for you and your buddy to each read a chapter of interest, and then prepare an informal presentation of the material. Include some questions or discussion points in your presentation. This presentation could be done face to face, via the telephone, over email or an Internet "chat".

This book is intended to be a resource, provide background and theoretical framework, and provide practical assistance. Whatever your situation, you will find this book most helpful if you keep it close to hand, and use it as a guide, inspiration and reinforcement in your role.

Reader's Guide to Chapters

Chapter	Main Themes	Target Audience	Related Chapters
1: The Nature of Developmental Disabilities	• What are developmental disabilities • The role of biological factors • What is meant by dual diagnosis	• Of interest to all audiences • Level of content appropriate to all audiences	• Chapter 2, The Mental Health Needs of Persons with Developmental Disabilities • Chapter 5, Comprehensive Screening and Assessment • Chapter 15, Dual Diagnosis in
2: The Mental Health Needs of Persons with Developmental Disabilities	• Psychosocial and emotional development within a developmental perspective • Factors related to vulnerability and resilience to mental health disturbances in persons with developmental disabilities • Ways to promote optimal mental well-being	• Of interest to all audiences • Level of content appropriate to all audiences	• Chapter 1, The Nature of Developmental Disabilities • Chapter 3, The Integrated Biopsychosocial Approach to Challenging Behaviours • Chapter 11, Developing Social Supports for People Who Have a Dual Diagnosis • Chapter 15, Dual Diagnosis in Children • Chapter 17, Mental Health Issues in Clients with Severe Communication Impairments

Chapter	Main Themes	Target Audience	Related Chapters
3: The Integrated Biopsychosocial Approach to Challenging Behaviours	• The integrative biopsychosocial model • How it differs from other approaches to challenging behaviour • How to develop a formulation based on the integrated biopsychosocial model	• Clinicians • Of interest to all audiences • Level of content appropriate to all audiences	• Chapter 2, The Mental Health Needs of Persons with Developmental Disabilities • Chapter 5, Comprehensive Screening and Assessment • Chapter 7, Collaborative Treatment Approaches • Chapter 10, The Interdisciplinary Mental Health Team • Chapter 17, Mental Health Issues in Clients with Severe Communication
4: The DSM-IV and How it Applies to Persons with Developmental Disabilities	• What DSM-IV stands for; its format and basic application • Identify which categories are listed in the Manual • Describe how these categories apply to persons with developmental disability, both children and adults	• Physicians • Of interest to all audiences • Level of content appropriate to all audiences	• Chapter 2: The Mental Health Needs of Persons with Developmental Disabilities • Chapter 5: Comprehensive Screening and Assessment • Chapter 7: Collaborative Treatment Approaches

Section	Learning Objectives	Audience	Related Chapters
5: Comprehensive Screening and Assessment	• Why screening and assessment are important • Specific instruments that are used for biopsychosocial assessments • How to conduct a biopsychosocial assessment	• Clinicians • Of interest to all audiences • Level of content appropriate to all audiences	• Chapter 1, The Nature of Developmental Disabilities • Chapter 3, The Integrated Biopsychosocial Approach to Challenging Behaviours • Chapter 7, Collaborative Treatment Approaches • Chapter 10, The Interdisciplinary
6: Person-Centred Approaches to Services and Supports	• What person-centred planning is • Why person-centred planning approaches were developed • How to design person-	• Of interest to all audiences • Level of content appropriate to all audiences	• Chapter 9, Building Responsive Service Systems • Chapter 11, Developing Social Supports for People who have a Dual Diagnosis
7: Collaborative Treatment Approaches : Integrating Medication with Non-pharmacological Treatments	• Appreciate the value of a collaborative, interdisciplinary approach to challenging behaviours in individuals with developmental disabilities. • Understand the role of objective monitoring of the signs and symptoms of	• Clinicians, physicians • Of interest to all audiences • Level of content appropriate to all audiences	• Chapter 4: The DSM-IV and How it Applies to Persons with Developmental Disabilities • Chapter 8: Psychopharmacological Treatments in Persons with Developmental Disabilities

Chapter	Main Themes	Target Audience	Related Chapters
8: Psychopharmacological Treatments in Persons with Developmental Disabilities	• Identify the categories of psychotropic medications • How to identify side-effects • Learn the protocols on how to use PRN medications	• Physicians • Of interest to all audiences • Level of content appropriate to all audiences	• Chapter 3: The Integrated Biopsychosocial Approach to Challenging Behaviors • Chapter 7: Collaborative Treatment Approaches • Chapter 15: Dual Diagnosis in Children • Chapter 16: Aging and Dual Diagnosis
9: Building Responsive Service Systems	• Understand how culture and philosophy have influenced the development of services for the dually diagnosed • Learn strategies for building a community support	• Administrators • Of interest to all audiences • Level of content appropriate to all audiences	• Chapter 1: The Nature of Developmental Disabilities • Chapter 10: The Interdisciplinary Mental Health Team • Chapter 11: Developing Social Supports for People who have Dual Diagnosis
10: The Interdisciplinary Mental Health Team	• Roles and functions of health professionals who work with persons with a dual diagnosis • The role of the core team within a consultative model • When to consider asking for an evaluation and how best to prepare for it	• Of interest to all audiences • Level of content appropriate to all audiences	• Chapter 3, The Integrated Biopsychosocial Approach to Challenging Behaviours • Chapter 5, Comprehensive Screening and Assessment • Chapter 7, Collaborative Treatment Approaches • Chapter 17, Mental Health Issues in Clients with Severe Communication Impairments

Topic	Objectives	Audience	Related Chapters
11: Developing Social Supports for People who have a Dual Diagnosis	• Define social supports and describe why social supports are important in the lives of persons with dual diagnosis • Identify how to effectively develop social supports	• Agency support workers • Of interest to all audiences • Level of content appropriate to	• Chapter 2: The Mental Health Needs of Persons with Developmental Disabilities • Chapter 6: Person-Centred Approaches to Services and Supports
12: Offenders Who Have a Developmental Disability	• Why persons with developmental disability are more vulnerable for offending behaviour • How the socio-environmental factors can be a risk to offending behaviour • How the judicial and criminal justice system create risks for persons with dual diagnosis	• All involved with offenders • Of interest to all audiences • Level of content appropriate to all audiences	• Chapter 1: The Nature of Developmental Disabilities • Chapter 2: The Mental Health Needs of Persons with Developmental Disabilities
13: Sexuality and Mental Health Issues	• Compare sexual wellness of persons with developmental disabilities vis-à-vis non-disabled persons • Define sexual abuse and its applicability to persons with developmental disabilities • Identify appropriate treatment options	• Of interest to all audiences • Level of content appropriate to all audiences	• Chapter 1: The Nature of Developmental Disability • Chapter 2: The Mental Health Needs of Persons with Developmental Disabilities • Chapter 3: The Integrated Biopsychosocial Approach to Challenging Behaviors

Chapter	Main Themes	Target Audience	Related Chapters
14. Substance-related disorders in persons with a developmental disability	• Know what substance abuse disorders are. • Learn how frequently they are diagnosed in this group of people. • Know how they affect these persons. • Learn how we can treat and manage these disorders effectively in persons with developmental disabilities.	• Clinicians, physicians • Of interest to all audiences • Level of content appropriate to all audiences	• Chapter 5: Comprehensive Screening and Assessment • Chapter 7: Collaborative Treatment Approaches • Chapter 8: Psychopharmacological Treatments in Persons with Developmental Disability • Chapter 13: Sexuality and Mental Health Issues
15: Dual diagnosis in children	• Different disorders that are usually diagnosed in childhood • Factors that contribute to behavioural and emotional problems in children and adolescents with developmental disabilities	• Persons working with children • Of interest to all audiences • Level of content appropriate to all audiences	• Chapter 1, The Nature of Developmental Disabilities • Chapter 2, The Mental Health Needs of Persons with Developmental Disabilities • Chapter 4, The DSM-IV and How it Applies to Persons with Developmental Disabilities

16: Aging and dual diagnosis	• Understand the nature of health problems of persons with developmental disabilities as they grow older • Know the mental disorders in persons with developmental disabilities • Learn how aging has been conceptualized as a biomedi-	• Persons working with aging population • Of interest to all audiences • Level of content appropriate to all audiences	• Chapter 1: The Nature of Developmental Disability • Chapter 4: The DSM-IV and How it Applies to Persons with Developmental Disabilities • Chapter 8: The Psychopharmacological Treatments for Persons with Developmental Disabilities
17: Mental Health Issues in Clients with Severe Communication Impairments	• Conventional and nonconventional forms of communication • How communication impairments can have a negative impact on the social and emotional well-being of persons with a developmental disability	• Those working with persons with severe communication problems • Of interest to all audiences • Level of content appropriate to all audiences	• Chapter 2, Mental Health Needs of Persons with Developmental Disabilities • Chapter 3, The Integrated Biopsychosocial Approach to Challenging Behaviours • Chapter 5, Comprehensive Assessment and Screening • Chapter 10, The Interdisciplinary
18. Legal issues and ethical dimensions of dual diagnosis	• Develop an understanding of how law develops and changes. • Become aware of the ethical dimensions underlying laws that affect people with dual	• Clinicians, physicians • Of interest to all audiences • Level of content appropriate to	• Chapter 1: The Nature of Developmental Disability • Chapter 2: The Mental Health Needs of Persons with Developmental Disability • Chapter 5: Comprehensive Screen-

Forward

Jo Anne Nugent
Chairperson
Habilitative Mental Health Resource Network

An Introduction to the Mental Health Needs of Persons with Developmental Disabilities represents a breakthrough!

For some years now, it has been acknowledged that one of the most serious barriers to the provision of effective support to persons with a dual diagnosis has been the lack of readily available education related to dual diagnosis. Many useful books exist that deal with various aspects of dual diagnosis. Several types of training and education related to dual diagnosis have been offered on a short-term basis. But there has never been a systematic, thorough campaign to provide dual diagnosis education across an entire province or state until now!

The Habilitative Mental Health Resource Network is the Ontario Chapter of the National Association on Dual Diagnosis. In that capacity, we have a provincial perspective on dual diagnosis and a responsibility that pertains to persons with dual diagnosis living throughout Ontario.

Four years ago, our Chapter decided that one of its priorities was to pursue avenues by which dual diagnosis education could be provided consistently and equitably across our province. We recognized that we had many strengths in Ontario: pockets of specific expertise, a great many excellent staff, concerned parents, post secondary educational institutions with an

interest in dual diagnosis, and a structure of local dual diagnosis committees. It was agreed that whatever process we developed would build on these strengths.

From our perspective, the missing element was a comprehensive training curriculum that could meet the needs of a variety
of participants. Therefore, the Habilitative Mental Health Resource Network developed a plan to obtain funding for a curriculum which would be utilized in a carefully planned way
across Ontario. Our goals were twofold. First, we wanted to
provide the information itself. Second, and in some ways
more importantly, we wanted to establish a system of dual diagnosis training that would exist permanently.

In 1998, we submitted a proposal to the provincial government
to fund the development and dissemination of an introductory
dual diagnosis training curriculum. This proposal was approved in 1999. Significantly, this funding was cross sectoral
since it came from both the Ministry of Community and Social
Services, which is responsible for Developmental Services,
and the Ministry of Health and Long Term Care, responsible
for Mental Health Programmes. An editorial committee was
struck by our Chapter and the process was under way!

After two years of hard work, all as volunteers, the members
of the Editorial Committee brought to completion the production of the book you are now reading. Our debt to them is
enormous, and we thank them all most sincerely.

Several factors make *An Introduction to the Mental Health
Needs of Persons with Developmental Disabilities* unique:

☆ it has been produced with the specific purpose of being disseminated at cost to thousands of readers across the vast province of Ontario

☆ its purpose is to ensure that there is a basic introductory level of dual diagnosis education throughout the province

☆ it has been written in a user friendly format so that it will be of benefit to a diverse audience including parents, staff who work in direct contact daily with the individuals who are labelled as dually diagnosed, and staff who work in more clinical and/or consultative roles

☆ it will be accompanied by trainer's materials, including overheads and exercises, so that the materials can be taught at local levels by existing educators in a variety of settings

☆ each local area will decide how the curriculum can most effectively be utilized in its own area to compliment other work occurring in its region

☆ it is appropriate for use as a course text in college or university

☆ the authors, with two exceptions, are from Ontario, which means that they are accessible to readers who might wish further information

☆ the information is applicable to a broader readership beyond Ontario

☆ it represents the most up-to-date research and practice

In conclusion, I can only try to convey how proud our Chapter is of this book and those who have been part of its creation. As it is utilized for training across Ontario, we are confident that it will make a significant contribution to the lives of our citizens with a dual diagnosis and to their families.

Preface

Jim Johnston
Parent Representative
Habilitative Mental Health Resource Network

Our understanding of the needs of individuals who have developmental disabilities and mental health needs (a dual diagnosis) is constantly changing and growing. New insights from research and the experience of families and professionals in the field have improved our provision of service to people with a dual diagnosis. It is essential that men and women who work in this field have access to the latest information and training so that they can provide the most effective service. This book is designed for that purpose.

For persons with a dual diagnosis, whether they live independently or with their families, educated workers can make a significant difference in their lives. If their mental health needs are not recognized, crises begin to develop. If no one understands the most effective intervention methods, the crises will deepen. Although much still needs to be understood about the nature of mental health issues in this population, we can do a much better job of delivering services with the knowledge we have today if staff receive the most current information and education.

The current level of ongoing education on this topic in the Province of Ontario is minimal. Education is received 'on the job' or in the occasional seminar. This is inadequate to train professionals who can recognize and help a person with a dual diagnosis. The complexity of mental health needs in this population can only be addressed with ongoing and in-depth education on a wide range of related topics. This book is the foundation for an education programme that attempts to cover the most recent research and best practices in key areas. This is a start, but must be accompanied by a commitment at all levels to continually include new research, and to make this an ongoing quest to educate all those who can improve the quality of lives of our children.

Certain service providers show an unwillingness to serve someone with a dual diagnosis. Service providers are under funded with unrealistic staff/client ratios. Providing service to someone with mental health needs in addition to his/her developmental disability is seen as time consuming, and may take resources away from other clients in need. Certainly, those with a dual diagnosis require more support, but a significant contributing factor is a lack of education. If the provider does not have trained staff to screen, assess, and plan interventions and integrated supports for the individual, then much more time is spent dealing with the inevitable crises that will develop. Of course, these crises will tend to emotionally affect the entire client base that is in contact with the person in crisis, creating even more requirements for staff interventions. Education can be very effective in alleviating these crises, and when the crisis is not preventable, in handling it in the most effective way possible.

There are many areas that cry out for more staff training. Offenders who have developmental disabilities, sexuality issues, substance-related disorders, and aging concerns are all areas in which the most recent research is made available to service providers through this education.

Having a child with a dual diagnosis creates immense pressures in the family. As the mental health issues emerge, sometimes later in life, the family is bewildered about how to help its family member. Stress and frustration affect everyone. Help seems fragmented and remote. Occasionally a professional will have the knowledge and training to really help the family member and also help the family better understand the issues and what techniques to best use. The difference these professionals can make is profound.

As a parent, I am excited by this collaborative effort between the Habilitative Mental Health Network, the Government of Ontario, and the many expert authors who contributed to this work. The 'train the trainer' approach will ensure that this information will be spread as widely as possible.

I trust that those who read this book will find that it assists them in helping persons with a dual diagnosis and their families, and that they will commit themselves to continuing their education as our knowledge of these subjects continues to develop.

Introduction

Dorothy Griffiths, Ph.D.
Chrissoula Stavrakaki, M.D., F.R.C.P.
Jane Summers, Ph.D., C. Psych.
(Editors)

This book is designed to provide state-of-the-art information regarding how mental illness presents in persons with developmental disabilities, along with providing assessment and treatment options that are reflective of best practice. This book was conceived as a way to help overcome many of the philosophical and practical obstacles that exist because of the way our service systems in Ontario are currently organized. It is our hope that, as a result of this book, there will be greater continuity of service between agencies and professionals, and improved service evaluation, delivery and follow-up.

As such this book has two objectives:

- ✓ first, that the reader should learn about the current state of the field and gain information that will assist in supporting persons with dual diagnosis return to a state of mental wellness;
- ✓ second, the reader will gain heightened awareness of the areas where early intervention and proactive support can enhance the emotional well-being of persons with developmental disabilities, as well as help in the prevention of mental illness and promotion of mental wellness in this population.

It is our hope that the readers will find this book useful in their workplace or home life, and that it will spark a renewed interest in this most challenging field. The book contains 18 chapters dealing with general areas from the nature of developmental disabilities and the mental health needs of this population, to areas of assessment and intervention. The authors of the book advocate an holistic approach to support and intervention for the person with developmental disabilities who presents with mental health problems, including biomedical, psychosocial and socio-environmental approaches. This theme is a common thread throughout this book.

Another integrating thread is the value placed on providing cross-sectorial collaboration, and defining the role of multiple disciplines working in collaboration. There are several chapters on integrated approaches to assessment and treatment and creation of multidisciplinary teams, social supports and responsive services for persons with dual diagnosis.

We have also included special chapters that address the lifespan issues of persons with dual diagnosis, and special considerations for issues related to sexuality, offending behaviour, substance abuse, and legal matters.

The book is a blend of theory, science and practical information. Each chapter is organized to provide learning objectives, an introduction and expansion of the chapter topic, review questions, and resource lists to direct the interested reader to more material. Case examples are used throughout to illustrate how the material may be applied to real life situations.

This book was written with the help of 34 professionals who represent the following:

- various service sectors (health, social and developmental services, and criminal justice)
- a variety of programmes (medical, psychiatric, psychological, behavioural consultation, community support for persons with intellectual disabilities and head injury, district health councils, community policing, and specialized dual diagnosis programmes)
- disciplines of psychiatry, psychology, behaviour analysis, speech and language, occupational and physiotherapy, law, nursing, police, developmental services, social work and education.

We are also represented by authors from eight colleges and universities. The complement of authors brings a unique richness and breadth to the material.

Because of the different disciplines and training, you will notice a variety of discipline-specific terminology throughout the book that we have attempted to clarify through a glossary. However, the reader will also note that terminology differs between disciplines, and in accordance to where people were trained. The politically accepted phrasing of "person first" language is adhered to throughout the book. However, different disciplines and cultures refer to persons with intellectual disabilities in different terms: Canada now employs *intellectual disability*, the United States uses *mental retardation*, the United Kingdom uses *learning disabled* and many individuals universally use the broader and more encompassing term of *developmental disability*. Although there is some variation throughout the book that remains to respect discipline-specific use, the majority of our authors have selected the broader term of *persons with developmental disabilities*.

The authorship of this book is largely selected from professionals in Ontario, Canada. This is the origin of our training initiative. It also reflects a province with a large number of professionals dedicated to this area of study and practice. Ontario has long been dedicated to ethical and effective intervention for persons who are labelled as dually diagnosed. Ontario's recent past has seen many fine mentors and teachers who paved the way for today's services and visions. This book represents the work of many of today's leaders. It is our hope that we will in some way inspire tomorrow's clinicians, researchers and advocates.

Acknowledgements

The editors are indebted to the thirty-four authors who devoted their time and expertise to the completion of this project. We also wish to thank the many agencies that they represent for donating time for their employees to complete this project.

We also wish to thank our many reviewers, particularly the Board of Directors of the Habilitative Mental Health Resource Network of Ontario. Their feedback and critiques were most appreciated and valued.

This book could never have been completed without the assistance of Shelley Watson (Publication Co-ordinator); her organization, dedication and skill are unparalleled. We also wish to thank Nancy Miodrag (Technical Editor), Donald Lesco (Stylistic Editor) and Usha Meister (Cover Designer). Each contributed enormously to this task.

We also acknowledge that this book could never have been created without the learning that the authors acquired at the hands of persons with disabilities, their families and support workers. They have taught us so much, and we hope this book will give something back to them.

The Habilitative Mental Health Resource Network is indebted to the Government of Ontario. The Habilitative Mental Health Resource Network acknowledges the financial support of the Government of Ontario. The views expressed are the views of the authors and do not necessarily reflect those of the Government of Ontario.

Chapter 1

The Nature of Developmental Disabilities

Frances Owen and Jacqueline MacFarland

Learning Objectives

Readers will be able to:

1. Define developmental disabilities
2. Describe several types of developmental disabilities
3. Describe the changes in our understanding of developmental disabilities over the past 200 years

First, A Focus On Language:

The fact that language is powerful in shaping how we think and feel is well known. However, this is a critical fact to bear in mind when studying the history of services for persons who have what we now call developmental disabilities. If you think back to your days in elementary school, playing in the school yard at recess, you will recall people being called "retarded" by their peers in a spirit of taunting. This inappropriate and hurtful use of a clinical term is the fate that has tended to befall most terms used to describe persons who have intellectual disabilities. For this reason, and for reasons of improved accuracy, the labels used to describe people who have these challenges tend to be changed on a fairly regular basis. In the mid 20th century, terms such as "mental deficiency, feeblemindness, mental subnormality, mental handicap, and oligophrenia" (Scheerenberger, 1983, p. 217) were all used to label people. These labels send chills through us as we stand at the dawn of the 21st century. However, just as these terms developed negative meaning through misapplication and careless use, so it is likely the same will happen for the terms we use today. In Canada, we tend to use the term developmental disabilities; whereas, in the United States and in Europe, the term mental retardation is more common, and in the United Kingdom, the term learning disabilities is common.

Labels, regardless of what they may be, tend to change the way people interact with the person who has the label. For this reason, the Canadian Association for Community Living abandoned its former name (Canadian Association for the Mentally Retarded) in response to feedback from people with intellectual disabilities who resented the term "mental retardation" (CACL, 2000). The Association is committed to the use of inclusive language, and has identified preferred terms to include "...people who have an intellectual disability, people who have a mental handicap, and people who have a developmental disability" (CACL, 2000).

In 1982, Bogdan and Taylor wrote a powerful biography of two people who had been labeled "mentally handicapped." One of these people, Ed Murphy, spoke eloquently about the challenges he faced: "The problem is getting labeled as being something. After that, you're not really a person. It's like a sty in your eye – it's noticeable" (p. 33). Think for a moment about all the labels with which you live, and how each of those labels changes how those around you react to you. Think also about the expectations that people have of you as a result of each label. For example, what social expectations are attached to the labels "student" or "professor"? Consider also how social expectations others have for you change as you move from being a student to being a worker. We all live with other labels as well. We may be sons or daughters, mothers or fathers, aunts or uncles, husbands or wives, friends and neighbours. Each of these labels carries with it both privileges and responsibilities that are socially determined. People who have been labeled as having a developmental disability may have many of these labels, but because of the power of language, their one label tends to override all the others, and colours the expectations and perceptions others have of them.

What is Developmental Disability?

This is far from a straightforward question. The definition of developmental disability has undergone many changes, some driven by medical and other research advances, and others driven by advocacy and policy revision. As Landesman and Ramey (1989) point out, "changes in the definition reflect shifting professional consensus (usually by a select group charged with establishing diagnostic criteria), as well as fluctuating political and social agendas (e.g., limiting how many are eligible for services, avoiding over-representation of certain subpopulations, and including a new group of special needs children)" (p. 409).

While many organizations around the world address issues related to developmental disabilities, in terms of definitions, we in North America tend to look to the American Association on Mental Retardation (AAMR) for leadership. On their website (http://www.aamr.org/Policies/faqmentalretardation.html), AAMR identifies mental retardation as "a particular state of functioning that begins in childhood and is characterized by limitation in both intelligence and adaptive skills." Evidence of limitations in adaptive functioning must occur in two or more of the following: "communication, home living, community use, health and safety, leisure, self-care, social skills, self-direction, functional academics, work." AAMR emphasizes that the definition includes the 'fit' between the capabilities of individuals and the structure and expectations of their environment. This contextual focus is clarified in the DSM – IV (Diagnostic and Statistical Manual– 4th Edition) where impairments in adaptive functioning are identified as "the person's effectiveness in meeting the standards expected for his or her age by his or her cultural group" (American Psychiatric Association, 1994, p. 50).

In the United States, the Developmentally Disabled Assistance and Bill of Rights Act of 1994 (PL 104-183) offers a definition of the term **developmentally disabled:**

The term "developmental disability" means a severe, chronic disability of an individual 5 years of age or older that:

1. is attributable to a mental or physical impairment or combination of mental and physical impairment;
2. is manifested before the individual attains age 22;
3. is likely to continue indefinitely;
4. results in substantial functional limitations in three or more of the following areas of major life activity:
    self-care
    receptive and expressive language
    learning
    mobility
    self-direction

> capacity for independent living;
> economic self-sufficiency

5. reflects the individual's need for a combination and sequence of special, interdisciplinary, or genetic services,
supports, or other assistance that is of lifelong or extended
duration and is individually planned and coordinated, except that such term, when applied to infants and young
children means individuals from birth to age 5, inclusive,
who have substantial developmental delay or specific congenital or acquired conditions with a high probability of
resulting in developmental disabilities if services are not
provided.

The CACL (2000) defines an intellectual disability as "... an
impaired ability to learn. It sometimes causes difficulty in coping with the demands of daily life. It is a condition which is
usually present from birth, and it is not the same as mental or
psychiatric illness."

Intellectual Functioning

The definition of developmental disability describes the limitations in the area of intellectual functioning of the individual.
Subaverage intellectual functioning is usually translated as an
IQ score below 70-75 on standardized intelligence tests. However, the central role of the intelligence test in identifying developmental disability has been reduced over the years, since
research has shown that I.Q. tests have overidentified people
who lived in poverty, whose parents are identified as having a
developmental disability, and those who are members of certain racial and cultural minority groups (Scheerenberger,
1983). Nevertheless, the IQ is used to differentiate among levels of mental retardation.

Level of Mental Retardation	IQ Level
Mild	50-55 to approximately 70
Moderate	35-40 to 50-55
Severe	20-25 to 35-40
Profound	Below 20 or 25

(American Psychiatric Association, 1994).

Adaptive Skills

As mentioned earlier, to be identified as having a developmental disability, a person must have identifiable deficits in adaptive functioning as well as intellectual potential. The adaptive skill areas that are assessed include:

- *Communication* includes expressive and receptive language skills as well as interpreting the "body language" of others.
- *Self-care* includes activities of daily living such as grooming, toileting, appropriate eating skills, dressing and personal hygiene.
- *Home living skills* include areas related to housekeeping, general maintenance, food preparation, shopping and home safety.
- *Social skills* include appropriate skills such as making and keeping friends, demonstrating personal restraint in public places, smiling, and showing signs of appreciation. Inappropriate skills include lewdness, obscene words or gestures, inappropriately approaching others, bawdy behaviours, and tantrums.
- *Community use* includes the appropriate use of and access to community resources such as restaurants, transportation, shopping areas, and places of worship.
- *Self-direction* refers to the ability to make appropriate life decisions related to scheduling and personal endeavors.

- *Health and safety* issues include the ability to maintain an appropriate diet, basic preservation and health issues, and following directions.
- *Functional academics* include the basic academic information learned in school needed for the "world of work."
- *Leisure* includes activities such as games, sports, recreational activities and appropriate behaviors at those functions.
- *Work* includes the skills needed to maintain a job.

(AAMR, 1992)

Individual Differences

Beyond the definitions of developmental disability that are generally accepted, as with any other diagnosis, every person who has a developmental disability is an individual with unique talents, personality, and interests. As mentioned earlier in this chapter, it is important that people who have developmental disabilities not be seen simply in terms of this one label but, rather, as people who are multifaceted. In some cases, the talents and skills exhibited by people who have developmental disabilities may be quite remarkable. For example, the phenomenon known as Savant Syndrome is evident when a person has specific skills that are at a level that is inconsistent with his/her general intellectual functioning. The presence of these special talents has been documented for more than 200 years. Evidence of Savant Syndrome includes people with developmental disabilities who have outstanding abilities in music, number derivation, arithmetic, mechanical tasks, language, art and sensory sensitivity.

Regardless of the label used to identify these special skills and talents, it is important for everyone who associates with people who have developmental disabilities to be aware of not only their challenges, but more importantly their strengths, interests, gifts and talents.

Statistics

In Canada, the CACL (2000) reports that there are 899,000 people who have been identified as having an intellectual disability. In the United States, 5.6 million children (12.43% of the general population) have a disability (U.S. Department of Education). In Britain, Mencap, "the largest charity working on behalf of people with learning disabilities and their families" (What is Mencap? Http://www.gmp.police.uk/mencap/whatis.html) reports that 1.2 million people have been identified with learning disability.

The Case of Jack

Jack Crane's mother suspected that he was not developing in the way his older brother and sister had. He was slow to reach milestones such as holding his head up, rolling over and pulling himself to stand. He was a happy baby who seemed content wherever he was. Marg Crane talked to her family physician about her concerns, but after examining Jack briefly, he told her the baby was healthy, and reminded her that each child develops at his or her own rate. Marg tried to pacify herself with this reassurance, but by the time Jack was two years of age and he still had not said an intelligible word, she was very concerned. She revisited her family physician.

To this point, Jack's story is not particularly unusual. It is not unusual for parents to report that they suspected their child had a developmental concern before professionals recognized the difficulty. However, the next part of the story would vary sig-

nificantly depending on the time period in which Jack was born. If he had been born in the 1940s, chances are that as Jack's developmental delay became more obvious, the family physician would have suggested that he be institutionalized "for his own good and that of the family." If Jack had been born in the 1960s, he would probably have stayed at home as a preschooler, and then would have been enrolled in a special, segregated school for children who had developmental disabilities. If he had been born in the 1990s, it is likely that he would have been referred to a developmental pediatrician for assessment, an infant development program for in-home parent education, and he would have attended an integrated preschool program. He would then have gone on to attend the local elementary school where he would have been enrolled in a class with other children his age, and would have participated in classes modified to meet his needs.

While the level of support available in community services (such as preschools and in-home consultation programs), and in school systems varies from one jurisdiction to another, there is an increasing commitment to inclusion of persons with developmental disabilities in community and school programs. Over the past half century, the evolution of services to support people who have developmental disabilities has been dramatic, as is evident from the variations in Jack's life story. As you will see from the following brief history, Jack's circumstances would have been even more challenging if he had been born in the 19th century or even earlier.

A Very Brief Early History of Developmental Disabilities

Historically, people with developmental disabilities have been protected in some civilizations, reviled, taunted, abused and rejected in others. They were protected by the powerful Egyptian god Osiris in ancient times, but they faced rejection and even death in ancient Greece (Scheerenberger, 1983). In ancient Rome, unwanted children were left at Columna Lactaria where people employed by the state were assigned to rescue them. However, many of these rescued children faced a terrible fate. It was common that they would be physically mutilated to increase their potential earning power as beggars. Nevertheless, as the medical sciences developed in Rome, people such as Ascelpiades of Prusa and Soranus advocated for more humane treatment of persons who had various kinds of mental disorders (Scheerenberger, 1983).

The advent of Christianity helped to stem the tide of infanticide and child slavery in Rome. Other religions and religious leaders, notably Zoroaster, Budda, Confucius and Mohammed, also preached concern, caring and respect for all people, including those who had special needs. From ancient times to the Enlightenment (476-1799 A.D./C.E.), there was some increase in the understanding of developmental disabilities. However, religious prohibitions against medical research limited investigations that might have lead to more significant developments (Scheerenberger, 1983). Despite the fact that infanticide was less common in this period than it had been in ancient Greece and Rome, thousands of children suffered from abandonment, were sold into slavery, or were left to die. There is evidence to suggest that during the Inquisition, some people with developmental disabilities were even put to death as witches. The earlier practice of mutilating children to increase their value as beggars was also revisited in the 17th century. Many died when they could no longer beg effectively, prompting Vincent de Paul to start his eleemosynary programmes. He believed that mental disease was not different from physical disease, and that Christians were called to address both needs.

The programmes Vincent de Paul started in the 17th century were the precursors to the work of the reformers, Philipe Pinel and William Tuke (Scheerenberger, 1983).

Some encouraging medical progress was made during the 17th and 18th centuries. Walter Harris suggested the importance of examining heredity, and related children's ingestion of alcohol to their reduced intellectual functioning. Also during this period, Wolfgang Hoefer provided the first detailed description of cretinism, Phillippus Jacobus Duttel published a monograph on birth defects, and Robert Whytt described hydrocephalus. In 1801, Philipe Pinel wrote his influential A Treatise on Insanity in which he attempted to differentiate between dementia and idiocy, saying that "the latter condition involved the loss of both intellect and behavior" (Pinel, 1806 in Scheerenberger, 1983, p. 40). Pinel fought for the removal of restraints from patients, and instituted moral treatment of patients, including the provision of music, conversation, books and employment opportunities. By today's standards, these concepts are not novel, but at the time they were truly revolutionary.

During the same period, in England, William Tuke also advocated for and provided humane treatment for people who had a variety of mental health and developmental difficulties. Still, the distinction between mental illness and developmental disabilities was vague. Perhaps the most significant contributions to the field of developmental disabilities during this time period were made by philosophers such as Alexander Pope, Francis Bacon, RJnJ Descartes, John Locke, and Jean Jacques Rousseau. Rousseau argued for the basic goodness of human beings, which flew in the face of earlier church teachings, and further advocated for the education of children through self-directed exploration and sensory training, ideas that had an impact on later educators including Maria Montessori

(Scheerenberger, 1983).

The 19th century was a time of enormous progress in Europe as in North America. There was a rapid expansion in medical understanding, including the identification of clinical forms of developmental disabilities. General understanding of developmental disabilities and their treatment was greatly increased during this period. The century began with the work of Jean Marc Itard who worked with Victor, the so-called "wild boy of Aveyron." Itard worked with Victor for five years, and despite a prognosis of "irreversible mentality," was able to teach him letter and object recognition, some sensory discrimination and social skills. Throughout the first half of the 19th century, advocacy movements in support of people who had developmental disabilities grew, along with similar movements in support of other disadvantaged groups, including people who had other kinds of disabling conditions, as well as for prisoners and slaves. Building on the work of Itard and others, Johann Jacob Gugenbuhl built a new kind of facility in Switzerland for people who had developmental disabilities. "Guggenbuhl tried to 'awaken the souls' of his patients through 'habituation to regular routine, memory exercises, and speech training.' He even introduced into the group two children of normal intelligence who 'brought life into the institution' " (National Institute on Mental Retardation, 1981, p. 5). However, a cure for developmental disability was, of course, not found, and the fortunes of Guggenbuhl's Abendberg centre declined.

Undeterred by the prevailing belief that there was little hope for remediation of people who had developmental disabilities, Edouard Onesimus Seguin made great strides working with several children at a Paris hospital. He was able to help these children to learn some writing and counting skills, to improve their memory, and to make more effective use of their senses. The Paris Academy of Sciences declared in 1844 that he had "solved the problem of 'idiot education'" (National Institute on Mental Retardation, 1981, p. 5). Sequin's fame spread with his publication of a textbook on mental retardation. Political upheaval prompted him to move to the United States where in 1876, he was elected the first president of the Association of Medical Officers of American Institutions for Idiotic and Feeble-Minded Persons which later became the American Association on Mental Retardation.

Growth in Services for People with Developmental Disabilities in Ontario

The 19th century view that persons with developmental disabilities were in some way a threat to society and needed custody persisted in Ontario into the 1960s (Williston, 1971). At the turn of the 20th century, as Edouard Seguin's legacy was leaving an impact on education for people who were then described as "feeble minded" in the United States, similar work was being undertaken in Ontario under the leadership of Alexander Beaton and Helen McMurchy. The result of their work was the Special Classes Act passed in 1911 which provided for the establishment of educational classes for children who had tested IQs over 50 (Anglin & Braaten, 1978).

Residential services in Ontario began with the 1859 conversion of an Orillia hotel. What was later known as Huronia Regional Centre, started life as a branch of the "provincial lunatic asylum" (National Institute on Mental Retardation, 1981, p. 7). Within a few years, it was closed due to disrepair, but as the demand for services increased, the facility was reopened in 1876 as the "Orillia Hospital for Idiots and Imbeciles" (National Institute on Mental Retardation, 1981, p. 7). At its peak, this residential facility housed 2400 people (National Institute on Mental Retardation, 1981). Complaints about poor living conditions at the Orillia facility began as early as 1913 yet, changes were not made. Instead, another facility was built, the Ontario Hospital School in Smiths Falls, which opened in 1951. Parents and others concerned about the welfare of persons with developmental disabilities were unhappy with this focus on "the prevailing one-solution of a lifetime institutional care for retarded people" (Anglin & Braaten, 1978, p. 3). More people tried to keep their children out of institutions and at home, but there were few classes for them to attend until the Parents' Council for Retarded Children was formed in 1948. This lobby group subsequently joined with other similar groups to form the Ontario Association for Retarded Children (OARC), which later became the Ontario Association for Community Living. The lobbying efforts of the Parents' Council lead to the formation of school classes and integrated recreational programmes by the early 1950s.

Despite the push for community-based services, the large institutions were still thriving. However, the momentum of the deinstitutionalization movement was helped with Pierre Berton's scathing column describing the conditions at Orillia in 1959. This was followed by a film, commissioned by the Ontario Minister of Health, Dr. Matthew Dymond. The film, "One on Every Street remains a tribute to a courageous elected representative who dared to encourage the public to demand change" (Anglin & Braaten, 1978, p. 34).

The commitment toward the development of community services and the de-population of the traditional large institutions persisted through the 1960s. This process was given legitimacy with the 1967 passing of Dr. Dymond's "Bluebook" which advocated the support of children in their homes with the assistance of a coordinated system of community supports (Anglin & Braaten, 1978). A series of legislative reforms through the 1970s, 1980s and 1990s continued the process of deinstitutionalization in Ontario and the building of community support services.

The Ontario Association for Community Living (OACL) has continued to pursue the ideals of its founders. With a current membership of approximately 12 000, and over 100 affiliated associations across the province, the OACL's goal continues to focus on advocacy. "OACL's goal is 'that all persons live in a state of dignity, share in all elements of living in the community, and have the opportunity to participate effectively" (OACL, 2000). Its local member associations provide a wide variety of services across Ontario. The OACL provides information and resources for its member associations, and advocates with government to shape policy for Ontarians who have developmental disabilities (OACL, 2000).

In recent years a number of organizations have been formed to advocate and provide services for persons with developmental disabilities. These organizations, including the Habilitative Mental Health Resource Network, focus on a variety of issues of special interest to persons with disabilities, their families, and caregivers.

Biological Factors in Developmental Disabilities

In the case of Jack mentioned earlier, there were no obvious physical features that identified him as a person who had a developmental disability. This is the case with many people.

However, there are some conditions associated with developmental disability that include a variety of physical characteristics that make them identifiable. Every human being has approximately 100, 000 genes comprising a very complex jigsaw for researchers to piece together. However, with the formation of the international Human Genome Project (HGP) in 1988, the rate of genetic research has exploded. Every year, enormous strides are made toward the HGP's "goal of sequencing the entire human genome" (Hagerman, 1996, p. 416). The congenital origins of various forms of developmental disability have been uncovered; however, we have a long way to go before the biological roots of all disabilities will be known (Mehes & Kosztolanyi, 1998). In fact, in 30% to 50% of cases, it is not possible for physicians to determine the cause of developmental disability even after undertaking a complete evaluation (Daily, Ardinger & Holmes, 2000).

Chromosomal Abnormalities

Human genetic abnormalities are common, involving as many as 50% of humans conceived. Most genetic abnormalities result in spontaneous abortion; therefore, we do not see the result in the regular population. Although there are more than 100 genetic disorders, the most common are: Down syndrome, Phenylketonuria, and fragile x syndrome (Plomin, DeFries, & McClearn, 1980).

Down Syndrome

Down syndrome is a genetic disorder that accounts for about 10% of individuals labelled with moderate to severe retardation. Those with Down syndrome are easily recognized by their short stature, rounded face and almond eyes. Individuals with Down syndrome may also exhibit low muscle tone (hypotonia), short, broad hands with a single simian crease, hyperflexibility of the joints, and a small oral cavity which causes tongue protrusion. In addition, they may have accompanying physical complications such as heart, eye, respiratory, or ear problems.

As individuals who have Down Syndrome mature, they appear to have an increased disposition to depression, dementia, and Alzheimer's Disease as well as obesity (Loveland & Tunali-Kotoski in Burack, Hodapp, & Zigler, 1998).

Phenylketonuria

Phenylketonuria (PKU) is an unusual disorder that inhibits the production and performance of enzymes. The absence of a specific enzyme in the liver leads to a buildup of the amino acid *phenylalanine*. PKU can be treated using a specific diet. This diet puts stress on the family due to its requirements. PKU is detected at birth so the nutritional treatment can begin immediately. Mental retardation results if the diet is not begun soon enough or not adhered to (Smith, Polloway, Patton & Dowdy, 1998).

Fragile X Syndrome

Fragile x syndrome is the single most common inherited cause of mental impairment. Recent studies suggest that fragile x affects 1 in 2000 males, and 1 in 4000 females of all races and ethnic groups" (How prevalent is fragile x in the general population? 1997-2000). There is evidence that 1 in 259 women is a carrier of fragile x and, as such, has the capacity to pass it to her children. Men have been found to be carriers at a rate of 1 in 800. The vast majority of people who have fragile x syndrome have not been diagnosed (How prevalent is fragile x in the general population? 1997-2000). In 1992, a DNA based test was developed that identifies the presence of fragile x (Is there a way to test for fragile x? 1997-2000). The symptoms of fragile x include a wide range of intellectual disability including learning disabilities and intellectual disabilities, attention problems, anxiety, autistic-like behaviors, and physical features that include "long face, large ears, flat feet, and hyperextensible joints, especially fingers" (What are the common symptoms, 1997-2000). Behavioral and emotional difficulties tend to be present in both genders (What are the common symptoms, 1997-2000). However, boys tend to be more severely impacted than girls in terms of intellectual functioning. In fact, some girls have normal IQ levels, while approximately 80% of boys who have fragile x syndrome have a developmental challenge or disability, ranging from low-average intelligence to severe developmental disability (What are the common symptoms, 1997-2000; Hagerman, 1994).

Autism

Autism is a condition with lifelong implications. It is a Pervasive Developmental Disorder that is characterized by stereotypical, perseverative behaviors, resistance to environmental changes or change in routine, and unusual sensory experiences (Kirk, Gallagher, & Anastasiow, 2000). The expression of autism is variable with the symptoms ranging from close to normal to very severe symptoms. As a developmental diagnosis, the symptomatology varies with age. Diagnosis relies on the evaluation of a detailed developmental history, and it is important to note that autism can co-exist with other conditions. People who have autism function in a fairly wide intellectual range. By age five or six, 50% demonstrate significant delay in both non-verbal and verbal skills; 25% show delays in verbal skills but have normal nonverbal skills, while 25% function in the normal range in both verbal and nonverbal skills. Of even more importance is the assessment of adaptive functioning since this is a particularly problematic area for people who have autism (Freeman, http://www.autism-society.org/ packages/getstart_diagnosis.html).

Prader-Willi Syndrome

Prader-Willi Syndrome (PWS) is a complex genetic disorder that is typically characterized by low muscle tone, short stature, incomplete sexual development, cognitive deficits, behavior problems, and a chronic feeling of hunger that can lead to excessive eating and life-threatening obesity. Most cases of PWS are attributed to a spontaneous genetic error that occurs at or near the time of conception for unknown reasons. In a very small percentage of cases (two percent or less), a genetic mutation that does not affect the parent is passed on to the child, and in these families more than one child may be affected. A PWS-like disorder can also be acquired after birth if the hypothalamus portion of the brain is damaged through injury or surgery (Frequently Asked Questions – Prader-Willi Syndrome, 1999).

It is estimated that one in 12,000 to 15,000 people has PWS. Although considered a "rare" disorder, Prader-Willi syndrome is one of the most common genetic causes of obesity that has been identified. PWS is found in people of both sexes and all races (Frequently Asked Questions – Prader-Willi Syndrome, 1999).

In addition to their involuntary focus on food, people with PWS tend to have obsessive/compulsive behaviors that are not related to food, such as repetitive thoughts and verbalizations, collecting and hoarding of possessions, picking at skin irritations, and a strong need for routine and predictability. Frustration or changes in plans can easily set off a loss of emotional control in someone with PWS, ranging from tears to temper tantrums to physical aggression. While psychotropic medications can help some individuals, the essential strategies for minimizing difficult behaviours in PWS are careful structuring of the person's environment, and consistent use of positive behavior management and supports (Frequently Asked Questions – Prader-Willi Syndrome, 1999).

Although in the past many people with PWS died in adolescence or young adulthood, prevention of obesity can enable those with the syndrome to live a normal lifespan. New medications, including psychotropic drugs and synthetic growth hormone, are already improving the quality of life for some people with PWS. Ongoing research offers the hope of new discoveries that will enable people affected by this unusual condition to live more independent lives (Frequently Asked Questions – Prader-Willi Syndrome, 1999).

Cerebral Palsy

Cerebral Palsy (CP) is a group of disorders whose major feature is brain damage. Damage to the brain occurs before, during, or shortly after birth, and can be due to a variety of causes. Cerebral Palsy can result from a brain injury that may occur due to a fall down stairs, or a car accident. However, this is more commonly called Traumatic Brain Injury if the event occurs after the age of 3 (Types of Cerebral Palsy, 2000).

Unfortunately, many people automatically associate a physical disability with intellectual disability. If Jack, in the case described above, had had a mobility problem or unclear speech, it is likely that people would have assumed he had a developmental disability before it had been diagnosed. Because he was able to walk but did so at a slower rate than other children, his developmental disability was not obvious. On the other hand, many people who have mobility problems or other physical difficulties do not have an intellectual difficulty. The following description of the various types of Cerebral Palsy will help you to develop a more realistic view of the specific challenges associated with each.

There are four types of Cerebral Palsy: spastic, athetoid, ataxic, and mixed. Spastic or hypertonic Cerebral Palsy is characterized by tight muscles. Involuntary movements are present in athetoid (dyskinetic, hypotonic, dystonia) Cerebral Palsy. Ataxic Cerebral Palsy occurs when the cerebellum has been damaged, thus causing lack of coordination and jerky movements. Mixed is a combination of any of the above (Types of Cerebral Palsy, 2000).

Spastic Cerebral Palsy is the most common type of Cerebral Palsy, and it is present in about 50% of people with Cerebral Palsy. Spastic Cerebral Palsy may also be called hypertonic Cerebral Palsy since there is an over-abundance of muscle tone resulting in tightened muscles. It is common for individuals with spastic Cerebral Palsy to have learning disabilities or developmental disabilities. However, developmental disability is the exception, not the rule, and it is found in approximately 50% of those with spastic Cerebral Palsy, and 35-40% of the total population of people who have Cerebral Palsy (Types of Cerebral Palsy, 2000).

Among people who have athetoid or dyskinetic Cerebral Palsy, unintentional or uncontrolled movements will often be seen. This is due to an ever-changing level of muscle tone. This type of Cerebral Palsy accounts for up to 30% of all persons with cerebral palsy (Types of Cerebral Palsy, 2000).

Some Other Terms for Cerebral Palsy

- Traumatic Brain Injury
- Little's Disease
- Infantile Cerebral Paralysis
- Dyskinetic Cerebral Palsy or Dystonia (Athetoid Cerebral Palsy)

Did You Know...

United Cerebral Palsy Association (UCPA) estimates that between one and three of every 1,000 births will have Cerebral Palsy (Types of Cerebral Palsy, 2000).

Family Stress and Advocacy

Families that include a member who has a developmental disability face many special challenges. Parents must grapple with the loss of the child they anticipated, and with the challenges presented by their child's special needs. "When a child has a disability, the mismatch between child and parental expectations and behavior may be high; feelings of grief, denial, and profound disappointment are often experienced by the parents as they mourn the loss of the healthy baby they had hoped for" (Singer & Powers, 1993, p. 26). Siblings may be embarrassed by their brother or sister who has a disability. They may be asked to be their sibling's protector, or may be expected to take on extra responsibilities within the family (Powell & Gallagher, 1993).

On the other hand, some families who have a member with a disability grow stronger and closer. Key factors that contribute to the successful adaptation of families include their ability to mobilize personal, family, extended family and community resources, and the interpretation they give to the challenges they face. Those families who are able to mobilize their available resources successfully are more likely to adjust to the challenges associated with supporting a member who has a disability (Gladding, 1998).

These two opposing views, the family disruption approach versus the family resilience approach, have characterized the literature on families which include a member who has a disability. However, some researchers have suggested a middle ground: that families can be both disrupted in the face of challenges presented by a member with a developmental disability, but they can also exhibit resilience such as supportive emotional tone and interpersonal connectedness (Costigan, Floyd, Harter & McClintock, 1997). In the case discussed earlier in the chapter, Jack's mother certainly experienced stress as she sought answers to her concerns about her son's development. However, she was able to access the appropriate resources that could help him to develop, and could support her family. From the advent of the Parents for Retarded Children in Ontario, this need to find services for family members who have a developmental disability has been a driving force in the development of advocacy groups that have prompted service development and service evolution. Increasingly, people who have developmental disabilities have been actively involved in advocacy. Currently, six self-advocates hold positions on the Board of Directors of the Canadian Association for Community Living

(Canadian Association for Community Living, 2000).

Dual Diagnosis:

The term "dual diagnosis" is used when developmental disabilities are further complicated by mental illness. For many years, practitioners believed that it was not possible for a person to have both a developmental disability and a psychiatric diagnosis. Any behavioral differences were attributed to the developmental disability alone. Fortunately, as attitudes have shifted over the past twenty years, individuals who have both a developmental disability and psychiatric concerns have increasing access to both systems of care, and in some cases, to integrated care plans. Persons with a developmental disability, combined with significant behavioral or psychiatric problems, will require an holistic treatment plan which may include a range of services and supports, including various forms of psychotherapy, psychotropic medication, behavioral counselling, social supports and other individualized services to assist in their inclusion in society. Full inclusion in the community can be hampered by the individual's limitations in cognitive level, interpersonal skills, and adjustment problems both socially and in the world of work. Later chapters in this book will address diagnostic, therapeutic and social issues facing people who have both a developmental disability and a mental health problem.

Back to the Case:

Like many other people who have a developmental disability, the cause of Jack's delay has not yet been identified. However, as the international work of the Human Genome Project progresses, it is likely that the biological underpinnings of Jack's challenges will be uncovered. Whether this will lead to improved medical interventions, or to strategies for preventing future generations from developing similar difficulties remains to be seen. However, just as the quality of Jack's life would have been better had he been born at the end rather than at the beginning of the 20th century, the opportunities for improved treatment and quality of life are increasing as we enter the 21st century. Thanks to the availability of community-based services, Jack could expect to have the opportunity to move into a supported living programme, and to participate in the work force.

Summary

Throughout our history as human beings, we have developed various strategies for either victimizing or supporting those among us who have special needs. Developmental disabilities have been used as justification for pressing people into slavery, or putting them to death as witches. Religious convictions regarding care for the less fortunate helped to increase the resources devoted to support for people with various challenges. With the increase in our understanding of genetics and neurology, there has been an increase in our understanding of the nature of various conditions associated with developmental disabilities. Advances in psychopharmacaolgy, education and therapy have improved the quality of life for people with a variety of challenges related to developmental disability. Of even more importance with regard to life quality have been the advocacy movements and changes in public policy which have resulted in a shift from institutional to community support systems. Full inclusion of persons who have a developmental disability in all aspects of school, work and social life is far from being a reality; however, great strides continue to be made so that all people may have the opportunity to live the life they choose.

Do You Know?

1. How have attitudes and interventions for people who have developmental disabilities changed over time?
2. What impact has the deinstitutionalization movement had on the quality of life of persons who have developmental disabilities?
3. Why do siblings of individuals who have developmental disabilities tend to experience social and family pressure?
4. What role has an organized advocacy movement played in the development of services for people with developmental disabilities in Ontario?

Resources

Autism Society Ontario. Available: http://netrover.com/~southgve/autismso.htm (This is the home page for the ASO. It describes the organization's mission and includes links to other ASO chapters.)

Autism Society of America. Available: http://www.autism-society.org (This site includes a wide variety of material produced and distributed by the Society including conference and research information. The site also has a search engine.)

Canadian Association for Community Living. Available: http://www.cacl.ca (This site provides information about National and Provincial programmes that support people in community settings.)

Centers for Disease Control and Prevention: Division of Birth Defects , Child Development and Disability and Health. Available: http://www.cdc.gov/nceh/cddh/Default.htm (This site includes information and links related to the biological bases of child developmental concerns.)

Council   for   Exceptional   Children.   Available: http://www.cec.sped.org (This is the homepage for CEC which includes links to pages that describe the organization's training events, literature and public policy information.)

Mencap. Available:
http://www.gmp.police.uk/mencap/index.html (This site describes the work of the largest charity serving people who have learning disabilities in Britain.)

National Information Center for Children and Youth with Disabilities. Available:
http://www.kidsource.com/NICHCY/index.html (This site has links to a wide variety of material of interest to parents and others who are concerned about the needs of children who have various challenges.)

Roeher Institute. Available: http://www.roeher.ca/roeher (This site provides information about research, training and publications provided through this major research institute.)

The ARC (1998). Introduction to mental retardation. Available: http://thearc.org/gaqs/mrqa.html (This site developed by the ARC in the United States, provides a very basic introduction to mental retardation, its diagnosis, causes and prevention.)

References

AAMR Fact Sheet: What is Mental Retardation? Available: http://www.aamr.org/Policies/faqmentalretardation.html

American Association on Mental Retardation (1992). *Mental retardation: Definition, classification, and systems of support workbook.* Washington, DC: American Association on Mental Retardation.

American Psychiatric Association (1994). *Diagnostic Criteria from DSM – IV.* Washington, DC: American Psychiatric Association.

Anglin, B. & Braaten, J. (1978). *Twenty five years of growing together: A history of the Ontario Association for the Mentally Retarded.* Toronto: Canadian Association for the Mentally Retarded.

Bogdan, R. & Taylor, S. J. (1982). *Inside out: Two first-person accounts of what it means to be labeled 'mentally retarded'.* Toronto: University of Toronto Press.

Burack, J., Hodapp, R. & Zigler, E. (Eds.). (1998). *Handbook of mental retardation and development.* New York: Cambridge University Press.

Canadian Association for Community Living (2000). What we do. Available: http://www.cacl.ca/english/what.html

Costigan, C.L., Floyd, F.J., Harter, K.S.M., & McClintock, J.C. (1997). Family process and adaptation to children with mental retardation: Disruption and resilience in family problem-solving interactions. *Journal of Family Psychology, 11*, 515-529.

Daily, D. K., Ardinger, H.H. & Holmes, G.E. (2000). Identification and evaluation of mental retardation. *American Family Physician, 61,* 1059-1067 (abstract).

Freeman, B.J. Diagnosis of the syndrome of autism: Questions parents ask. Available: http://www.autism-society.org/packages/getstart_diagnosis.html

Frequently Asked Questions-Prader-Willi Syndrome (1999). Available: http://www.pwsausa.org/

Gladding, S.T. (1998). *Family therapy: History, theory and practice.* Upper Saddle River, NJ: Merrill.

Hagerman, R. (1994). Fragile X syndrome. Available: http://thearc.org/faqs/fragqa.html

Hagerman, R.J. (1996). Biomedical advances in developmental psychology: The case of Fragile X Syndrome. *Developmental Psychology, 32,* 416-424.

How prevalent is fragile X in the general population? (1997-2000) Available: http://www.fraxa.org/html/about_prevalence.htm

Is there a way to test for Fragile X? (1997-2000). Available: http://www.fraxa.org/html/about_testing.htm

Kirk, S., Gallagher, J., & Anastasiow, N. (2000). *Educating exceptional children.* Boston: Houghton Mifflin Company.

Landesman, S. & Ramey, C. (1989). Developmental psychology and mental retardation: Integrating scientific principles with treatment practices. *American Psychologist, 44,* 409-415.

List of Educational Statistics (1997). Available: http://nces.ed.gov/pubs99/digest98/listoftables.html

Mehes, K. & Kosztolanyi, G. (1998). Genetic evaluation of mental retardation. *Orv Hetil, 139,* 339-346 (abstract).

National Institute on Mental Retardation (1981). *Orientation manual on mental retardation.* Downsview, Ontario: National Institute on Mental Retardation.

Ontario Association for Community Living. Who we are and what we do. Available:
http://www.acl.on.ca/about/wwa.html

PL 94-103, Developmentally Disabled Assistance and Bill or Rights Act of 1975.

Powell, T.H. & Gallagher, P. A. (1993). *Brothers & sisters: A special part of exceptional families.* (2nd ed.) Baltimore: Paul H. Brookes Publishing Co.

Scheerenberger, R. C. (1983). *A history of mental retardation.*

Baltimore: Paul H. Brookes Publishing Co.

Singer, G. H.S. & Powers, L.E. (1993). *Families, disability and empowerment: Active coping skills and strategies for family interventions.* Baltimore: Paul H. Brookes Publishing Co.

Smith, T., Polloway, E., Patton, J., Dowdy, C. (1998). *Teaching students with special needs in inclusive settings.* Boston: Allyn and Bacon.

Types of Cerebral Palsy (2000). Available: http://dir.lycos.com/Health/Conditions_and_Diseases/C/Cerebral_Palsy/Types_of_CP/

What are the common symptoms? (1997-2000). Available: http://www.fraxa.org/html/about_symptoms.htm

What is Learning Disability? Available: http://www.gmp.police.uk/mencap/learndis.html

What is Mencap? Available: http://www.gmp.police.uk/mencap/whatis.html

Williston, W. B. (1971). *Present arrangements for the care and supervision of mentally retarded persons in Ontario: A report of the Minister of Health.* Toronto: Ontario Department of Health.

Chapter 2

The Mental Health Needs of
Persons with Developmental Disabilities

Elspeth Bradley and Lillian Burke

Learning Objectives

Readers will be able to:

1. Have an understanding of the mental health needs of persons with developmental disabilities from a developmental perspective
2. Be able to identify circumstances contributing to mental health disturbances in persons with developmental disabilities
3. Be able to identify circumstances contributing to optimal mental well being
4. Have an appreciation of how some mental health disturbances may be avoided

Introduction

We all have needs which, if met, serve to maintain optimal mental health. The mental health needs of the person with a developmental disability are fundamentally the same as for all other human beings. As humans, we are essentially social creatures; we are constantly seeking, and need shared experi-

ences with others. This validates our own experience and
daily reality, and is a necessary requirement in healthy growth,
development and mental wellness across the lifespan. The
person with a developmental disability may appear to be different from the non-disabled individual, behave differently,
and communicate differently; as such, we find it more difficult
to appreciate our shared human experience with that person.
The difficulty of the non-disabled person in relating to the human experience and emotional expression of the disabled person has been a particular tragedy for persons with developmental disabilities. As a result, they have suffered, and continue to suffer greater disadvantage in many aspects of their
lives (including health care) than might otherwise be the case.
If we could better understand their perspective, and better understand their unique ways of communicating, whether this be
about a physical illness, emotional distress, or some other upset in their daily environment, non-disabled people could respond more appropriately:

Mel relies on non-verbal behaviours to communicate the distressing experiences in his life (see case example 1 for An Introduction to Mel). To better understand his behaviour, it
would be prudent to imagine what it is like to attempt to communicate his daily needs, frustrations, and discomforts from
the limited vantage point of his world. His history, the nature
of his developmental disability, and his medical conditions
shed light on this. Without such perspective, we are at risk of
seeing his behaviour as needing to be controlled or eliminated
rather than as an attempt to communicate his needs to his caregivers.

The Case of Mel

Mel is a 29 year old man diagnosed with visual impairment and autism. Mel is not verbal, and communicates non verbally - which includes some gestures and a few signs. Mel lives in a group home, and while he has been assigned a day program, he is rarely able to attend. He has had the same support staff for many years, and maintains contact with his family. When he is doing well, he is generally pleasant, calm, affectionate and will participate in activities. However, if distressed he may scream, self-injure, strike out at others or cause destruction in his environment.

Mel has a history of many medical problems. Shortly after his birth, there was concern about his vision. Optic nerve damage was diagnosed; Mel now has no vision. He was reported very early to have indicators of autism, including stereotypies and unusual sensory behaviours, as well as communication and social impairments. Reports indicate that his sleep cycle has always been disturbed. He has a long history of rubbing his eyes aggressively, causing trauma to the surrounding tissue. He has many environmental allergies, and has been subject to frequent ear infections. He has also had grand mal seizures. Mel has been prescribed many oral and topical medications over the years for his various medical problems. Mel's history of self-injury, allergic reactions, and associated discomfort, seizures, and symptoms believed associated with an autistic disorder, and attempts to treat these have culminated in a cycle of distress. Those supporting Mel now feel it is beyond their resources to manage him. His cycle begins with signs of allergic reaction after which Mel scratches or rubs the irritated area intensely, causing bleeding and bruising. During these periods, he will also bang his head with objects, or strike his head against walls. Sedation and topical treatments are given at this time. The sedation is to calm him, while the ointments provide local relief and assist the healing process. Sometimes severe, self-injurious behaviour occurs before the sedation/topical treatments have been effective. Further, after healing has occurred, when medications are withdrawn, he has been known to have violent reactions which some have questioned may be withdrawal seizures.

Development across the life span

All of us are born with a potential for further growth and further development. Fully realized, this potential is associated with the extent to which environments are nurturing and supportive, and offer opportunities and challenges to which we can comfortably respond. Persons with developmental disabilities may have suffered brain damage (see biological contributions to developmental disabilities under mental health vulnerabilities) may have been exposed to environments in their early lives which have been insufficiently nurturing or lacking in opportunities (see environmental and socioeconomic contributions to developmental disabilities). These early circumstances can limit the individual's potential, and delay and / or distort normal developmental pathways. However, we are now also aware that, regardless of the individual's unique potential, society's response to the person with a disability has a profound impact on the extent to which the person is disabled as an adult. See Box 1 for definitions and further understanding of impairments, disabilities and handicaps.

Box 1. Prevention of further disabilities and handicaps

In the context of health experience the World Health Organization (1980) has defined **impairment**, **disability** and **handicap** as:

impairment:	any loss or abnormality of psychological, physiological, or anatomical structure or function
disability:	any restriction or lack (resulting from an impairment) of ability to perform an activity in a manner or within the range considered normal for a human being
handicap:	a disadvantage for a given individual resulting from an impairment or a disability that limits or prevents the fulfillment of a role that is normal (depending on age, sex, and social and cultural factors) for that individual

An example of a **hearing impairment** would be loss of hearing, resulting from damage to the inner ear from infection. Many aspects of our daily existence have developed around the capacity to hear (e.g. communication - speech; entertainment - music; danger sign - sirens). Persons without hearing are not able to listen (they then suffer a **hearing disability**), and are thus excluded from activities that rely entirely on being able to hear (giving rise to a **hearing handicap**). If our social world was organized around vision (e.g. communication - signing, entertainment - visual, danger sign - flashing light) the hearing impaired person would not be disabled or handicapped in this visual world. If the hearing impaired person is provided hearing aid he or she may no longer have a hearing disability.

Impairments ⓪ Disabilities ⓪ Handicaps

In working with persons with developmental disabilities, the goal is to prevent and/ or minimize the impairments, disabilities, and handicaps.

For example, **hearing impairment** can be eliminated or reduced by identifying persons at risk, screening vulnerable groups, providing early intervention and treatment with antibiotics for ear infections. **Hearing disability** can be reduced by screening for hearing impairments, and providing hearing aids and augmentative communication aids. **Hearing handicap** can be reduced by adapting the external environment, and the social behaviour of hearing carers, to meet needs of the hearing impaired individual.

Developmental patterns and pathways across the lifespan

We are now beginning to understand some of the particular challenges that certain syndromes such as Down, Prader Willi, and fragile x syndrome present to the individual at different stages of life. This information is helpful in planning optimal educational opportunities, and in helping to avoid secondary disabilities and handicaps, and further damaging experiences. However, this research is relatively recent, and much still needs to be understood. In the meanwhile, it seems reasonable to consider that the person with a developmental disability passes through similar developmental stages as the person without such disabilities, even though this may be at a slower pace, and he/she may not reach the same end point.

There are two major areas in human development where an understanding of the usual sequence of events across the lifespan is particularly helpful in trying to provide optimal and appropriate supports for the person with a developmental disability.

(a)   Cognitive development

Piaget (1896 - 1980), a Swiss biologist, has helped us understand normal cognitive development. He described four different types of thinking (cognitive structures), occurring at different stages of development: birth - 2 years; 2 - 7 years; 7 - 12 years; 12 years to adulthood. Humans pass through different thinking stages, each influencing the way the individual perceives and interacts with the world around him or her (See Box 2). An analogy might be made to the way some creatures such as amphibians pass though different stages requiring different supportive environments (e.g., tadpole with gills and limbs requiring aquatic environment; adult frog with lungs requiring air).

(b)   Psychosocial and emotional development

Erikson (1902 - 1994), an American psychoanalyst and scholar with interests in cultural anthropology, child development, social psychology and the study of man in history, has helped us understand patterns of emotional experience across the life span. He described 8 stages of psychosocial development from birth to old age. In these stages, issues in the development of trust, independence, initiative, self esteem, identity, intimacy, isolation, despair and success are encountered, and may or may not be successfully resolved (see Box 2).

Both Piaget and Erikson have rooted their developmental stages relative to the chronological age of normally developing individuals. Of course, there will be some variation between individuals both in the tasks that are achieved by a certain age, and the sequence by which these tasks are achieved. But for the most part, most individuals will, by a certain age, have achieved success in the age related tasks appropriate for that age, and will have achieved success in all previous age related tasks. A person with a developmental disability lags behind his/her non disabled age peers in many aspects of mental development. While both are the same chronological age, the

---

Box 2. Developmental Stages of Piaget and Erikson
(adapted from Papalia, Olds, & Feldman, 1989)

Psychosocial Development (Erikson)   *Cognitive Development (Piaget)*

Basic Trust vs. Mistrust
(Birth - 12-18 mon.) Learns whether
his (her) world is a place where he/
she can trust others

Sensorimotor (Birth - 2yr.) Infant
changes from primarily reflexive responses to learning about environment
through senses and motor actions.

Autonomy vs. Shame/Doubt
(1-3 yr.) Develops some independence from caretaker or experiences
shame/self-doubt

Preoperational (2-7 yr.) Develops a
representational system: e.g. words,
gestures.

Concrete operations (7-12 yr.) Logical
problem solving on here/now issues.

Initiative vs. Guilt (3-6 yr.) Develops
initiative through new experiences or
feels failure

Formal operations (12 yr. - adult)
Thinking in abstract terms and being
able to hypothesize.

Industry vs. Inferiority (6 yr. - Puberty) Learns skills of culture or feels
inferior to others

Identity vs. Role Confusion (Puberty -
Yg. Adult) Develops self-identify or
experiences confused sense of self

Intimacy vs. Isolation
(Yg. Adult) Develops relationships or
feels isolated.

Generativity vs. Stagnation (Adult)
Guides/supports the next generation

Integrity vs. Despair (Old Age)
Accepts one's life and accomplish-
ments or feels dissatisfied/despair.

---

person with a developmental disability is functioning at previous developmental stages. Cognitively, the person with a
developmental disability may not progress through all types of
thinking. However, socially and emotionally, he/she will con-

front the same issues. His/her cognitive limitations may in part inhibit resolution of these issues. It is important that care-givers recognize the developmental stages their client/relative has reached across the various domains of mental and emo-tional development. A clearer understanding of the client's ac-tual level of functioning, and the meaning of his/her life ex-periences can guide the carer in assisting the client to gain more mastery in life skills within his/her ability, and to de-velop a belief in his/her own competence. These latter experi-ences will, for the client, dispel the disquieting fear/anxiety of not being adequate.

How can an understanding of cognitive and emotional devel-opment help us to respond more optimally to Mel and provide him with more appropriate supports?

Mel has severe/profound developmental disability (as defined by APA, 1994). In addition, he has visual impairment or men-tal retardation, and has a diagnosis of autism. These three cir-cumstances will impact on his ability to function, and will combine to limit his ability to be aware of, and to process in-formation about his environment. Applying Piaget's under-standing, he is functioning in the Early Pre-operational stage (see Box 2), with some behaviours still in evidence from the Sensorimotor stage.

Mel is able to understand and respond to verbal information/ requests from others. He has been able to learn some sign lan-guage which he uses to make his needs known. These are indi-cators of a representational system, and are skills indicative of having reached the Pre-operational stage in some cognitive ar-eas. He shows an understanding of concepts that would have developed in the Sensorimotor stage: he can lead people to places to show what he wants, such as to the kitchen to get cookies (an indication of "object permanence"). He knows how some items in the house function/turn on and off (an indicator of "operational causality"). However, Mel still responds with many reflexive responses (e.g., oversensitivity to sounds/ touch), and engages in sensory-based activities (e.g., rocking or self injury in response to discomfort), at a level one would expect of someone still in the Sensorimotor stage.

Emotionally, Mel is in Erikson's second stage: Autonomy vs Shame and Doubt. He has developed some sense of the social world, and enjoys interactions with others. He does initiate in a limited way his own actions, such as going to lie down during the day, requesting food, or requesting an outing. However, he is still dependent on others for his basic needs, and often others are unable to respect or follow through with choices he makes for himself. He is not at the point of initiating new, unlearned acts.

The Case of Sam

Sam is a man in his thirties who has a mild developmental disability. His parents are high achieving professionals as are his older brother and sister. The family's lifestyle has allowed Sam to have many opportunities to which other persons with a developmental disability may not have had access. He has traveled extensively, enjoys recreational activities such as skiing, horseback riding, going to concerts and theaters. He is currently living in an apartment with a roommate and receives support from an agency staff. He attends a sheltered workshop part time, and programs offering training in daily living skills and recreational opportunities part time. He has a special female friend, but has no close male friends. His primary support, both for his needs and his socialization, continues to be family. Sam takes medication because he hears voices and re-acts overtly to them. These are not believed to be due to a psy-chotic disorder, but due to anxiety based in developmental ex-periences as outlined below.

Sam developed speech late, and was not talking when he started school. He was teased by classmates who called him "retard". Sam's family arranged activities for him, and tried to ensure he had stimulation and social interaction. Sam reports that many adults were also rude to him during his childhood. The most difficult period for him seemed to be adolescence when same-aged classmates were going to parties and on dates, and he was excluded. His older brother and sister were socially active, and this reinforced for Sam that he was differ-ent. Sam has vivid memories of a party his brother had, and when his brother was not in the room, the teenagers there taunted Sam and made rude comments to him.

Sam was an overachiever in school, having a good memory and being able to read beyond most of his peers with a comparable delay. His family encouraged him. Sam, striving not to be handicapped, seems to have pushed himself beyond his limits. He was accepted into an early childhood education program at a community college, and during that year had a "breakdown". He began to present as depressed, engaged in self-talk, and re-ported hearing voices. Usually, the voices told him he was "stupid" or "no good". The family wanted him diagnosed with a label and prescribed a cure. Those professionals supporting Sam, however, believed that he had pushed himself past his lim-its, and had recognized he could not achieve what he had been attempting. He was responding to voices from the past that had told him he was stupid and no good. He experienced high anxi-ety, and his self esteem was very low during this period. He has been treated with medication and individual therapy for about three years. Sam goes through long periods where he appears to experience few distressing symptoms. He goes through other periods where the voices become stronger. He responds overtly to them, and he has difficulty continuing his daily activities. There appear to be some events that trigger the anxiety and voices including: school beginning in the fall; visits from his siblings; parties/social events with unfamiliar people.

Sam's early experiences, including labeling, name calling and other negative social feedback seem to have had a profound and damaging influence on him, even though he has had a supportive family and many opportunities which other persons in his situation do not have. The memories which are triggered present much like a flashback does to people who have been traumatized. Many individuals we have worked with who have had negative social experiences, do have intrusive memories that have an impact on their vocational, social and daily lives. They are misunderstood by their friends, professionals and their caregivers.

Sam functions in the mild range of developmental disability (or mental retardation as defined by APA, 1994). Applying Piaget's understanding, he is functioning at the Concrete Operations stage.

Sam can read, write, do basic arithmetic, care for his daily hygiene, do some household chores/cooking, hold a job, take public transportation, and can solve basic problems if they are focused on the here and now (i.e., are concrete). He dates, shops with friends and attends social activities. Sam may not always be able to project into the future, so may not weigh the consequences of an action before he engages in it. Issues which are complex, such as legal and medical decisions with potential problems and implications require explanation.

Emotionally, Sam is in Erikson's sixth stage: Intimacy vs Isolation. He has not achieved resolution of all the issues at this stage. Many of his relationships have been arranged by family/care providers. These relationships come to a natural end, which leaves him feeling loss and rejection. Those which are naturally occurring relationships, such as that with his girlfriend, are few. Although he has reached this stage, he has not achieved full resolution of issues at previous stages – i.e., the fourth, Industry vs Inferiority. He is aware he is different from his family members, and can never achieve what they do, and he feels inferior because of this. As well, issues from Erikson's fifth state (Identity vs. Role Confusion) carry forward: his awareness of being different from others, his attempts to figure out where he fits, and his attempts to come to terms with himself and accept his own limitations.

What needs to be in place to help Mel and Sam reach their potential?

For Mel and Sam to reach their potential, those supporting them must understand the developmental stages and have awareness of where Mel and Sam are along that developmental path. Mel and Sam must be encouraged to take the next developmental steps without making huge leaps that place unrealistic expectations on them. For example, for Mel, it may be important to have more material/activities available, and to teach him how they are used so he can engage in independent activity. It may also mean providing him with a better communication system with which to express himself. For Sam, it may mean counseling to help him come to terms with his limitations, and to help him in recognizing the strengths he has, and the positive relationships he has been able to develop on his own. Identifying what is at the next developmental step, providing opportunities to learn tasks at that step, and providing reinforcement for success and encouragement when success is not quite achieved, will be most helpful in moving them toward their potential. Care-providers must also understand that there will eventually be limits to what each individual can achieve, and they should respect that rather than push the individual past that point.

Mental health: Vulnerability

We are now beginning to understand some of the factors that may leave some of us more **vulnerable** to mental health disturbances and psychiatric disorders. For example (1) loss of a primary caregiver (usually the mother) before the age of eleven may result in an increased risk for developing depression as an adult; (2) having a family history of anxiety or mood disorders may provide an increased risk for developing such disorders.

However, we are also beginning to understand what factors help to protect us from developing such disturbances. The same individual at risk for depression may develop **resilience** to depression by developing a supportive social network, by having a close relationship and satisfying partnerships with a spouse. Likewise, the individual with a genetic vulnerability to psychiatric disorder may become more resilient to the onset or impact of such disorder by identifying environmental stressors, becoming sensitive to the early development of symptoms, and being able to access preventive interventions as required, such as lifestyle changes, counseling, psychotherapy and medication.

There are many additional circumstances which predispose

persons with developmental disabilities to mental health disturbances; this predisposition also leaves them more vulnerable to the negative impact of normal life events. In addition, having a developmental disability predisposes the person to more negative life experiences and traumas; for example, persons with developmental disabilities are at greater risk than peers without such disabilities for physical and sexual abuses.

The biological, psychological and social circumstances that contribute vulnerability to mental health disturbances in persons with developmental disabilities are described below (see Box 3).

Box 3.   Vulnerabilities - Check List

Circumstances causing or contributing to mental health and behavioural disturbances in persons with developmental disabilities:

Biological
Brain Damage; Dementia; Epilepsy; Sensory (e.g., vision, hearing) impairments;   Sensory (e.g., visual , auditory) processing problems;   Physical illnesses other medical treatments

Psychological
Distorted personality development;   Separations / losses; Deprivation / abuse / trauma;   Other life events;   Positive / negative learning experiences;   Self-insight / self-esteem;   Communication difficulties;   Language disorders; Psychological impact of the above biological factors on the individual

---

Social
Attitudes - negative social feedback; Labeling; Rejection; Infantilization; Victimization; Unrealistic expectations; Few / limited repertoire of coping strategies; Inadequate supports / relationships; Inappropriate environments / services; Under-/ overstimulation; Valued / stigmatized roles; Financial / legal disadvantage

Family
Diagnostic and bereavement issues; Life cycle transitions / crises; "Letting go"; Psychiatric and emotional disorders in immediate family members;
Stress / adaption to disabilities; Relationships / resources (financial, emotional, supports)

(a) Biological

In persons without developmental disabilities, brain damage, epilepsy and dementia are all associated with an increased prevalence of behavioural disturbance and/or psychiatric disorder. As a group, persons with developmental disabilities have an increased prevalence of brain damage and seizure disorders. At least 25% of all cases of mental retardation are known to be caused by biological abnormalities which affect the brain (and often other body systems). Seizure disorders are increased proportionately as the level of cognitive disability becomes more severe (one in two individuals with profound developmental disability may have a seizure disorder). Dementia appears to be more prevalent in some conditions associated with developmental disability (e.g., most persons with Down Syndrome over the age of forty show the neuropathological changes of Alzheimer's dementia, and some go on to develop the disease at an earlier age than the population without developmental disability).

Some syndromes associated with developmental disability appear to be associated with an increased risk for certain psychiatric disorders (e.g., mood and anxiety disorders in persons with Autism and Down Syndrome). Some syndromes run in families (e.g., fragile x). In the general population, there is a genetic predisposition to certain psychiatric disorders (e.g., some mood and anxiety disorders are more prevalent in some families). A person with a developmental disability with a family history of psychiatric disorder may also, therefore, be at increased risk for such disorder.

As a group, there is a greater prevalence of physical illnesses, such as ear, nose, mouth problems, congenital heart disease and gastrointestinal disorders, physical disabilities such as Cerebral Palsy and sensory impairments and unusual physical appearance. Any illness, physical disability or unusual appearance usually has associated psychological consequences for the individual as he/she comes to terms with the loss or absence of a fully functioning sense of self. The addition of these problems, and others' reactions to these problems, may add to the negative self image and low self esteem experienced by many persons with developmental disabilities.

Persons with developmental disabilities as a group are less able to share their inner experiences and describe their experience of pain and bodily discomforts. As such, they are at greater risk for medical misdiagnoses (e.g., misattributing oesophageal reflux induced sleep disturbance to the behaviour of someone with a developmental disability, otherwise referred to as "diagnostic overshadowing"), and negative outcomes from therapeutic interventions (e.g., side effects from medications). These latter "iatrogenic" biological factors can also contribute to mental health and behavioural disturbances.

It is very important to identify an individual's biological vulnerabilities. It offers the opportunity to design and implement interventions that will serve to increase resilience associated with these vulnerabilities. For example, in recent years, there has been an explosion of knowledge in understanding certain syndromes associated with developmental disability, such as Down, Prader Willi, fragile x, and 22 Deletion Syndromes. Proactive health guidelines are now available for many of these syndromes.

(b)   Psychological

All of us express our temperament early in infancy. That is, we will have differences in activity level, mood and how we adapt to changes in the environment. Throughout the developmental period, temperament will influence how people respond to us and how we respond to others. The experiences we have in our social environment, influenced by our temperament, are said to result in our own unique personality. Our personality is made up of characteristics others see in us such as introversion/extroversion, and which allow others and ourselves to anticipate how we will act in a certain situation. For example, the introvert is shy and withdrawn, and tends to focus on his internal world; the extrovert is comfortable in social situations, and seeks out others.

When a person has a developmental disability, his/her personality will develop in that same manner as it does for the rest of us. However, there are often some differences in the developmental experiences of persons with developmental disabilities. These atypical experiences during development have allowed researchers to predict how this will affect the personality of the person with a developmental disability. For example, a person with a developmental disability is often excluded from activities (e.g., minor sports, teenage parties). He/she may have to endure stigmatizing perceptions and negative social reactions and comments. He/she often begins early in childhood by requiring more assistance than others would in physical, communication and learning areas. People may become accustomed to helping him/her, and he/she may become accustomed to being helped, so that the experience of managing with less assistance is not developed. Personality characteristics often seen in persons with developmental disabilities include overdependence, lack of confidence, poor self-identity, or low self-esteem. These characteristics may also decrease the person's development of good ways to cope with psychological, social and biological experiences the person may encounter, and may increase his/her vulnerability for psychological/emotional difficulties. When the person with a developmental disability encounters life events such as separation/loss, personal or family milestones, or experiences requiring learning and/or insight, illness of self or others, or extreme events such as deprivation, abuse or trauma, the individual may have poor coping strategies, and may be more vulnerable to a range of mood and anxiety disorders.

(c)   Social

Individuals with developmental disabilities are often socially isolated or have social networks that are made up of primarily family members and "artificial" friendships. While some people with developmental disabilities may have more normal friendships or play relationships early in childhood, their differences separate them from same-age others as they reach adolescence and on into adulthood. Usually persons with developmental disabilities are not included in the activities of their classmates, and are in fact, often overtly shunned. Family tends to arrange social activities for them. This may include bowling or swimming for persons with disabilities, special needs workers or volunteers to take the person out and to assist in teaching social and adaptive skills. Other social engagements tend to be with family or with the friends of the parents. When the person with a developmental disability reaches an age where he/she may leave home, usually an agency or family decides where the person will live, and who he/she will live with. If the person doesn't get along with roommates, he/she is often identified as having behavioral problems. He/she may have few, if any, naturally developing relationships; and thus start to identify staff as friends. This can be problematic because staff leave and the individual may feel repeatedly rejected.

The individual with a developmental disability is easily victimized. He or she may have poorly developed social boundaries because of a lack of experience in social situations, may be easily intimidated or coerced because (s)he's been taught to comply, and may appreciate attention paid, even if its inappropriate attention. Therefore, the person with a developmental disability is prone to be exploited sexually, financially and in many other ways.

If an individual has been encouraged and given the opportunity to develop a good social network, has had access to realistic role models, and has been taught to value him/herself, he/she will feel included and achieve some degree of social success/

happiness. However, if the individual has not achieved a positive social network, and has poor self-identify/low self-esteem, the individual may strive to belong or be accepted without always having appropriate or realistic role models from whom to base expectations of him/herself. Television and movies portray beautiful and successful people, and put high value on relationships. The person with a developmental disability who has poor self-perception or low self-esteem may have a life that, by comparison to successful siblings or TV soap stars, may feel unhappy and unsuccessful. He or she may express anxiety behaviours, changes in mood or other behavioral disturbances, including those which may be misinterpreted as psychosis, such as an active fantasy life or self-talk.

In what way might Mel (Case Example 1) or Sam (Case Example 2) be vulnerable to mental health disturbances?

Mel is unable to communicate his needs apart from a few non specific gestures and a few learned signs. This leaves him unable to communicate pain (resulting in medical conditions and bodily discomforts remaining unrecognized), anger, frustration, happiness, and many of his feelings outside of behaviours which reflect or cxpress these in some way. Mel is dependent on others to identify the causes of his upset behaviours. He is dependent on others to take him places, and to provide his basic needs. This means he must place a great deal of trust in people. Because he cannot communicate things that frighten him, or relate experiences of his past that may have been terrible for him, those care providers may inadvertently put him in a situation which is daunting to him. This inability to express his experiences of pain and bodily discomforts, his needs and feelings, the need to trust when venturing into the unknown, and the possible occurrence of being retraumatized without others knowing, make Mel vulnerable to mental health disturbances.

Sam has many skills and abilities. However, he is aware he is never going to be able to accomplish the same things as those to whom he is closest. Therefore, he is in a constant state of feeling different/inferior. As Sam grew up, others pointed out his differences, and said things to him which he has held in his memory and has not resolved, often because it reflected what he found was true – he **was** different. Sam has limited ability to problem solve, or project into the future. Therefore, he feels stuck in a situation that he finds difficult, and he has no way to plan how to change that. His feeling of inferiority, which has been reinforced by events in his life, and his inability to find a positive path for himself, makes him vulnerable to mental health problems. His difficulty in communicating his inner experiences to his doctor adds to difficulties in the treatment of his depression.

Resilience and Optimal Supports

As caregivers, we can help our clients become more resilient to the vulnerabilities previously discussed Resilience is a characteristic in some individuals which is protective, or which lessens the negative impact of stressors for them. Resilience is thought to be an aspect of the personality, and some features of a person's environment may increase a person's resilience. These include:

- early emotional support from one's family of origin
- few risk factors in one's environment (examples of such risk factors would be exposure to financial distress, disruption in the family structure, abusive relationships)

- encouragement to learn independent problem solving
- supportive environments outside of the home
- development of positive self image.

If we think of persons who have developmental disabilities, as individuals who have experienced negative social feedback, have poor self-images, or have not been able to cope with experiences without mediation, then we would assume that these individuals will enter adulthood without much resilience. Considered in other terms, they have less protection against the negative impact of stressors, and are therefore more vulnerable to mental health problems.

An individual's protection against life stressors can be increased by developing optimal supports. These supports would aim to increase competence, and increase self-esteem and better regulation of mood. Optimal supports would also decrease an individual's anxiety by decreasing stressful circumstances in the person's life, and by providing support to develop positive ways to cope with unavoidable stressors (See Box 4).

Emotional, psychiatric and behavioral disorders (dual diagnosis)

People who have developmental disabilities can have any of the same physical, psychiatric or emotional difficulties as any other person. However, because of the experiences described earlier, they are more likely to develop emotional or mental health problems. Often, these disturbances are first recognized by others because of changes in the person's behaviour. It is important to remember that a behaviour is not an isolated event - it results from one or a combination of developmental, social, family, medical, psychological/emotional, or environmental circumstances that impact on the individual. When a behaviour occurs, it is communicating something about the person, either in terms of something that has happened to him/her, something he/she needs or wants, or some internal experience such as feelings or bodily discomfort. Individuals who have developmental disabilities often have difficulty sharing verbally such experiences and for some individuals, a change in non verbal behaviour is the **only** way they can communicate to others that something is amiss. For individuals without developmental disabilities, bizarre or unusual behaviour is often the first indication that a psychiatric disorder is present. Health care personnel unfamiliar in working with persons with developmental disabilities, and in particular, unfamiliar with their ways of communicating distress or their emotional responses, may automatically conclude that such changes in behaviour reflect an underlying psychiatric disorder, and frequently antipsychotic medication is prescribed. The opportunity to conduct a full functional analysis as to what the behaviour change may truly be communicating is lost, and because of the sedative and other side effects of the medication, individuals are often left less able to effectively communicate what may be causing their distress. Under these circumstances, behaviour often escalates. At this point, the medication may be increased or further medication added without a clear understanding of what is being treated; the individuals are effectively "gagged", and doomed to continue suffering in silence. In any psychiatric evaluation of someone with a developmental disability, the primary goal is to understand what any change in verbal or non verbal behaviour is communicating for that individual. This requires a comprehensive assessment by health care staff experienced in working with individuals across the spectrum of disability from mild to profound developmental disability (or

Box 4. Resilience and Optimal Supports Check List

The onset of anxiety and mood disorders for example, in persons with developmental disabilities, can be prevented and /or their impact minimized by:

Decreasing Stress in the environment and Helping the Individual feel more Competent:

- Increase opportunities for success in work / leisure
- Increase opportunities for satisfying social/ life experiences
- Ensure ability to communicate and make choices
- Offer medical intervention / therapy when appropriate
- Offer information / education on how to cope with frustration, issues of sexuality, loss
- Redefine person / situation to allow for new approaches (i.e., externalize the problem so the person does not see it as part of himself)
- Encourage expression of and validation of emotions
- Assist individual in developing supportive social networks
- Ensure social and other supports sufficient to meet individual's health and emotional needs

Attention to the above contributes to:
- Increased emotional and social supports available to client

And client experiences:
- Increased coping skills
- Increased self esteem
- Fewer stressful life events
- Decreased anxiety
- Greater ability to regulate mood

mental retardation as defined by APA, 1994) (see Box 5).

The Impact of Systems on Mental Health, Vulnerability, Resilience and Optimal Supports

Persons with developmental disabilities and their carers live within larger systems that can impact positively or negatively on mental well-being. In many industrialized countries such as North America and Europe, people with developmental disabilities used to be admitted to institutions when they were very young, and essentially lived lives separated from same-age peers without such disabilities. In the 1960s, there were increasing concerns being expressed about the negative physical and social conditions in these institutions. Subsequently, in the 1970s and 1980s, many families, activists and politicians began taking action to keep those with developmental disabilities with their families, or in their communities and to move those in institutions back to their home communities. Below we describe support systems currently in place in Ontario.

(a)   Community supports

In Ontario, the Ministry of Community and Social Services is the branch of government that funds institutions, agencies with vocational and residential opportunities for persons with developmental disabilities, assessment and treatment centres which offer services to those with developmental disabilities, and pensions for person with disabilities who cannot work, or who form of independent income. Originally, funds were transferred from the Ministry to agencies to plan and provide residential (group home/supported independent living) situations and vocational opportunities (life skill training workshops have no other supported employment) for individuals. We are now in a transition period where, while this model is still in

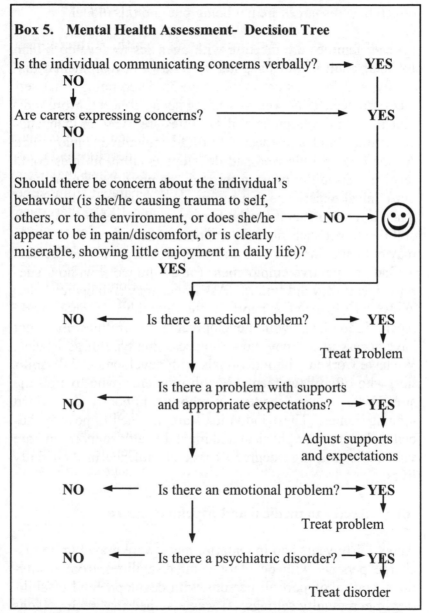

Box 5.   Mental Health Assessment- Decision Tree

Is the individual communicating concerns verbally? → **YES**
   NO
   ↓

Are carers expressing concerns? ————————————→ **YES**
   NO
   ↓

Should there be concern about the individual's
behaviour (is she/he causing trauma to self,
others, or to the environment, or does she/he → **NO** → ☺
appear to be in pain/discomfort, or is clearly
miserable, showing little enjoyment in daily life)?
                     YES

NO ← Is there a medical problem? → **YES**
                                          ↓
                                   Treat Problem

NO ← Is there a problem with supports
           and appropriate expectations? → **YES**
                                            ↓
                                   Adjust supports
                                   and expectations

NO ← Is there an emotional problem? → **YES**
                                          ↓
                                   Treat problem

NO ← Is there a psychiatric disorder? → **YES**
                                            ↓
                                   Treat disorder

(Bradley & Summers, 1999) Reprinted with permission from *Developmental Disabilities in Ontario*, p. 414, Toronto, Canada: Front Porch.

effect, new resources are not being put into this model.

Instead, families are meeting with agencies to develop a plan for their adult son or daughter who has a developmental disability, and families are more active in determining what services are needed, as well as finding such services. More individuals with developmental disabilities are living in independent settings, and are expected to find competitive employment. At one time, people who had developmental disabilities could receive a disability pension through the province. It has been our clinical experience that recent changes in the system have made it more difficult for the persons with developmental disabilities to get such financial support. These same individuals may not have families who can support them, may not be able to find competitive employment (or do the work without support even if they did find it). Assistance may also be needed to apply for financial support if the individual cannot work. Again individuals with developmental disabilities may not have access to or know how to access this type of assistance. We have worked with individuals with developmental disabilities, who often have mental health problems, who live on the street, who frequent shelters, or who live in poorly maintained lodging homes. These individuals are destined to poverty, social isolation, poor physical and mental health support, and are vulnerable to a high degree of risk of violence in their daily lives.

(b)   Access to medical and psychiatric care

About thirty years ago in Ontario, plans were drawn up to discharge persons with developmental disabilities from institutions, and to support all persons with developmental disabilities in community settings. It was assumed that such persons would access health care in the same manner as persons without such disabilities. In principle, persons with developmental disabilities continue to have *equal* access to health care (equal rights for all Canadians are protected under the Canadian Charter of Rights and Freedoms). However, many studies have now substantiated that persons with developmental disabilities do not have *equity* of access to health care (Beange, 1996; Gelinas & Ross-Greenside, 1993; Gitta, 1993; Turner & Moss, 1996). In other words, often, they do not receive either the same level or the same quality of health care enjoyed by non disabled persons. As a consequence, even some basic health needs remain unmet. The reasons for these unmet needs include:

- persons with developmental disabilities are not "typical" patients. They are often unable to communicate their concerns verbally, and health care personnel are not trained to understand their atypical ways of communicating pain and discomfort. Misdiagnoses, and consequently inappropriate interventions and treatments are common.
- health care personnel often have negative stereotypes of persons with disabilities which interfere with the services they may be able to provide.
- in the health care arena there is a general lack of knowledge and recognition of specific health vulnerabilities associated with developmental disabilities.
- persons with developmental disabilities often take longer to assess and treat; for example, it is necessary to meet with families and caregivers, review medical records and past assessments, consult with other colleagues involved in the client's care, as well as to provide direct clinical care to the client. Generic services are rarely resourced to provide the time necessary for all these activities.

- routine tests and procedures often need to be adapted if they are to be accessed by the person with a developmental disability.
- preventative information is not offered in a format which is easily accessed/understood by those who have a developmental disability.

As a consequence of these barriers, persons with developmental disabilities often receive poor and inadequate health care. The same picture prevails for psychiatric care. Frequently, we encounter clinical situations where the psychiatric crises and distress suffered by the client has been made worse by system deficits as outlined above. See the MATCH Project (1996) for further consideration of these concerns.

Evidence indicates that the model of "access to generic health care" for persons with developmental disabilities is not sufficient on its own to meet their health needs, particularly in the absence of training in developmental disabilities of health care personnel in these generic settings. See Aspray, Frances, Tyrera, and Quilliam, 1999 for recent editorial.

The Needs of Families and Caregivers

It has been pointed out that when a child is born with an obvious disability, the typical celebration and congratulations at birth are restrained or non-existent. Parents may blame themselves for contributing to the disability, even if the cause is unknown or outside of their control. If a disability becomes apparent later in childhood, families often "shop" for new assessments and answers to determine what went wrong. Interventions begin early to try to "correct" the problem to whatever extent is possible. Therefore, the child, from the time of the first recognition of his disability, is thought of with some sense of not being fully able and needing help. As families seek help and interventions, the child and the family will have the perception of this "difference" reinforced. The family may seek help, experience guilt, and must learn about the "systems" that can offer support.

In traditional families, mothers have most often been thought of as the parent who provides both physical care and nurturing. When a child is born who has a disability, there are additional special needs for care. One parent may have to give up a career in order to become a full time care provider, meeting the special needs of the individual, and acting as an advocate for service. This person is most often the mother. At the same time, she must continue to address the needs of the rest of the family. The time and energy involved in care provision may make her less able to attend to her own needs, and to those of the rest of the family. In the role of advocate, if she is not persistent, she may not get services. If she is persistent, she may be viewed by the system as a problem.

There are high rates of dissolution of marriages following the birth of a child with a disability. Fathers of children with disabilities more often experience depression, have less enjoyment in their children, and have lower self-esteem than fathers of non-disabled children. Siblings of children with disabilities are also affected. They may have to assist with provision of care, or may have less access to their parents' time and energy than other children do. As the person with a developmental disability ages, the siblings are often expected to replace the parents in offering support to the disabled person, and arrange appropriate service provision.

Support systems providing services to persons with developmental disabilities tend to be too few, not well-linked and not well advertised. When services are found, the resources available are often not adequate to meet the needs, whether, these are medical, social, educational or supportive. Service providers overextend themselves to provide services; yet, families and individuals with disabilities tend to be on long waiting lists, or to receive incomplete services. Therefore, everyone within the system is under stress. The search for appropriate services is often frustrating, and families often have to rely on other families to tell them how to navigate the system. While such family linkages may be supportive, the need to be constantly seeking advice or giving advice takes further time and energy away from the family unit.

Summary

There is a recognized increased prevalence of behavioural, emotional and psychiatric disorders in persons with developmental disabilities compared to the general population. In this chapter, we have tried to outline the broad spectrum of circumstances that can contribute to the vulnerability of persons with developmental disabilities to mental health disorders. However, the fact that someone is vulnerable does not mean (s)he will go on to develop such a disorder. By identifying certain vulnerabilities, and by understanding the nature of resilience to mental health disturbances, and how to promote such resilience in persons with developmental disabilities, we can both prevent some of these disorders from occurring, **and** lessen the impact of those that do develop. Biological, psychological, social, cultural, and political circumstances, and particular philosophies of care and support, combine in complex and intricate ways. They determine how vulnerable the person with a developmental disability may be to mental health disorders, and whether such disorders develop. When someone with a developmental disability presents with a significant change in usual behaviour, or with behavioural disturbance, clinical assessment involves evaluating the relative contributions of each of these circumstances in contributing to or maintaining the client's mental distress. From such an assessment, an appropriate treatment program is formulated. Invariably, given the complexity of circumstances contributing to mental health disturbances in persons with developmental disabilities, such treatment programs usually require the active participation of both the client and his/her direct caregivers Frequently, caregivers also have to act as advocates in helping to make the environmental and system changes necessary to promote healing and maintain optimal mental health.

Do You Know?

1. How may understanding of an individual's emotional and cognitive development contribute to an understanding of his/her disturbed behaviour? How may this understanding affect the treatment plan?

2. Describe some of the medical, emotional, psychological and psychiatric disorders that contribute to behaviour disturbance in individuals with developmental disabilities.

3. Optimal mental well-being is related to optimal physical health, optimal psychological functioning, and optimal treatment of psychiatric illness. Describe how you would promote optimal well being in your client.

4. Many mental health disturbances (emotional, behavioural and psychiatric) can be avoided. Describe how mental health disturbances arise. Select two examples and describe how these might be avoided.

Resources

Developmental Disabilities Program. http://www.psychiatry. med.uwo.ca/ddp/. For access to a range of Developmental Disability Web Sites and resources.

References

American Psychiatric Association, American Psychiatric Association, & Task Force on DSM-IV. (1994). *Diagnostic and statistical manual of mental disorders DSM-IV.* (4th ed.). Washington, DC: American Psychiatric Association.

Aspray, T. J., Francis, R. M., Tyrer, S. P., & Quilliam, S. J. (1999). Patients with learning disability in the community. *British Medial Journal, 318*, 476-477.

Beange, H.P. (1996). Caring for a vulnerable population: Who will take responsibility for those getting a raw deal from the health care system. *Medical Journal of Australia, 164*, 159-160.

Bradley, E. A., & Summers, J. (1999). Developmental disability and behavioural, emotional and psychiatric disturbances. In I. Brown & M. Percy (Eds.), *Developmental disabilities in Ontario* (pp. 409-428). Toronto: Front Porch Publishing.

Brown, I. & Percy, M. (Eds.). (1999). *Developmental disabilities in Ontario.* Toronto: Front Porch Publishing.

Gelinas, K. M. & Ross-Greenside, J. (1993). The health care coordination project: Interim report and future concerns. *Clinical Bulletin of the Developmental Disabilities Program 4(1)*, 1-3.

Gitta, M. (1993). Community health issues in Southwestern Ontario 1992-1993. *Clinical Bulletin of the Developmental Disabilities Program, 4(3)*, 1-2.

Papalia, D.E., Olds, S.W., &.Feldman, R.D. (1989). *Human*

development   (4th ed.)   New York, NY: McGraw Hill Books.

The MATCH Project. (1996). *Creating a continuum of supports and services: A resource document.*   Toronto: MATCH.

Turner, S. & Moss, S. (1996). The health needs of adults with learning disabilities and the Health of the Nation strategy. *Journal of Intellectual Disability Research, 40,* 438-350.

World Health Organization. (1980). *International Classification of Impairments, Disabilities and Handicaps.*   Geneva. Author.

Chapter 3

The Integrated Biopsychosocial Approach To Challenging Behaviours

Dorothy M. Griffiths and William I. Gardner

Learning Objectives

Readers will be able to:

1. Explain limitations of unidimensional assessment and the benefits of multimodal assessment and treatment approaches for complex behaviours,
2. Identify strengths of an integrated biopsychosocial model, and develop a case formulation based on the integrated biopsychosocial model.

Introduction

Persons with psychiatric disorders who present complex challenging behaviours require complex assessment and intervention strategies. Often challenging behaviours appear to have a pattern, but the pattern often is not totally predictable or consistent in time, place, frequency, duration, or severity (Gardner, 1998). In most cases, there is no single cause or solution to these challenging behaviours. Gardner (1998) has noted that a number of different conditions may influence expression of the behaviours at different times, and in different situations. In fact, it is not uncommon for persons who know individuals with a dual diagnosis to hold different opinions about the causes of the behavioural challenge.

The reality is that complex challenging behaviours may reflect the influences of multiple medical, psychiatric, psychological and environmental conditions. It is difficult to determine which combinations of conditions represent the most critical influences. If more than one hypothesis about conditions of influence is correct, such related issues as the following may be raised: "What is the magnitude of influence of each?" "How do the separate effects interact with each other to influence the occurrence and severity level of the behaviour?"

Historically, treatment for challenging behaviour has been unidimensional and unidisciplinary in nature. The type of treatment provided often reflected the professional discipline of the clinician rather than being based on a comprehensive case formulation of the challenging behaviour. Resulting treatments derived from the case formulation would be matched to each of the multiple relevant features of the individual and/or the environment.

In this chapter, a multimodal (bio-psycho-social) model that fosters integration of both diagnosis and treatment for challenging behaviours is described. This model represents a state of the art integrative approach in the field of dual diagnosis. Other models are discussed and compared to this integrative approach. The following case example illustrates the need for such an integrative model.

The Case of Mr. Jones

Mr. Jones has a long history of periodic self-injury. The episodes increased following a new vocational placement. In 1992, Mr. Jones was sent for an IQ test in order to be eligible for funding. His IQ had decreased considerably and as a result he was placed in a programme with persons with more severe challenges.

Following this change his self-injury increased in frequency. He also had other behaviours that were problematic at work, such as leaving the work area and wandering around. The vocational staff collected frequency data on the behaviours at work and found self-injury occurred an average of fifteen times a week, and leaving the work area occurred about 5 times a day. Self-injury was more frequent in certain situations such as upon arrival at work, during lunch and breaks, and when doing assembly tasks. Following each self-injurious episode, he was sent out of the room and told to calm down. The staff believed that this approach was appropriate because the behaviour stopped when he was removed. However, the behaviour did not change in frequency, and in fact increased in severity.

In 1993, noise and disruption of other clients were noted as relevant antecedents. When another client would scream or cry, Mr. Jones would begin to self-injure. As a result, he was placed in a relaxation training programme offered at the vocational setting. All persons presenting challenging behaviour took part in this 4-week programme. Mr. Jones appeared to enjoy the class. But the relaxation failed to demonstrate a change in his behaviour when in the work setting,

In 1997, his vocational counsellor noted that Mr. Jones appeared very anxious prior to the self-injury. This occurred when working across from other workers in the workshop or when required to have eye contact and during lunches and breaks. He was referred to a psychiatrist who sent him for genetic testing for fragile x syndrome due to discernible physical features and anxiety problems. The test was positive. Mr. Jones was provided medication for excessive anxiety that often is associated with fragile x. His self-injury decreased somewhat, but continued to occur. The family discontinued the medication after finding it ineffective in eliminating his behaviour.

In 1998, a behaviour analyst completed a functional analysis and determined Mr. Jones was self-injuring to escape from the three undesired situations (a) noise, (b) assembly tasks, and (c) routine changes. The behaviour analyst suggested that Mr. Jones should be taught an alternative way to escape undesired activities. Staff, however, did not believe it was appropriate for Mr. Jones to be able to escape these situation. They discontinued the time-out programme and began a positive reinforcement program to motivate him to stay in the undesired activities. Mr. Jones went into crisis.

Mr. Jones' situation is not that unusual. Persons with dual diagnosis often have long histories of challenging behaviour and related lists of interventions that have been tried with varying degrees of success. Why were none of these successful? Prior to addressing this and related questions, a brief review of various treatment models used with persons with developmental disabilities and significant mental health concerns is provided as background information.

Models of Intervention for Challenging Behaviour

In recent decades, significant attention has been given to the treatment of challenging behaviour in persons with developmental disabilities who present mental health concerns. Two major models-- *psychopharmacological and behavioural*-- have guided most treatment efforts. An unidimensional approach to treatment of behavioural challenges in persons with a dual diagnosis too often has resulted in behaviourally-responsive symptoms being inappropriately treated with medication, and biomedically-responsive symptoms being treated with behaviour reduction procedures (Gardner, 2000). The field has experienced an overuse of medications and a misuse of behavioural procedures to suppress symptoms in the absence of an adequate comprehensive diagnostic understanding (Gardner, 2000). The psychopharmacological and traditional behavioural approaches, while reducing the frequency of some behaviours, seldom have been successful in changing the conditions producing the behaviour or taught functional alternative skills (Gardner, 2000). Dissatisfaction with this unidimensional approach to intervention for persons with mental health concerns has prompted the field to embrace an integrative biopsychosocial model.

An integrative biopsychosocial model is based on the premise that behavioural and emotional challenges faced by persons with developmental disabilities represent the *dynamic* influence of biomedical, including psychiatric and neuropsychiatric, psychological and social environmental factors (Griffiths, Gardner, & Nugent, 1998). Each factor not only may play an individual role in the expression of symptoms, but also may interplay to influence features of the behavioural challenges. It is this understanding of the dynamic interplay that brings the field to a new level of focus on the complexity of the behavioural challenges presented by persons with a dual diagnosis. The integrative biopsychosocial model has been described by Gardner and colleagues in a number of publications (e.g., Gardner & Cole, 1984b; Gardner & Sovner, 1994; Gardner, 1996; Gardner & Whalen, 1996; Griffiths, Gardner, & Nugent, 1998).

This model differs initially from behavioural models in how behavioural challenges are viewed. The challenging behaviour, rather than being the focus of assessment and intervention, is viewed as a symptom of other conditions. In viewing behavioural challenges as a symptom, the diagnostic and intervention attention immediately is shifted from the behaviour to those conditions that produce the behavioural symptom. The behaviour itself tells us nothing about the controlling conditions that influence its occurrence, severity, variability, or durability. Self-injury, for example, may be influenced by medical, psychiatric, and neuropsychiatric influences, social interactions, physical and programme environmental events, psychological needs or distress, or may reflect the absence of alternative ways to deal with any of the above. Thus, reduction or elimination of the behavioural challenge is not the goal of the clinical approach. Rather, identification and modification of the various conditions (causes) do represent the focus.

Nature of an Integrated Biopsychosocial Assessment

Gardner (1996) suggested that a challenging behaviour is a non-specific symptom relative to controlling influences and remains so until a thorough assessment has been completed of conditions that influence its occurrence, severity, variability, and durability. The assessment would include careful analysis of potential biomedical, social-environmental and psychological factors that influence the behaviour, and the interplay of those factors. Results of this integrative comprehensive bio-psycho-social assessment provides the needed basis for deriving diagnostically-based interventions.

> ## Areas of Assessment for the Integrated Biopsychosocial Model
>
> **BIO (medical)-** *medical, psychiatric, medication reactions, syndromes, neurological state*
>
> **PSYCHO (logical)-** *current psychological features and skill deficits*
>
> **SOCIAL-** *environmental, interpersonal, programmatic, physical*

A biopsychosocial perspective is not new in the literature (Engel, 1977; Sadler & Hulgus, 1992). However, the application of this model to the field of dual diagnosis often has led to singular hypotheses (e.g., psychopharmacology vs. behavioural) or linear applications (e.g., medical then psychophar-

macology then behavioural). Complex clinical cases, particularly involving persons with a dual diagnosis, seldom reflect
unidimensional or unrelated influences. Thus, the separate biopsychosocial assessment and intervention efforts were not integrative in nature. To repeat, this approach fails to account for
the roles assumed and magnitude of effects exerted by the different sources of influence, or the interactions of these various
influences. This dynamic interplay of influencing factors frequently accounts for the seemingly unpredictable and bewil-
dering behaviours commonly observed in persons with a dual
diagnosis (Gardner, 1998).

A brief example will demonstrate the nature of this interplay.

The Case of Mr. Abrahams

*Mr. Abrahms is 32 years old. He experienced severe de-
pression following the sudden death of his mother in a
car accident. Mr. Abraham had lived with his mother
since the death of his father when he was 15 years old.
Mr. Abrahms and his mother were inseparable. Since
finishing school at age 21 years, he worked with his
mother in their corner store. He was in the local bowling league, and was a regular church member. Following his mother's death, he was moved into a residential
program on an emergency basis. The home was transitional in nature, and often persons remained for only
short periods. Often, the persons in the home presented
severe challenging behaviours. In the past seven
months, Mr. Abrahms has almost stopped eating, rarely
sleeps at night, does not bathe or change his clothes,
and has been highly irritable. He recently was observed
hitting one of the other residents, a behaviour never be-*

fore seen. He currently spends most of his days in his room, and comes out to the living room at night when everyone else is sleeping. He seems to have no interests, and says he wants to die so he can be with his mom.

Mr. Abrahms meets the criteria for a major clinical depression (DSM-IV, APA, 1994). His irritable mood, diminished interest in all activities, lack of interest in food, insomnia and recurrent thoughts of death clearly are symptoms of a depressed mood. However, the symptoms were not present until after the death of his mother. Although the physician prescribed medication to address these mood symptoms, the death and the resulting bereavement precipitating the depressive episode were not addressed. Mr. Abrahms appears to be lacking skills to deal with grief and loss. Further, he has not been afforded the counselling and support needed for him to understand, and to cope with his grief. He was not allowed to go to his mother's funeral because his uncle felt that Mr. Abrahms might become disruptive and would not understand.

Reduction in the dysphoric mood and related somatic symptoms through psychopharmacology, although helpful, represents only one aspect of a more comprehensive set of needed interventions. Counselling and support are needed to deal with the grief regarding his mother and the other multiple losses in his life. He lost his mother, job, home, lifestyle, and best friend. Moreover, the environment that he lives in is transient, disruptive, and not structured to provide long term support. One of the other residents taunts and pinches him. In his irritable state, Mr. Abrahms responds by hitting back. Placement in a safe and comfortable home, meaningful work, leisure activities that offer pleasure and success, and positive relationships with others whose interactions provide emotionally satisfying experiences all represent components of a more comprehensive treatment strategy. None of the programme components in isolation will meet his multiple medical and psychosocial needs. To illustrate, drugs alone will not address his psychosocial needs; counselling alone will not address his psychiatric, social, or environmental needs; a healthy life-space alone will address only one component of the multiple factors that influence his depressive condition.

For more in-depth analysis, let's revisit Mr. Jones, described earlier, and translate what we know from our case notes into the integrated biopsychosocial perspective. We know the following aspects about Mr. Jones:

BIO (medical)- *Mr. Jones has fragile x syndrome, and demonstrates anxiety symptoms typical of persons with fragile x.*

PSYCHO (logical) - *Mr. Jones has limited coping skills. He appears to have a low tolerance for certain stressors.*

SOCIAL- *Mr. Jones self-injures and wanders more in certain situations (i.e., at lunch or breaks, upon arrival at work, when doing assembly tasks) and self-injury follows certain events (i.e., noise, demands for eye contact, change in routine). The behaviours appear to allow him to escape from undesired situations.*

Although it is of value to sequentially list these various assessment insights, this information is incomplete in describing the various roles and magnitude of effects, and the interaction effects on the challenging behaviour. Previous efforts with Mr. Jones showed that anxiety medication on its own was insufficient to eliminate the behaviour. Relaxation training in isolation failed to have an impact on the behaviour. Attempts at punishing him appeared to have actually strengthened the behaviour. In this case, no single diagnostic insight or intervention in isolation was sufficient. A comprehensive programme that integrates insights from different modes of influence, viz. biomedical, environmental and psychological, appears to be warranted. It is not sufficient, however, simply to treat each area independently since the influences are dynamic or interactive in nature. To accomplish an integrative treatment approach, it is valuable to determine the role that each plays in influencing the behaviour. This assessment step provides information to account for why the behaviour occurs with the frequency and pattern that it does.

Various influences having their origin in medical, psychiatric, psychological, or environmental conditions may act as (a) *instigating* conditions (b) *vulnerabilities/risk* influences, and (c) *maintaining* conditions for the behaviour. Following brief explanation of each circumstance, interventions based on each are suggested for Mr. Jones.

Instigating Conditions

Instigating conditions are "stimulus events that signal occurrence of challenging behaviours" (Gardner, 1998). Instigating conditions can exist in many forms:
- *physical environment* (e.g., noise, smells, heat, crowding)

- *social environment* (e.g., specific people, types of interactions, change or withdrawal of social contact)
- *programme environment* (e.g., changes in routines, unpredictability, excess leisure time, terminating a preferred activity or programme time)
- *psychological conditions* (e.g., specific fears, boredom, arousal states)
- *medical conditions* (e.g., those that create psychological distress resulting from pain, disorientation or irritability)
- *psychiatric/neuropsychiatric* conditions (e.g., those that produce cognitive, perception, motor, somatic, or affective symptoms that create psychological distress)

Instigating stimulus conditions can exist as either *triggering* stimulus conditions, or as *contributing* stimulus conditions. Triggering stimulus conditions refer to those events that precede and prompt behavioural occurrence. The behaviour does not occur unless antecedent triggering events specific to an individual are present. Contributing stimulus conditions, while not sufficient in isolation to produce a specific challenging behaviour, may serve to increase the likelihood of occurrence when combined with a triggering event. The influence of antecedent conditions is demonstrated by Mr. Jones in the following example:

> *The triggering conditions for self-injury include noise, demands to engage in eye contact, or unexpected change in his routine or care-providers. In the presence of these events, and only in the presence of one of these events, self-injury occurs. However, there are additional events that contribute to the behaviour. The challenging behaviour is more likely to occur when he is confronted with one of these contributing events in situations that are crowded and noisy. These*

> *situations, while serving to increase the likelihood of the challenging, are insufficient in isolation to produce the behaviour. Only when the triggering events occur does self-injury result.*

Vulnerability Conditions

A vulnerability may reflect either a personal feature of the individual, or a feature of the environment that places the person at increased risk for challenging behaviours. Personal features may reflect psychological deficits (e.g., limited communication or coping skills) or pathologies (e.g., inflexibility, suspiciousness, ritualism), and biomedical abnormalities (e.g., sensory or neurological impairments, psychiatric disorders). Environmental features representing either deficient or excessive conditions may be physical (e.g., limited sensory stimulation level), social (e.g., limited opportunity for social contact or excessively crowded classroom), or programmatic (e.g., type, frequency or pacing of activities) in nature. To repeat, vulnerabilities represent features of the person (biomedical and psychological) and/or the environment (physical and social) that create *increased risk* for challenging behaviours when a person is exposed to conditions of instigation. As examples, Miss Smith may have low frustration tolerance; Mr. King may have limited anger management skills; Miss Brown periodically gets migraine headaches; Mr. Alexander has manic-depressive episodes; Miss Craighead lives with abusive parents. All represent vulnerability conditions that increase the risk of the challenging behaviour when these individuals are exposed to those instigating conditions that control occurrence of their challenging behaviours. As noted, some vulnerability features represent personality characteristics (e.g., suspiciousness), others reflect skill deficits (e.g., limited anger management skills), while others reflect medical (e.g., migraines) or psychiatric (e.g., bipolar disorder) conditions. At times, features of the social environment may represent vulnerability conditions (e.g., crowded classroom, abusive parents).

In sum, vulnerabilities may represent features of:

*   *physical environment* (e.g., noisy, crowded, potentially aversive temperature variations)
*   *social conditions* (e.g., abusive, taunting or demanding interactions, absence or infrequent positive social interactions or feedback)
*   *programme conditions* (e.g., unpredictability, limited or excessive stimulation, limited or excessive structure),
*   *psychological conditions* (e.g., limited or absence of skills of coping, communication, problem solving, daily living; motivational features such as excessive dependency on a specific type or limited range of reinforcing events, emotional over-arousal on exposure to numerous social or environmental cues)
*   *medical conditions* (e.g., recurring migraine headaches, chronic arthritis, recurring episodes of general fatigue, recurring earaches)
*   *psychiatric/ neuropsychiatric conditions* (e.g., Bipolar Mood Disorder, anxiety disorder, compulsive rituals, episodes of irritability.)

Sometimes vulnerabilities representing several modalities may be present and interact both to produce and strengthen behavioural challenge.   Mr. Jones presents the following vulnerabilities that increase the risk of behavioural challenges when he is exposed to triggering conditions.

Fragile x syndrome presents a biomedical vulnerability, which can explain certain behavioural phenotypes, such as loss of IQ (which is not a loss of skill but a lack of acquisition of new skills), short-term memory and anxiety problems, aversion to eye contact and sequencing tasks, and the tendency to be over-aroused to noise and crowds. This explains the vulnerabilities the person is experiencing and helps in identifying possible contributing and triggering events for the self-injury. Therefore in situations of excess crowding or activities involving sequencing, he responds with high levels of anxiety with which he lacks the skills to cope. He is vulnerable to engage in behavioural challenges due to his (i) fragile x syndrome and the resulting tendency to become easily over-aroused,, (ii) repeated exposure to aversive environmental conditions (i.e., excessive noise, and sequencing tasks requiring short term memory), and (iii) lack of appropriate skills to cope with the distress.

Maintaining (Reinforcing) Conditions

Challenging behaviours increase in likelihood of being repeated as a result of consequences produced by the behaviour. Challenging behaviours can be reinforced by the attention or reactions from other individuals, by environmental pay-off such as tangibles or activities, sensory stimulation, or environmental change (Feldman & Griffiths, 1997). These and similar *positive reinforcers* may be viewed as pleasant or desired by the person. As noted, these consequences increase the likelihood that behaviour producing these effects will be repeated. Additionally, behaviour may be strengthened through a process of negative reinforcement if the behaviour results in avoidance, termination, reduction, or delay of an event or situation that is unpleasant, painful, unwanted or aversive to the person. In summary, both positive and negative reinforcement experiences increase the likelihood that the challenging behaviour that produces these effects will be repeated.

Reinforcing influences may involve a range of medical, psychiatric, psychological, and social and physical environmental conditions:

- *physical environment* (e.g., removal, reduction, or avoidance of unpleasant physical conditions such as noise, heat or access to desired environment)
- *social* (e.g., avoidance of undesired social contacts, access to desired social interactions, creating distress in others)
- *programme* (e.g., avoidance of boring or difficult programme, access to desired changes in programme activity)
- *psychological* (e.g., pleasant sensory stimulation, decrease in discomfort or anxiety)
- *medical* (e.g., reduction in physical pain or distress)
- *psychiatric/neuropsychiatric* (e.g., decrease in aversive events related to disorientation, hallucinations, or dysphoria; increase in comforting social attention during periods of depression)

It should be noted that reinforcing factors are quite individual in nature. For example, Barrett et al. (1989) suggested that self-injury in a 12-year-old girl with autism and mental retardation was reinforced by the endogenous production of opiates which provided her a biological source of sensory reinforcement. A number of writers also have suggested that challenging behaviour, while frequently treated by behavioural procedures, actually may be instigated by aberrant neurological or neurochemical influences as seen in temporal lobe epilepsy or other poorly understood neurological conditions (e.g., Matson & Gardner, 1991; Mace & Mauk, 1999).

As noted earlier, reinforcing influences cannot be examined independent of the specific antecedents involved in the occurrence. It is insufficient to report that a person's behaviour is strengthened by "negative reinforcement" without describing what the individual is avoiding, and why this is aversive to him or her. The reinforcing condition must be examined in its contexts. As described earlier, Mr. Jones did not always attempt to escape from the work area. What were the internal or external conditions that activated the escape behaviours at a specific time? There were specific times of the day when he was more likely to be self-injurious, and this behaviour appeared to be reinforced by his being able to leave the room. Why did he wish to leave the room—too warm, too noisy, fearful of peers, bored, too crowded? It is important to collect information about situations in which behaviours occur in order to establish the contextual instigating-maintaining dyads, and then to understand these in the context of vulnerability conditions.

Gardner and Sovner (1994) and Gardner (1998) describe the use of small index cards to collect valuable observational data for later analysis. For each incidence of a specified behavioural challenge, the situation, triggering events, behaviour, consequences, and the possible contributing instigating influences are recorded at the time of the occurrence. The cards can later be examined and sorted into categories depending on the type of antecedent instigating condition, features of the behaviour (e.g., type, severity, victim), and the possible maintaining or reinforcing consequences. These data, as well as other situational conditions such as time of day, location, programme being provided, physical location, presence of specific peers or staff, and the like, are used to develop hypotheses about instigating conditions and related consequences influencing the behaviour. Vulnerability influences can be added to provide a number of diagnostic hunches to guide treatment programme development.

Sample Incident Recording Card for Mr. Jones

Name: Mr. Peter Jones   Observer: A. Staff
Date: Feb 8/00   Time: 9:00 a.m.
Situation: *Peter arrived at work.*
Triggering Event: *There was a lot of noise and crowding in the lobby. Two clients were fighting.*
Behaviour: *Peter tried to leave the building but was stopped. He began to bite himself.*
Consequence: *Peter was taken into the building and sent immediately to an empty workroom to calm down.*
Possible Contributing Instigating Factors: *Peter became very anxious and started to rub his hands together.*

With this background information, incidents occurring throughout a day's attendance at a vocational setting in the life of Mr. Jones are offered to illustrate the use and value of lodging these behavioural occurrences in their various contexts. Typically in clinical settings, one would collect data for at least a week or two for relatively high frequency behaviours, and often several weeks for low frequency behaviours.

Data Collection for Mr. Jones

Mr. Peter Jones   **Date: Mon. Feb 8, 2000**
                                       Setting: St. Andrews Workshop

Instigating Events	Behaviour	Maintaining Events
9 a.m.: Peter arrived at work. Two clients were fighting. Note on Possible Contributing Factors: Peter appeared anxious and was rubbing his hands.	Peter tried to leave the building but was stopped. He began to bite his hand.	He was brought into the building and sent immediately into the empty workroom to calm down.
12 noon: Peter entered the lunch room. Staff directed him to sit down to eat his lunch. He resisted and was physically guided. Note on Possible Contributing Factors: Peter appeared distressed by the music that was playing.	Peter bit his hands.	Staff warned him that if he did that again he would be sent to the sick room to calm down and miss lunch.
12:06: Peter quickly ate his lunch. A staff member approached to ask him to slow down.	He got up and walked out of the room.	Staff followed and directed him to the sick room. Note: Peter seemed less anxious once outside the lunchroom.
1:55: Peter assigned to an assembly task . 2:05 He was redirected back to work. The instructor sat across from him and requested he look at her while she instructed him in the task.	Peter got up and left the work area. Peter began to bite his hands.	He walked around for 10 minutes outside of the work area then was redirected back to work. Peter was sent to calm down in the quiet room

Instigating Events	Behaviour	Maintaining Events
2:25: Peter was told that his favourite counsellor was sick and he would be working with someone else. He began to pace and rub his hands. Note on Possible Contributing Factor: Sally was screaming .	Peter began to bite himself.	He was removed from the area and a staff counselled him about his behaviour
2:30: At break, several clients were playing a game and so he could not sit in his favourite spot in the corner.	Peter began to rub his hands and began to bite his hands.	He was removed from the group.
4:20: After getting ready to go home, the clients had to wait twenty minutes in the hallway because the bus was stuck in the snow. Note on Possible Contributing Factors: Peter was pacing back and forth and rubbing his hands together. Several peers were yelling at each other.	Peter began to bite his hands.	He was taken to the classroom until the bus arrived.

A summary of the multiple conditions presumed to influence Mr. Jones' behaviours is located on the following page.

Biopsychosocial Analysis of Peter

	Instigating Factors Triggering/ Contributing	Vulnerabilities	Reinforcing Conditions Positive/ Negative
Biomedical • Medical/ • Medication • Psychiatric/ neuro psychiatric	Anxiety when faced with social instigating conditions.	Fragile x syndrome and the resulting tendency to anxiety and overarousal.	**Negative Reinforcement:** Self-injury results in his escape to a less stressful environment. Anxiety (physical and psychological) discomfort is reduced.
Psychological • Current features • Skill deficits		Peter lacks appropriate means of coping with anxiety and overwhelming environmental stimulation.	Self-injury serves to produce the desired reduction in anxiety level
Social • Physical • Social • Programmatic	Excess noise, forced eye contact and changes in routines trigger self-injury. Being required to attend to an assembly task and presence of lots of people in one area can trigger escape behaviour and contribute to self-injury.	His current work environment is very noisy, crowded and has many individuals who also have behavioural challenges.	**Negative Reinforcement: His** self-injury and wandering behaviour allow him to escape from undesired social, programmatic and physical influences.

From Hypotheses to Intervention

Hypotheses relating to the instigating (both triggering and contributing), vulnerability, and maintaining conditions for Mr. Jones's self-injury suggest, as illustration, interventions that:

- Reduce the internal contributing instigating influence of anxiety by providing anti-anxiety medication and periods of relaxation that compete with anxious arousal.
- Remove or reduce the contributing instigating events for self-injury (socio-environmental changes such as increased structure and an adapted schedule).
- Alter his reactions to the instigating stimulus events by teaching alternative ways of coping with these events via coping skills training.

Sample Consultation Using the Integrated Biopsychosocial Model

Name: Mr. Peter Jones

Consultation Members:

Mr. and Mrs Jones (parents) and Peter Jones, Day Programming Staff of the Workshop, Dr. Adams (psychiatrist), Mr. Frazer (behaviour analyst), and Mrs. Dufour (social skills instructor).

Selected reports were also reviewed prior to the visit. Mr. Peter Jones was observed in his day programme environment. A contextual analysis was conducted of his behaviour for a two week period.

Presenting Challenges:

Mr. Jones demonstrates a number of challenging behaviours:

•Self-injury
•Avoidance, escape from programming environment

Background:

Mr. Jones is a 21 year old man with fragile x syndrome He has longstanding behavioural challenges. Many programmes have been attempted without significant alteration of his behaviour. Several strategies had been tried. However, the key to success appears to involve reduction in his vulnerabilities, including those created by fragile x syndrome, and how these interplay with his environment. This interplay will be essential in developing a proactive management plan and an appropriate replacement teaching programme.

Integrated Biopsychosocial Intervention Plan

- *Biomedical Formulations:*

Hypothesis: Fragile x syndrome creates various vulnerabilities which contribute to Mr. Jones's challenging behaviours:

- *Anxiety*
- *Sensory overloading*
- *Problems with noise sensitivity, crowding and space*

- *Attention and short term memory problems*
- *Gaze aversion*
- *Difficulty with assembly tasks*
- *Challenges learning new things*

Programme Objectives:

To minimize levels of anxiety and overarousal

Interventions:

1. *Dr. Adams will reintroduce the medication for anxiety.*

2. *Provide options for Mr. Jones and his family to learn about fragile x syndrome, connect with support groups and access genetic counselling (if desired).*

3. *Training for staff about the unique issues facing a person with fragile x syndrome.*

Environmental Formulations:

Hypotheses:
- *Sensitivity to over-stimulation caused by crowded situations and demands to do sequencing (assembly) tasks are common challenges for someone with fragile x syndrome. In this case, exposure to these conditions increases anxious arousal that serves as a trigger for Mr. Jones's wandering and self-injury and contributes to self-injury.*

- *Pressure to directly look at people, excess noise, and changes in routines, expectations and people in his life can serve as triggering events for self-injury.*

Programme Objectives:

To minimize and/or eliminate those aversive environmental (physical, social, programmatic) conditions that contribute to the hitting.

Interventions:

The workshop environment is very noisy and over-stimulating especially at transition times, such as during the morning or at break-times. Mr. Frazer (behaviour therapist) will assist the workshop staff to adapt the routine and environment to accommodate Mr. Jones' anxiety related to his special sensitivities.

1. *Develop one room in the building that Mr. Jones could CHOOSE to use during times that are unusually busy or during transition or break times.*

2. *Mr. Jones would benefit from daily structure. Develop a <u>predictable written</u> daily routine that is based on his strengths (expressive communication, daily living and domestic skills, enjoyment of the outdoors, physical activity, and music), and does not weigh heavy on his weaknesses (short-term memory or sequencing problems).*

3. *Provide a programme to teach alternative ways of dealing with anxiety (such as deep muscle relaxa-*

tion , music relaxation, or an exercise programme). He should have access to these routinely throughout the day as needed and upon request. Previously he was unable to apply his relaxation approach in the face of the anxiety triggers; this approach allows him to remove himself appropriately to a setting where he can use a variety of relaxation techniques.

Psychological Formulations:

Hypothesis: Deficit skills in social coping with changes in expectations, routines (especially when changes occur or during transitions) and frustration represent vulnerabilities.

Hypothesis: Mr. Jones's wandering and self-injury serve several functions:

- *Escape from an undesired activity, interaction, environment or demand*
- *Avoidance of an undesired activity, interaction, environment or demand*
- *Reduction in anxiety-provoking stimuli (i.e., crowding, sequential task demands).*

Programme Objectives:

1. *to teach Mr. Jones's alternative ways of coping with aversive events*

2. *to establish reinforcement for the new coping skills*

to ensure both maintenance and generalization of the skills

3. *to teach tolerance for reasonable delays.*

Interventions:

Mrs. Dufour, a social skills instructor, plans to develop a programme to teach Mr. Jones alternative strategies to cope with aversive events. She has outlined the following steps she will follow:

Step One: *Perform a complete contextual analysis to identify the specific instigating conditions (both triggering and contributing) and the maintaining conditions for his challenging behaviours.*

Step Two: *Select for each condition a method of that is appropriate for Mr. Jones to use as an alternative way to self-manage the situations where he is currently wandering or self-injuring.*

Step Three: *Initially set up an individual training programme to ensure that he learns the new coping strategies. Because of his fragile x, the programme will include the use of imitation and modelling, which are his best learning approaches. He needs to be given time to respond to auditory cues; responses may be delayed.*

Step Four: *Transfer the new coping skills to the natural environments.*

Step Five: *Provide staff and parent training to ensure* *consistent reinforcement for the new skills. For the skills to be used in the natural environment, it is critical that skills be generalized to the natural environment and re-inforced there. As example, Mr. Jones demonstrates early signs that indicate that he is getting anxious, and may need to use his new coping system (i.e., he rubs his hands). At those times, it is important that the early signs be detected and that prompts be provided for him to use one of his coping strategies rather than resorting to self-injury.*

Step Six*: Insure that Mr. Jones finds the new behav-iours to be more effective than self-injury at gaining him escape or avoidance from aversive situations.*

Step Seven*: Once the new behaviours are well estab-lished, Mr. Jones will be taught to tolerate reasonable delay. However, this would only begin once the new skills are well established as alternative ways of coping with the triggering conditions that currently produce self-injury.*

Staging the Changes

There are both pragmatic and empirical reasons for producing a staging plan. Practically, it is difficult to initiate all segments of a complex multimodal plan simultaneously. Empirically, changes that are progressively sequenced allow for assessment of the relative influence of the various interventions. However, there is a risk that caregivers may lose interest or motivation if short-term interventions produce reduction in the behavioural challenges. If these initial intervention approaches are well designed and implemented, the challenging behaviour may be significantly reduced. This reduction may reflect the effects of (a) changes in the instigating stimulus conditions, (b) presentation of stimulus conditions for alternative prosocial behaviours, and (c) consequences that have been altered to reduce reinforcement or to inhibit occurrence of the challenging behaviours. However, these initial procedures, while supportive of long-term therapeutic effect, frequently do not produce durable changes (Gardner & Cole, 1987). These authors suggest that short-term behaviour management effects, when used independent of active treatment, neither provide the person with competency skills nor ensure durable behaviour change across times and conditions.

Best Practice Features of an Integrated Biopsychosocial Model

The integrated biopsychosocial model:

1. Incorporates the roles and magnitude of effects of biomedical and psychosocial factors on occurrence, severity, variability, and durability of challenging behaviours, and how these influences interrelate.

2. Uses assessment information to guide selection of diagnostically-based interventions.

3. Identifies the skills and related emotional/motivational supports required by the individual to cope effectively with the multiple biopsychosocial influences involved in producing the challenging behaviours.

4. Is proactive in focus.

5. Provides for translation of multiple modalities of influence into a common explanatory paradigm, i.e., conditions of instigation, vulnerability or risk influences, and maintaining influences.

6. Provides an integrated multimodal treatment and management plan.

7. Recognizes that mental health consists both of the presence of personal contentment, and the relative absence of psychological distress. The major treatment focus is that of improvement in quality of life via enhancing the competencies of the person, and providing a person-centred environment. Reduction in behavioural challenges is a natural result of these routine changes.

Summary

Persons with developmental disabilities who also demonstrate mental health needs represent a complex challenge to clinicians and service providers. In the past, intervention has often been overly simplistic and narrow. The complexity of the individual and the relationship of biomedical, psychological and social influences were often lost in a hurried attempt to eliminate a behavioural symptom. Too often, the personal experiences of the individual were not explored, and a cookbook strategy to treatment was considered selected.

Current philosophy and related practice emphasize the personal experiences of the person with a dual diagnosis as the key to assessment and treatment. Best practice requires comprehensive biomedical assessment, psychological and skill evaluation, and social-environmental investigation as a basis for understanding the multiple contexts in which the person expresses various behavioural challenges. Intervention programs derived from this understanding represent the essence of the integrative biopsychosocial model.

Do You Know?

1. Behavioural symptoms typically are not the direct product of neurochemical abnormality, and thus do not completely subside following treatment with medication.

2. There is a growing feeling among clinical researchers that there has been too much behaviour modification in the field, and not enough comprehensive multimodal contextual analysis.

3. Comprehensive assessments include a thorough contextual analysis of the behaviour including the antecedent instigating conditions, vulnerability influences, and consequences. These influences may reflect a range of biomedical and psychosocial conditions.

4. The most successful treatments include multiple components of intervention (both behavioural and psychopharmacological), environmental manipulation and education.

5. The integrated biopsychosocial model is based on the understanding that the behavioural and emotional challenges faced by persons with developmental disabilities reflect the *dynamic* influence of these biomedical, including psychiatric and neuropsychiatric, psychological, and social environmental factors.

Resources

Dykens, E.M., Hodapp, R.M., & Finucane, B.M. (2000). *Genetics and mental retardation syndromes: A new look at behavior and interventions.* Baltimore, MD.: Paul H. Brookes.

Friefeld, S., Rosenfield, J, Laframboise, K, MacGregor, D., Marcovitch, S., Teshima, I., & Vachon, V. (1990). The Fragile X Syndrome: A multidisciplinary perspective on clinical feature, diagnosis and intervention. *Journal of Developmental Disabilities, 2,* 56-72.

Griffiths, D., Gardner, W.I., & Nugent, J. (1998*). Behavioural supports: Individual centered interventions- A multimodal functional approach.* Kingston, NY: NADD Press.

References

American Psychiatric Association (1987). *Diagnostic and statistical manual of mental disorders-Fourth edition.* Washington D.C.: Author.

Bambara, L.M., Mitchell-Kvacky, N. A. & Iacobelli, S. 1994) Positive behavioral support for students with severe disabilities: An emerging multi-component approach for addressing challenging behaviors. *School Psychology Review, 23,* 263-278.

Carr, E.G., Taylor, J.D., Carlson, J.I., & Robinson, R. (1991). Reinforcement and stimulus-based treatments for severe behavior problems in developmental disabilities. *Proceedings of the consensus conference on the treatment of severe behavior problems in developmental disabilities.* Washington, DC: National Institutes of Health

Engel, G. L. (1977). The need for a new medical model: A challenge for biomedicine. *Science, 196,* 129-136.

Feldman, M.A. & Griffiths, D. Comprehensive assessment of severe behaviour problems. In N.N. Singh (Ed.), *Prevention and treatment of severe behaviour problems: Models and methods in developmental disabilities* (pp. 23-48). Brooks/Cole: Pacific Grove, CA.

Gardner, W. I. (1996). A contextual view of nonspecific behavioral symptoms in persons with a dual diagnosis: A psychological model for selecting and monitoring drug interventions. *Psychology in Mental Retardation, 21*, 6-11.

Gardner, W.I. (2000). Behavioral therapies: Using diagnostic formulation to individualize treatment for persons with developmental disabilities and mental health concerns. In R. J. Fletcher (Ed.), *Effective therapy approaches with persons who have mental retardation* (pp. 1-25). Kingston, NY: NADD Press.

Gardner, W. I. (1998). Initiating the case formulation process. In D. M. Griffiths, W. I. Gardner, & J. Nugent (Eds.), Behavioral supports: *Individual centered behavioral interventions: A multi modal functional approach* (pp. 17-66). Kingston, NY: NADD Press.

Gardner, W. I., & Cole, C. L. (1994a). Aggression and related conduct difficulties in the mentally retarded: A multi-component behavioral model. In S. E. Bruening, J. L. Matson, & R. P. Barrett (Eds.), *Advances in mental retardation and developmental disabilities* (Vol. 2, pp. 41-84). Greenwich, CT: JAI Press.

Gardner, W. I., & Cole, C. L. (1994b). Use of behavior therapy with the mentally retarded in community settings. In F. J. Menolascino and J. A. Stark (Eds.), *Handbook of mental illness in the mentally retarded* (pp. 97-153). New York, NY: Plenum Press.

Gardner, W.I., & Sovner, R. (1994). *Self-injurious behaviors: Diagnosis and treatment.* Willow Street, PA: Vida Publishing.

Gardner, W.I., & Whalen, J.P. (1996) Discussion: A multi-modal behavior analytic model for evaluating the effects of medical problems on nonspecific behavioral symptoms in persons with developmental disabilities. *Behavioral Interventions, 11*, 147-161.

Griffiths, D., Gardner, W.I., & Nugent, J. (1998). *Behavioral supports: Individual centered interventions: A multi-modal functional approach.* NADD Press: Kingston, New York

Mace, F. C., & Mauk, J. E. (1999). Biobehavioral diagnosis and treatment of self-injury. In A. C. Repp & R. H. Horner (Eds.), *Functional analysis of problem behavior* (pp. 78-97). Belmont, CA: Wadsworth Publishing.

Sadler, J. Z., & Hulgus, Y. (1992). Clinical problem solving and the biopsychosocial model. *American Journal of Psychiatry, 149(10)*, 1315-1322.

Chapter 4

The DSM-IV and How It Applies to Persons with Developmental Disabilities

Chrissoula Stavrakaki

Learning Objectives

Readers will be able to:

1. Describe what DSM-IV stands for, its format, and basic applications
2. Identify which categories of mental disorders are listed in the manual
3. Describe how these categories apply to persons with developmental disabilities, both children and adults.

Introduction

Consider a mental health problem in a client with a developmental disability. Try to recollect the ways that the mental health problem was presented, and what formal diagnosis, if any, this person received through a Psychiatric Clinic or Mental Health Community Centre. What were your impressions?

The use of a diagnosis based on certain criteria or ways that professionals communicate with one another has been in practice for a long time. Updated criteria based on new ways of

our understanding of mental health problems have been devised across continents in an effort to improve and enhance the
way these criteria apply to all persons with different cultural
backgrounds, religious affiliations and varying degrees of disabilities.

In this chapter, an effort has been made to present the Diagnostic and Statistical Manual (DSM-IV) criteria, the various
categories listed in it, and more specifically, how they apply to
the developmentally disabled population. It is easily understood that any set of criteria that attempts to address all issues
relevant to mental health and/or psychiatric pathology/illness/
disorder, would present challenges and have limitations, especially as they apply to exceptional groups of people such as
those with a developmental disability. DSM-IV presents such
limitation as it addresses this population. Despite these difficulties, DSM-IV is an improved version of previously accepted diagnostic criteria, and it can successfully apply to the
higher functioning developmentally disabled person.

Let us try to get to know what DSM-IV actually is, and its appropriate application to our clients.

What Is DSM-IV?

DSM-IV stands for Diagnostic and Statistical Manual of Mental Disorder. It is presently in its fourth edition, the latest publication of its kind. It is published by the American Psychiatric Association in Washington, DC. It was first published in
May of 1994. DSM-IV was a team effort. More than one
thousand people and numerous professional organizations
have helped the editorial committee in its effort to develop and
provide a helpful guide to clinical practice. The resulting pub-

lication is being used by many and diverse groups of clinicians, researchers and educators with many different orientations and/or specializations. For example, psychiatrists, other physicians, psychologists, social workers, nurses, occupational and rehabilitation therapists, counsellors, and other health and mental health professionals have used this publication.

DSM-IV has been used across settings such as inpatient, outpatient, partial hospital care, consultation-liaison clinics, private practice, primary care and community settings. Its primary aim has been, and remains to be, the communication and description of the various mental disorders in order to improve understanding of these disorders by professionals. In this vein, the DSM-IV is a very important and extremely useful tool for all groups of professionals, irrespective of specialization, level of care, and/or orientation.

DSM-IV has also attempted to bridge the gap amongst the various continents. Its writers collaborated with the World Health Organization Committees to achieve continuity and harmony in the understanding of mental disorders not only in North America, but internationally by using similar concepts as the International Statistical Classification of Diseases and Related Health Problems (ICO-10) (World Health Organization; WHO; 1994), thus enhancing their compatibility.

A DSM-IV Text Revision (TR) was undertaken in 1997 by a working team of experts who in conjunction with the professionals initially involved in the DSM-IV looked at :

A. Any factual errors in DSM-IV and attempted to correct them
B. Updated the material presented in DSM-IV
C. Made changes to reflect new information
D. Made improvements to enhance the educational value of DSM-IV and
E. Updated the ICD-9 (World Health Organization) codes which had changed with the introduction of DSM-IV.

Major attributes of the DSM-IV have been:

- acknowledgement that, despite what its definition implies, a "mental disorder" is as much a physical disorder, and that a physical disorder influences the mental disorder.

- provision of clarification of categories that divides mental disorders into types based on criteria with defining features.

However, the use of individual, professional, clinical judgement is very important in the appropriate use of the DSM-IV. Thus, DSM-IV is *a tool only* to be used in conjunction with other clinical data and judgement. Specific caution should be exercised when DSM-IV categories, criteria and descriptions of mental disorders are applied. For example, for the forensic population, the legal determination of competence, clinical responsibility, or disability can vary vastly from the set terms as defined by the DSM-IV.

Special effort has been made in the preparation of DSM-IV to incorporate an awareness that the manual is used in culturally diverse populations in North America and internationally. Thus, DSM-IV includes three types of information specifically related to cultural considerations:

1. A discussion of cultural variations and the presentation of mental disorders
2. A description of culture-bound syndromes that have not been included in the DSM-III-R
3. An outline for cultural formulation to assist in evaluating and reporting the information of the individual's cultural context

Use of the Manual

What is a Multiaxial System?

DSM-IV is a multiaxial system, which involves an assessment on several *axes or levels*, each of which refers to a different domain of information that may help the caregiver to plan treatment and predict outcome.

There are five axes included in DSM-IV, each of which refers to a different diagnostic area:

AXIS I: Clinical disorders/mental illnesses
AXIS II: Personality disorders and mental retardation/ developmental disability
AXIS III: General medical conditions
AXIS IV: Psychosocial and environmental problems
AXIS V: Global assessment of functioning

Table 1: AXIS I- Clinical Disorders/Mental Illnesses

Clinical Disorders

- Delirium, Dementia, and Amnesic and other cognitive disorders
- Mental disorders, due to a general medical condition
- Substance-related disorders
- Schizophrenia and other psychotic disorders
- Mood disorders
- Anxiety disorders
- Somatoform disorders
- Factitious disorders
- Dissociative disorders
- Sexual and gender identity disorders
- Eating disorders
- Sleep disorders
- Impulse-control disorders not elsewhere classified
- Adjustment disorders

Axis I includes the various clinical subcategories of the mental illnessess such as mood and anxiety disorders, scizo-phrenias, somatoform, dissociative etc.

Table 2: AXIS II- personality disorders and mental retardation/developmental disabilities

- Paranoid
- Schizoid
- Schizotypical
- Antisocial
- Borderline
- Dependant
- Obsessive-Compulsive
- Histrionic
- Narcissistic
- Avoidant

Mental Retardation/Developmental Disability/ Delay
- Mild
- Moderate
- Severe
- Profound

Axis II includes the various personality disorders and the clinical subgroups of the mental retardation/developmental disabilities.

Table 3: Axis III- General medical conditions

- Infectious and parasitic diseases
- Neoplasms
- Endocrine, nutritional and metabolic diseases
- Diseases of blood and blood forming organs
- Diseases of nervous system
- Diseases of circulatory system
- Diseases of respiratory system
- Diseases of digestive system
- Diseases of the genitourinary tract
- Diseases of musculoskeletal system and connective tissue

Axis III Includes any medical/physiological illnessess of all body systems such as blood, nervous system, circulatory and respiratory systems, neoplasms, infections etc.

Table 4: Axis-IV- Psychosocial/Environmental problems

- Problems with primary support groups
- Problems related to the social environment
- Educational problems
- Housing problems
- Economic problems
- Problems with access to health care services
- Problems related to interaction with the legal system-crime
- Other psychosocial and environmental problems

Axis IV Includes any Psychosocial/environmental problems such as school, housing, financial , service delivery issues etc.

Axis V: Global Assessment of Functioning

It refers to the clinician's judgement of the individual's overall level of functioning. It is usually done by using the Global Assessment of Functioning Scale or GAF Scale. The scale is rated from 1 to 100. *The higher the number, the better the functioning of the individual in a specified time*. For example, 70 GAF in the past year refers to reasonably high level of functioning during the past year. (See Table 5)

**Table 5: Global Assessment of Functioning Scale
          GAF) Scale**

Scale	Wellness/Illness
100-91	Superior functioning– no symptoms
90-81	Absent or minimal symptoms (mild anxiety but generally well functioning)
80-71	Symptoms present but transient and expectable reaction to stressors
70-61	Some mild symptoms but generally functioning well
60-51	Moderate symptoms in social, occupational, school functioning
50-41	Serious symptoms/impairment in social, occupational, school life
40-31	Some impairment in reality, testing, or communication or work/school/family/judgment
30-21	Delusions or hallucinations; serious impairment in communication of judgment
20-11	Some danger of hurting self or others/ gross impairment in communication
10-1	Persistent danger of severely hurting self or others/ inability to maintain self care

This scale considers the psychological, occupational, and social functioning of an individual or a hypothetical continuum of mental wellness/illness.

The Case of Mr. C.

Mr. C., a 45-year-old man, lives in a group home, and has a mental age equivalence of an 8-10 year old level (severe degree of intellectual disability). Over the past three months, Mr. C. has become withdrawn, has lost any feelings of pleasure in life such as visiting the neighbourhood store, and has refused to walk and ride in the car, all activities which he used to love prior to this phase in his life. He has become more and more dependent on staff, and has lost his ability to self-care.

Mr. C. has also lost his appetite and his weight is now less by ten pounds. His sleep pattern has also changed so that Mr. C. wakes up during the night (2-3 a.m.), and is unable to return to sleep, which disturbs the other clients. When asked, he tends to deny any difficulties, and withdraws even more.

It seems that at the point when his symptoms started, Mr. C. lost his day program due to lack of sufficient work activity and resources available. On interview, Mr. C. is rather withdrawn, does not talk spontaneously, and clings to the staff. However, he denies hearing any voices and/or seeing things.

Mr. C.'s Multiaxial DSM-IV evaluation is as follow:

Axis I	Major depressive disorder, single episode, severe without psychotic features
Axis II	Severe mental retardation
Axis III	Unclassified brain dysfunction
Axis IV	Loss of day program
Axis V	GAF: 35 (current).

DSM-IV TR Classification

The list of categories referred to in this text is primarily the one commonly applied to persons who have a developmental disability persons of any age. Substance related disorders, and sexual and gender identity disorders are not included in this chapter, since they are being dealt with elsewhere in this text.

A.   Disorders that are usually first diagnosed in infancy, childhood or adolescence.

Mental Retardation/Developmental Disability.

Communication Disorders
- Expressive language disorder
- Mixed expressive-receptive language disorder.
- Stuttering
- Phonological disorders

Pervasive Developmental Disorders
- Autistic disorder
- Rett's disorder
- Asperger's disorder
- Childhood disintigrative disorder

Attention Deficit and Disruptive Behaviour Disorders
- Attention deficit/hyperactivity disorder
- Conduct disorder
- Oppositional and defiant disorder
- Disruptive behaviour disorder

Feeding and Eating Disorders of Infancy or Early Childhood
- Pica
- Rumination disorder
- Feeding disorder of infancy or early childhood

Tic Disorder
- Tourette's disorder
- Chronic motor or vocal tic disorder
- Transient tic disorder
- Tic disorder NOS

Elimination Disorder
- Enuresis
- Encopresis

Mental Retardation/Developmental Disabilities/Delay

The most important reference of DSM-IV-TR classification, as it applies to developmentally disabled persons, is its section on mental retardation/developmental disability. As already mentioned in Chapter 1, the essential feature of Mental Retardation/Developmental Disability/Delay is a significantly subaverage general intellectual functioning *(criterion A)* that is accompanied by concurrent deficits or impairments in adaptive functioning significant limitation in adaptive functioning in at least two of the following areas *(criterion B),* onset before age 18 *(criterion C).*

Mild Degree of Developmental Disability: Potential and mental health risks

This group constitutes the largest segment (about 85%) of all persons who are developmentally disabled. This group was formerly referred to as *educable*. Persons with this degree of disability can acquire academic skills up to approximately the sixth grade level, and typically have social and communication skills with minimal impairment at the sensorimotor areas. During adulthood, they usually achieve social and vocational skills adequate for minimal self-support.

Various causes are responsible for the occurrence of this degree of disability; the person may be affected prior to birth or after birth due to infections, medical conditions, and traumas. This group of persons, frequently, suffers from increased levels of anxiety and mood disorders (Borthwick-Duffy & Eyman, 1990; Stavrakaki & Mintsioulis, 1995; Gitta & Goldberg, 1995), since academic and social demands are often greater than their cognitive limitations allow them to reach. They also recognize the differences that exist between themselves and the general population. This increases their level of anxiety, and lowers their self-esteem. Another important factor in the development of mental illness in this specific group is the very traumatic and adverse experiences that these individuals have to face throughout their lives (school, work and societal barriers). Remaining other mental disorders are as prevalent in this group as in the general population (Reid, 1976).

Moderate Degree of Developmental Disability: Potential and mental health risks

This group constitutes about 10% of the entire population of persons with developmental disabilities. Individuals with moderate levels of intellectual disability usually are able to reach the second grade level in academic subjects, and can profit from vocational training. They also can attend to their personal care with moderate supervision. They may as well learn to travel independently in familiar places. During the early childhood years, persons who are moderately developmentally disabled acquire limited communication and self-care skills. During adolescence, due to difficulties in understanding and appropriately responding to social cues and stimuli, they may find themselves socially isolated with limited or nonexistent peer network. During adult life, the majority of these persons are able to perform unskilled or semiskilled work under supervision in sheltered workshops, or in the general workforce.

Mental health concerns and the development of mental disorders in this group, are generally higher than that of the general population. Sleep and adjustment disorders are also more prevalent in this group. Anxiety and mood disorders are more prevalent amongst this group (Stavrakaki & Mintsoulis, 1997, 1999; King, 1999; King & McCarthy., 1999). Certain types of schizophrenias are more frequent than were earlier believed such as Catatonia, disorganized subtypes of Schizophrenia (Menolascino 1972; Hucker, 1979; King, 1994).

Severe Degree of Developmental Disability: Potential and mental health risks

This group constitutes 3-4% of individuals with developmental disabilities. They acquire limited or no traditional communications skills, intelligible speech, or elementary self-care skills. Their gains in pre-academic subjects are limited to sight-reading of some "survival words". In adult years, they may be able to perform repetitive simple tasks in closely supervised settings. Most adapt well to life in the community, either with their families, or in group homes.

It is well established that the greater the degree of developmental disability, the greater the risks of developing mental health concerns and mental disorders (Heaton-Ward, 1977; Gostason, 1985; Gillberg, Persson, Guffman, & Themner, 1986; Borthwick-Duffy, 1990). It is also fair to state that the greater the degree of developmental disability, the greater the concurrent physical and medical disabilities (Heaton-Ward, 1977; Blackman, 1997).

This group is subject to higher prevalence of mental disorders during childhood through to adult life. During early childhood years, attention deficit hyperactive disorder, and self-injurious behaviours, with associated eating and tic disorders, were found to be very common (Reid, 1980; Quine, 1986). Other authors such as Einfeld and Sovner have reported increased prevalence of Autism (up to 40%), psychoses and disruptive behaviour disorders. Epilepsy and pervasive developmental disorders were found to be significantly higher than in the general population (up to 37%) with male vs. female ratios of 3:1. Sleep disorders and disruptive behaviour disorders have also been found to prevail in this group (Sovner & Hurley, 1986). Anxiety and Obsessive-Compulsive disorders are more common in this group (Stavrakaki & Mintsoulis, 1995; 1997). Affective mood disorders, and bipolar disorders as well, are more prevalent in this group as compared to the general population (Reid, 1976; Heaton-Ward 1977; Hucker, Day, George, & Roth, 1979; Stavrakaki et al, 1997, 1999; King, 1999; King, Fay, & Croghan, 2000). With adequate supports, this group of individuals can settle in the community in high support settings and/or group homes.

Profound Degree of Developmental Disabilities: Potential and mental health risks

This group constitutes 1 to 2 percent of people with developmental disability. Most individuals with this diagnosis have an identified neurological condition that accounts for the disability. They exhibit significant impairment in their cognition and sensorimotor functioning. Self-care and communication skills are limited to non-existent. Many will benefit from highly structured environments with constant supervision and support as well as an individualized relationship with a caregiver.

Mental disorders and mental health issues are, by far, more prevalent in this group. However, due to the cognitive limitations of this group, the diagnosis, assessment and treatment are challenging. Based on the criterion that is accepted (DSM-III-R), Sovner and Des Noyers–Hurley (1989) suggested that there were four factors that interfered with the application of the DSM criteria to persons with developmental disabilities. These factors are:

- *Intellectual distortion* refers to the effects of the diminished ability to think abstractly and communicate effectively.
- *Psychosocial masking* refers to the effects of the developmental disability upon the content of the psychiatric symptoms.
- *Cognitive disintegration* refers to limited coping skills and cognitive impairment that tends to affect this group in becoming disorganized under stress. This process is similar

to the one that occurs in pseudodementia.

- *Baseline exaggeration* describes how pre-existing behavioural challenges of a less significant level or maladaptive coping strategies may increase during periods of increased stress or psychiatric distress, and be dismissed as possible symptoms of a psychiatric disorder because of their pre-existence.

The DSM-IV criteria are very difficult to apply when individual clients are functioning at a severe to profound level of developmental disability. The best criteria and tools to be used in these instances are the *clinician's own experience, and the behavioural descriptions and clinical observations* that lead to an improved understanding of the mental disorders specifically found in these groups. Modifications to the criteria to apply in persons with developmental disability are currently being developed by a team of experts in the US.

Symptom clusters can be misleading in their applicability and diagnosis of the mental disorder in these groups. For example, many persons suffering from developmental disability are seen at various psychiatric or medical clinics because of the prevailing symptoms that are, in the majority, aggressivity, impulsivity, agitation and self-injurious behaviours (King, Carlo De Antonio, McCracken, Forness, & Ackerland, 1994; Stavrakaki & Mintsoulis, 1995; Gitta & Goldberg, 1997). These symptoms can be the manifestations of a number of medical and/or mental health issues or disorders, such as, anxiety disorder, depressive illness, and/or major psychotic illness. The preferred diagnosis in this case should be based primarily on the clinical experiences and observational data. *It is of utmost importance that staff, family members, school and other professional personnel collect and provide information on behav-*

ioural patterns and symptom presentation. It is critical to evaluate how patterns have altered and deviated from earlier, accepted and established patterns for the individual concerned.

Communication Disorders: These disorders are very common, and frequently coexist with developmental disabilities. Frequently, individuals experiencing this combination of disorders tend to exhibit other mental health problems, since any language deficits create stress and frustration for the individuals concerned. Anxiety, depressive and adjustment disorders are commonly linked with this group (Stavrakaki, et al., 1995). Treatment and/or assistance in improving language or adopting alternate ways of communicating are very important in modifying and ameliorating mental health problems in this group (primary prevention).

Pervasive Developmental Disorders: These disorders are characterized by severe and pervasive impairment in several areas of development:

- Reciprocal social interaction skills
- Communication skills
- Presence of stereotyped behaviour, interests and activities

These disorders are linked with developmental disabilities. Up to 40% of persons with developmental disabilities experience or have been diagnosed with any of the subcategories of these disorders especially as seen in autism. The coexistence of these two disorders usually indicates major neurological damage. Mental health problems such as anxiety and depressive disorders further complicate the clinical picture, and create inordinate amounts of stress to the individuals, further lowering their already limited level of functioning. Treatment of coexisting mental health problems assists individuals and their families in better adjusting to the primary disability, and diminishes the support they are required to receive.

Attention Deficit and Disruptive Disorders: The essential feature of the Attention Deficit-Hyperactivity Disorder is a persistent pattern of inattention and/or hyperactivity- impulsivity that is more frequent and severe than is typically observed in individuals at a comparable level of development.

This disorder plagues persons with developmental disabilities and increases the difficulties that he/she experiences in his/her life. The coexistence of these disorders with a developmental disorder points to a major neurological deficit. It also increases the likelihood of other mental health disorders such as disruptive behaviour, anxiety, and depression as well as substance related and sexual disorders. However, it is a challenge to identify these disorders in the developmentally disabled group for two reasons. First, many of the cardinal symptoms of these disorders are either inherent in the developmental disability (short attention span, excessive motor activity, or impulsivity). Second, the presence of qualities such as deliberateness and independence are sometimes incompatible with the developmental disability.

Thus, Oppositional Defiant Disorder is very rarely, if at all, diagnosed in this group. Attention deficit/disruptive disorders can only be diagnosed in the presence of the main symptoms, (i.e., attention deficit, hyperactivity, or impulsivity) when developmentally disabled persons present these in excess to their peers with a similar degree of disability.

Feeding Disorders: The primary disorder of this category is pica, the persistent eating of non-nutritive substances for a period of at least one month. Pica is very common amongst persons with developmental disabilities. It is very difficult to modify pica; various treatment modalities and interventions have been used with limited success.

Eating Disorders: Anorexia, the individual's refusal to maintain a minimally normal body weight, and bulimia, binge eating and inappropriate methods to prevent weight gain, are very rarely diagnosed in this population. This is primarily due to the fact that the diagnosis relies heavily on the individual's subjective feelings and intent, qualities that are generally lacking especially in the lower functioning groups.

On the other hand, compulsive overeating and patterned overeating are major issues in this population. This is, in part, due to the use of food for comfort and pleasure, and in part, due to the use of food as reinforcement to alter undesirable behaviours. Overeating is not usually diagnosed as one of the main eating disorders. However, excessive weight gain affects this group disproportionately, and leads to lower mobility, physical health issues, and low self-esteem.

Tic Disorders: A tic is a sudden, rapid, recurrent non-rhythmic, stereotyped motor movement or vocalization. Tic disorders may be associated with developmental disability. Adequate diagnosis of these disorders is challenging, since tics and movements tend to be inherent to some disability conditions. However, the repetitive, stereotypic movement encountered in Autism and other developmental disabilities does not constitute a tic disorder.

Elimination Disorders: Enuresis, the repeated voiding of urine day and night into bed or clothing, and *Encopresis,* the repeated passage of faeces into inappropriate places, are very frequently associated with persons labelled as developmentally disabled.   The greater the degree of disability, the more frequent the coexistence of these disorders. It is accurate to state that these conditions may also be the result of lack of opportunity of appropriate training.   In these instances, the persons with developmental disability can profit from behavioural/ learning opportunities/training.

These disorders are very difficult to prevent and/or treat, since they are often neurologically driven or developmentally determined.   They can also be a manifestation and/or expression of emotions such as anger, fear, or agitation.   Physical complications such as urinary tract infection are frequently present.   As a result, social and psychological problems may also develop.

B.   Disorders associated with any age group

Mood Disorders

- Depressive disorders
- Bipolar disorder

Anxiety Disorders

- Panic disorder without agoraphobia
- Panic disorder with agoraphobia
- Specific phobia
- Social phobia
- Obsessive-Compulsive disorder
- Post-traumatic stress disorder

- Acute stress disorder
- General anxiety disorder

Eating Disorders

- Anorexia Nervosa
- Bulimia Nervosa

Sleep Disorders

- Dyssomnias
- Parasomnias

Adjustment disorders

- With depressed mood
- With anxiety
- With both depressed mood and anxiety disorder

Personality disorders

- Paranoid
- Schizoid
- Antisocial
- Borderline
- Histrionic
- Narcissistic
- Avoidance
- Dependent
- Obsessive-Compulsive

Schizophrenias

* Schizophrenia
* Schizophreniform disorder
* Delusional
* Brief psychotic disorder
* Psychotic due to medical conditions

Specific characteristics of the above mentioned disorders as they apply to the developmentally disabled group

The aforementioned mental disorders associated with any age group are also prevalent in the developmentally disabled population. The higher the degree of cognitive ability, the higher the occurrence of these disorders.

Let us now examine the specific features with which these disorders are associated when they coexist with developmental disability.

Mood Disorders: These disorders are characterized by a disturbance in mood as the predominant feature. As mentioned earlier, these disorders are quite common for adults who are mildly and moderately developmentally disabled. The criteria referred to in the DSM-IV clearly can apply to the developmental disabled population. In the cases where the cognitive ability is rather limited (severe and profound degrees), and verbal or augmented communication is limited or non-existent, the main symptoms of these disorders (lack of pleasure, excessive emotions, tearfulness, irritability, changes in sleep, appetite and sexual behaviour), can only be recognized as *deviations from previously exhibited behaviour.* Their diagnosis is heavily based on clinical observations and accurate data collection of sleep patterns, eating habits, and daily activities. Recently, great interest has been shown in both depressive and bipolar disorder for persons with developmental disabilities.

Anxiety Disorders: Similar interest has been expressed in these disorders. The DSM-IV criteria apply without modifications in higher functioning developmentally disabled persons. In the lower categories, again, behavioural observations are of utmost importance in diagnosing these disorders. Clients who do not verbalize or communicate adequately, exhibit certain behaviours linked with these disorders (avoidance behaviour when faced with certain stimuli, autonomic arousal by becoming hyper-vigilant, panicky, tremulousness with excessive motor activity, and agitation and/or aggressivity). These changes are frequently associated with other physical signs (i.e., paleness, increased heartbeat, sweating and dry mouth). Wetting, loose stools and/or constipation can also accompany them.

Eating Disorders: In the adult population, as in children and adolescents, both anorexia and bulimia rely heavily on the subjective feelings of the individual and, as such, are very seldom diagnosed in persons who have developmental disabilities. Issues of overeating apply equally to this group. However, there are also distinct syndromes such as Prader-Willi, where excessive eating is the cardinal symptom. In these instances, the eating takes the form of an obsessive-compulsive disorder, and its treatment requires addressing the obsessive-compulsive nature of the eating disorder.

Sleep Disorders: Sleep disorders are very common in this group, and are either the direct result of the underlying neurological deficit, or a symptom of another co-existing mental disorder. They are usually associated with anxiety and depressive disorders, as well as bipolar disorders. These disorders can be continuous for a lengthy period of time, or can be intermittent, as in bipolar disorders, reflecting the underlying pathology. Many times, treatment of the underlying disorder resolves the sleep disorder. In a few situations, they can be prolonged and difficult to address. In these cases, the sleep disorders themselves can be the cause of disruptive behaviours, irritability, agitation and/or aggressivity. Re-establishing a healthy sleep pattern can be sufficient to modify the ensuing disruptive behaviours. Again, accurate and appropriate data collection is very important in the diagnosis and treatment of these disorders.

Adjustment disorders: The symptoms of these disorders are very similar to those of anxiety and depressive disorders. They follow a specific psychological or physical trigger, and usually last a self-limiting time. They are quite frequent in the persons labelled with mild and moderate developmental disabilities since they go through environmental changes during their lives. The presence of these disorders and their diagnosis in persons labelled with severe or profound developmental disabilities, remain a challenge, and are based on observed behavioural changes, and deviation of usually accepted normative behaviour patterns.

Personality disorders: They are enduring patterns of inner experience and behaviour that deviate markedly from the expectation of the individual's culture. Symptoms characteristic of these disorders in the adult general population apply also to the developmentally disabled group. Again, the level of cognitive ability determines how closely these symptoms resemble the ones applied to the general population as defined by DSM-IV. Clinicians are challenged in diagnosing these conditions in the lower functioning groups (severe and profound degrees).

Schizophrenia: It is a disturbance that lasts for at least six months, and includes at least one month of active-phase symptoms such as, delusions, hallucinations, disorganized speech, grossly disorganized or catatonic behaviour, and negative symptoms. These criteria can apply in diagnosing schizophrenia in the higher functioning developmentally disabled group. In the lower groups, due to limited or total absence of communication, the diagnosis of schizophrenia remains a challenge. These individuals cannot convey experience such as hallucination and/or delusions. In certain instances, however, some developmentally disabled individuals can display evidence of response to hallucinations, or adapt catatonic postures, so that the diagnosis of schizophrenia can be made.

C. Disorders commonly but not exclusively associated with the aging population

- Delirium
- Dementia
- Amnesic disorders
- Other cognitive disorders

Delirium: The essential feature of delirium is a distubance of consciousness that is accompanied by a change in cognition that cannot be accounted for by a pre-existing or evolving dementia. In persons with developmental disability, as in the general population, delirium can be the result of one of the following conditions:

- General medical conditions
- Substance intoxication/withdrawal

Delirium can also produce symptoms similar to schizophrenia and/or other psychotic conditions. Careful physical and mental status examinations are very important in understanding and diagnosing delirium. The treatment of delirium requires addressing the medical crisis and the underlying cause.

Persons with developmental disabilities are more frequently afflicted by delirium since they are more vulnerable to medical conditions that lead to delirium. They are also very sensitive to medications and/or other substances which are used to treat physical ailments for mental health problems.

Dementias: Dementias are characterized by the development of multiple cognitive deficits (including memory impairment). Dementia is due to the direct physiological effects of a medical condition, the persisting effect of a substance, or multiple etiologics suggestiing cerebrovascular disease and/or Alzheimer's.

The main symptoms of Dementia are:

- Memory impairment
- Apraxia (impaired ability to execute motor activity despite intact motor ability)
- Aphasia (deterioration of language function)
- Agnosia (failure to identify or recognize objects despite intact sensory function)
- Disturbance in executive functioning (ability to think abstractly, plan, initiate, sequence and stop complex behaviours)

Many persons with developmental disabilities suffer from underlying pathologies that predispose them to dementias. Genetic conditions such as Down Syndrome and other chromosomal anomalies are known to be linked with dementias in earlier ages than that of the general population. Due to the cognitive limitations that already pre-exist in persons with a developmental disability, it is very difficult to diagnose dementias in this population. *The diagnosis can only be based on evident deterioration of the pre-existing level of cognition, and on behaviours that indicate a greater loss of abilities.*

Table 7: Characteristics of Mental Disorders in Persons with Developmental Disability

A. Disorders associated with infancy, childhood, and adolescence

Mental Disorders	Developmental Disability
Communication Disorders	*Frequency*: High *Associations*: Anxiety, Depression, Adjustment disorders
Pervasive Developmental Disorders	*Frequency:* 40% *Associations*: Anxiety and depressive disorders, major neurological deficit
Attention Deficit/Disruptive Disorders	*Frequency*: High *Associations*: Disruptive behaviours, anxiety depressive disorders, sexual and substance abuse disorders *Symptoms*: Have to be higher than other persons with DD in similar circumstances
Feeding Disorders Pica	*Frequency*: High *Associations*: Neurological deficit
Eating Disorders Anorexia/Bulimia Compulsive/patterned overeating	*Frequency*: Very rare as diagnosis relies heavily on the individual's feeling of intent *Frequency*: Very common Not usually diagnosed as one of main eating disorders

(Table continues)

Mental Disorders	Developmental Disability
Tic Disorders	*Frequency*: Common but difficult to diagnose *Associations*: Autism and repetitive stereotypic movements are not
Elimination Disorders Enuresis Encopresis	*Frequency*: Very common especially in the lower levels of ability

B. Disorders Associated with Any Age Group

Mood Disorders	*Frequency:* High *Symptoms:* Lack of pleasure, excessive emotions, tearfulness, irritability, changes in sleep and appetite and sexual behaviours *Recognition*: Only if deviation is noted from previously exhibited behaviour
Anxiety Disorders	*Frequency:* High *Symptoms:* Avoidance of certain stimuli, autonomic arousal, panic, tremulousness, excessive motor activity, agitation, aggressivity, pallor, increased heart beat, sweating, dry mouth, wetting, loose stools and/or constipation *Recognition:* Only if deviation is noted from previously exhibited behaviour
Eating Disorders	Same as in disorders in childhood
Sleep Disorders	*Frequency*: High Associations: Neurological deficit, co-existing mental disorder, may cause mental health problems

(Table continues)

Adjustment Disorders	*Frequency*: Moderate *Symptoms:* Similar to anxiety depressive disorders *Associations*: Follows a specific trigger, self-limiting
Personality Disorders	*Frequency*: Moderate *Symptoms*: Similar to general population *Recognition*: Difficult in lower functioning persons
Schizophrenias	Frequency: Moderate Symptoms: Delusions, hallucinations, disorganized speech, grossly disorganized or catatonic behaviour and negative symptoms Recognition: Easy when display above symptoms. Clinical observations in lower functioning group of behaviours resembling abnormal phenomena such as hearing voices or suspiciousness/paranoia. Also in certain instances, total personality disintegration

C. Disorders Associated with Aging

Delirium	*Frequency*: Moderate *Symptoms*: Disturbances of consciousness, change in cognition *Associations*: Medical conditions, substance abuse, mental disorders
Dementias	*Frequency*: High *Symptoms*: Memory loss, apraxia, agnosia, aphasia, disturbance in executive function *Associations*: Genetic conditions such as Down Syndrome and other trisomies, medical conditions

Summary

This chapter addresses the DSM-IV and Text Revision criteria in their application to developmentally disabled persons.
These criteria are best applied with few modification when the
individual clients are functioning at the mild, and in some instances, moderate level of disability. The DSM-IV-TR criteria
are very difficult to apply when the individuals are severely or
profoundly disabled. Best criteria and tools used in these
cases are the clinician's own experience and familiarity with
these groups, and the behaviour descriptions and clinical observations of caregivers that assist the experts in diagnosing
mental disorders in these groups.

We all agree that appropriate diagnosis is vitally important in
the understanding of Mental Disorders, and in turn, the use of
proper therapeutic interventions including specific medications,   behaviour   techniques,   psychotherapies,   milieu
(environmental) therapies and social interventions. Therefore,
the Diagnostic and Statistical Manual is an important, but not
exclusive, diagnostic tool available to clinicians in their attempt to apply criteria to properly diagnose Mental Disorders
in the developmentally disabled group. Clinical observation
and other diagnostic tools are very important in establishing
the correct diagnosis of mental disorders in persons with developmental disability.

Do You Know?

1.   What is the DSM-IV and its application?
2.   What are some of the common diagnoses of Mental disorders in the Developmentally Disabled group?
3.   What is the multiaxial system?
4.   What primarily determines the application of the DSM-IV criteria without any modifications?
5.   What are some of the barriers in the use of DSM-IV criteria for the Developmentally Disabled persons?

Resources

King, B.H., Carlo DeAntonio, B.A., McCracken, J.T., Fomess, S.R., & Ackerland, V. (1994). Psychiatric consultation and profound mental retardation. *American Journal of Psychiatry, 151,*1802-1808.

Sovner R., & Hurley, A.D. (1989) Ten diagnostic principles for recognizing psychiatric disorders in mentally regarded persons. *Psychiatric Aspects of Mental Retardation Reviews, 8,* 9-14.

Stavrakaki, C. (1999) Depression, anxiety and adjustment disorders in people with developmental disabilities. In N. Bouras (Ed.), *Psychiatric and behavioral disorders in developmental disability and mental retardation* (pp. 175-187.) Boston: Cambridge University Press;

References

American Psychiatric Association (1987). *Diagnostic and statistical manual of mental disorders, Third edition revised.*

Washington, DC: Author.

American Psychiatric Association (1994). *Diagnostic and statistical manual of mental disorders, Fourth edition.* Washington, DC: Author

Blackman, J. A. (1997). *Medical aspects of developmental disabilities in children: Birth to three. Third edition.* New York: Aspen Publishers.

Borthwick-Duffy, S.A., & Eyman, R.K. (1990). Who are the dually diagnosed? *American Journal on Mental Retardation, 94,* 586-595.

Einfeld, S.L. (1984). Clinical assessment of 4,500 developmentally delayed individuals. *Journal of Mental Deficiency Research, 28,* 129-142.

Gillberg, C., Persson, E., Grufman, M., & Themner, U. (1986). Psychiatric disorders in mildly and severely mentally retarded urban children and adolescents: Epidemiological aspects. *British Journal of Psychiatry, 149,*68-74.

Gitta, M.Z.& Goldberg, B. (1995). Dual diagnosis: Psychiatric and physical disorders in a clinical sample, part II. *Clinical Bulletin of Developmental Disabilities Program, 6,* 1-2.

Gostason, R. (1985). Psychiatric illness among the mentally retarded: A Swedish population study. *Acta Psychiatrica Scandinavica, 71* (Supplement 318), 1-117.

Heaton-Ward, A. (1977). Psychosis in mental handicap. *British Journal of Psychiatry, 1330,* 525-533.

Hucker, S.J., Day, K.A., George, S., & Roth, M. (1979). Psychosis in mentally handicapped adults. In F.E. James & R.P. Snaith (Eds.), *Psychiatric illness and mental handicap (pp. 27-35).* London: Gaskell Press.

King, R. (1999). Clinical implication of comorbid bipolar disorder and obsessive-compulsive disorder in individuals with development disabilities. *The National Association of Developmental Disabilities Bulletin, 2,* 63-67.

King, B.H., Carlo DeAntonio, B.A., McCracken, J.T., Forness, S.R., & Ackerland, V. (1994). Psychiatric consultation and profound mental retardation. *American Journal of Psychiatry, 151,*1802-1808.

King R., Fay, G., & Croghan, P. (2000). Rapid cycling bipolar disorder in individuals with developmental disabilities. *Mental Retardation, 38(3),* 253-261.

King, R. & McCartney, J. (1999). Charting for a purpose. Optimal treatment of bipolar disorder in individuals with developmental disabilities. *Mental Health Aspects of Developmental Disabilities, 2 ,* 1-9.

Menolascino, F.J. (1972). Primitive, atypical, and abnormal-psychotic behavior in institutionalized mentally retarded children. *Journal of Autism and Childhood Schizophrenia, 3,* 49-64.

Quine, L. (1986). Behaviour problems in severely mentally handicapped children. *Psychological Medicine, 16,* 895-907.

Reid, A.H. (1976). Psychiatric disturbances in the mentally handicapped. *Proceedings of Royal. Society of London, 69,* 509-512.

Reid, A.H. (1980). Psychiatric disorders in mentally handicapped children: a clinical and follow-up study. *Journal of Mental Deficiency Research, 24,* 287-298.

Sovner R. & Hurley, A.D. (1989). Ten diagnostic principles for recognizing psychiatric disorders in mentally regarded persons. *Psychiatric Aspects of Mental Retardation Reviews, 8,* 9-14.

Stavrakaki, C. (1999). Depression, anxiety and adjustment disorders in people with developmental disabilities. In N. Bouras (Ed), *Psychiatric and behavioral disorders in developmental disabilities and mental retardation* (pp. 175-

187). Boston: Cambridge University Press.

Stavrakaki, C. & Mintsioulis, G. (1995). Pharmacological treatment of obsessive-compulsive disorders in Down's syndrome individuals: Comparison with obsessive-compulsive disorders of non-Downs mentally retarded persons. In *Proceedings of the International Congress II on the Dually Diagnosed*. pp. 52-56.

Stavrakaki, C. & Mintsioulis, G. (1997). Anxiety disorders in persons with mental retardation: Diagnostic, clinical, and treatment issues. *Psychiatric Annals, 27*, 182-189.

World Health Organization. (1974). *International statistical classification of diseases and related health problems* (ICD-9). Geneva: Author.

World Health Organization. (1994). *International statistical classification of diseases and related health problems* (ICD-10) (1994). Geneva: Author.

Chapter 5

Comprehensive Screening and Assessment

Jane Summers, Chrissoula Stavrakaki, Dorothy M. Griffiths, and Thomas Cheetham

Learning Objectives

Readers will be able to:

1. Identify two reasons why assessment and screening are important
2. Provide an example of an instrument that is used with persons with developmental disabilities in each of the following areas: diagnostic and health care screening, biomedical assessment, psychological assessment and social-ecological assessment
3. Understand how the range of assessments assist in development of a comprehensive biopsychosocial profile

Introduction

Why are screening and assessment important?

This chapter contains a review of different instruments that are used during the biopsychosocial assessment of mental health problems in persons with developmental disabilities. Some of these instruments have been developed for "screening" purposes – that is, to identify those individuals who are likely to require more in-depth assessment or particular types of service. Screening tools can be used on an individual basis, or on a larger scale with groups of people. They are helpful in the clinical decision-making process about whether to proceed to the next level of assessment. They are useful for detecting potential problems that may not have been recognised, or for formulating a tentative diagnosis. In doing so, they can lead to faster and more specific treatments, and can minimise the time and cost involved with unnecessary assessment.

The dominant theme throughout the book is the biopsychosocial approach to assessing and understanding mental health problems in persons with developmental disabilities. Often, mental health problems present as non-specific behavioural challenges. Griffiths (2001) noted the need for differential diagnosis for behavioural challenges in order to determine the underlying factor or factors. For instance, a behaviour can be or do any of the following:

- reactive to biomedical influences or traumatic events
- responsive to ecological events, interactions or conditioned stimuli
- function to enhance stimulation or reinforcement, to avoid discomfort or unpleasant events
- provide communication.

In order to diagnose the different factors that may be working alone or together to produce the behaviour, a comprehensive screening and assessment process must be conducted at multiple levels. Box 1 illustrates how a single behaviour such as aggression may be associated with numerous factors or conditions. Without a thorough biopsychosocial assessment, it is impossible to make a differential diagnosis. Moreover, without a well-conceived hypothesis (or hypotheses), the selection of an appropriate treatment is like shooting in the dark.

BOX 1 - Ten Factors to Consider in the Differential Diagnosis of Aggression (Lowry & Sovner, 1991)

> 1. Medical illness
> 2. Medication side-effects
> 3. Pre-seizure irritability
> 4. Irritability secondary to mania, depression, or organic mental syndrome
> 5. Rage attacks
> 6. Task-related anxiety
> 7. Schizophrenia-related paranoid delusion
> 8. Inability to express needs
> 9. Means to gain positive reinforcement
> 10. Means to avoid or escape an unpleasant event.

A comprehensive assessment process involves gathering the existing data and background information, interviewing the individual and relevant others, making observations in the natural environments, and synthesising the information into working theories that make sense to explain why the person may be behaving in this way. Often, further tests or measures are needed to confirm or eliminate hypotheses. However, the assessment is a scientific process of elimination and confirmation of potential influences, based on all available data, and taking a broad-based perspective.

No one person or member of one particular professional discipline can possess the breadth of knowledge and skills that are needed to perform such a comprehensive assessment. For instance, the expertise and scope of practice for a behaviour analyst is quite different from that of a medical doctor. That is why an interdisciplinary approach, that involves a synthesis of input from professionals from several different disciplines, is considered to be "best practice" when assessing and treating individuals with developmental disabilities and mental health problems (see Chapter 10: The Interdisciplinary Mental Health Team for more detail). But, it is not professional input alone that is taken into consideration during a comprehensive assessment. Information from the individual, his or her family, and caregivers is a critical part of the process.

Isn't dual diagnosis just another label?

A comprehensive biopsychosocial assessment provides you much more than a label, although sometimes a new label or diagnosis may emerge. For instance, the person may be given a psychiatric label, such as depression, mania, or post-traumatic stress disorder. The reason for the label is twofold:

- It provides understanding. It is descriptive to other people working with the individual so that they can respond appropriately, and with full knowledge of the challenges the person faces.
- It is also key to treatment. Persons who are deemed to have clinically significant depression are often, based on that diagnosis, prescribed a path of chemical intervention and cognitive therapy to alter the mood state. Thus, the label helps to guide appropriate treatment.

At times, the assessment may uncover a genetic disorder that can give rise to a characteristic pattern of behaviour (a behavioural phenotype). The diagnostic label can be helpful in putting the individual's behaviour in context. For example, as we learned in Chapter 3– The Integrated Biopsychosocial Approach to Challenging Behaviour, individuals with a diagnosis of fragile x syndrome can be expected to share certain features and vulnerabilities. Knowledge of the underlying syndrome can lead to more focused assessment and treatment (see Appendix A for a list of common genetic syndromes and their associated features). The outcome of assessment is not just a diagnostic label, but a profile of the person's biomedical, psychological and social conditions as they influence the behaviour. This assessment then, is the foundation on which treatment and intervention are built.

Type of Assessments:

What does it mean to do a comprehensive biopsychosocial assessment? Does it mean completing a comprehensive biomedical work-up, performing psychological evaluations, and conducting a social or contextual analysis? The answer is maybe and maybe not. The assessment flows from the nature of the background information and observations made by the team members.

A. Biomedical Factors

Challenging behaviours can be influenced, directly or indirectly, by physical conditions, medications, and/or psychiatric conditions. Some common medical conditions that have been noted to relate to challenging behaviours are seizure disorders, sleep apnea, otitis media, blocked shunt, migraine headaches, and premenstrual problems. Hyper/hypo thyroidism, autoimmune disorders, upper respiratory tract conditions, eating disorders, or heart conditions (e.g., mitral valve prolapse), can present like depression, mania, or anxiety/panic disorder. Ryan and Sunada (1997) noted that an overwhelming percentage of clients who present with behavioural challenges actually have undiagnosed medical conditions. These medical conditions may be directly related to the behavioural challenge (e.g., headbanging to alleviate severe pain caused by a migraine headache), or they may play a more indirect role (e.g., sleep deprivation due to sleep apnea ⇒ irritability ⇒ aggression in response to a minor provocation). A thorough assessment should include a careful medical and medication history and physical examination (Loschen & Osman, 1992). It may involve a laboratory work-up, a mental status examination, neurological testing, sleep studies and diagnostic imaging (x-rays or MRI scans).

Specific observation charts have been developed to assist in gathering biomedical data that can be used for diagnostic purposes. As an example, sleep disturbance is an important factor in multiple DSM-IV diagnoses, either as a criterion for a disorder, or as an associated feature of a disorder. Sleep data can serve as a general index of psychological status, and should be included as a routine component of any biomedical data collection package (Carr, Neumann & Darnell, 1998). Sovner and Hurley (1990) developed an overnight observation sleep chart to record when a person actually sleeps (as opposed to when the person goes to bed or gets up). This chart was modified slightly by Carr et al. (1998). See Figure 1.

Figure 1–Monthly Sleep Chart

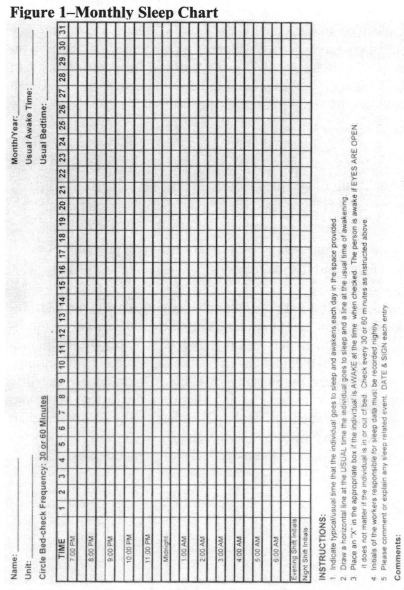

Reprinted with permission from Psych-Media. Originally printed in article by Carr, E.G., Neuma, J.K., & Dornell, C.L. (1998, Apr-June). The clinical importance of sleep data collection: A national survey and case reports. *Mental Health Aspects in Developmental* Disabilities, 1(2).

Certain syndromes are associated with an increased risk of medical or mental health conditions. Health care screening guidelines have been developed for a number of these syndromes. For adults with Down syndrome, for instance, some of the following investigations are recommended by the Down Syndrome Medical Interest Group (1999):

- annual thyroid screening
- auditory testing
- ophthalmologic evaluation
- cervical spine x-rays as needed for sports participation
- enquire about sleep apnea symptoms
- monitor for signs of skill loss or behavioural change
- anemia and liver screening

The timing and nature of the challenging behaviour can provide a valuable clue to potential medical and mental health issues (i.e., cyclical behaviours may relate to allergies or menses in women; to medication effects or side effects; to seasonal changes caused by Seasonal Affective Disorder, or related to Post Traumatic Events; to shifts between depressive behaviour and mania as seen in Bipolar Disorder). The following chart (Figure 2) developed by Sovner and Hurley (1990) is an excellent example of how these cyclical shifts can be tracked.

Figure 2– Bipolar Mood Chart

CLIENT'S NAME: _____

MONTH: _____

Each day, assess the client's mood state for that day by circling the appropriate mood scale item. Your rating should be based on observations for the entire day and evening. If the client is both manic and depressed during the day, carry out separate ratings based upon 12-hour time periods. When completing the log, please use the following anchor points for your mood state ratings:

+3 = markedly manic
+2 = moderately manic
+1 = mildly manic
0 = normal mood for the day
-1 = mildly depressed
-2 = moderately depressed
-3 = markedly depressed

DAY:	1	2	3	4	5	6	7	8	9	10	11	12	13	14	15	16	17	18	19	20	21	22	23	24	25	26	27	28	29	30	31
	+3	+3	+3	+3	+3	+3	+3	+3	+3	+3	+3	+3	+3	+3	+3	+3	+3	+3	+3	+3	+3	+3	+3	+3	+3	+3	+3	+3	+3	+3	+3
	+2	+2	+2	+2	+2	+2	+2	+2	+2	+2	+2	+2	+2	+2	+2	+2	+2	+2	+2	+2	+2	+2	+2	+2	+2	+2	+2	+2	+2	+2	+2
	+1	+1	+1	+1	+1	+1	+1	+1	+1	+1	+1	+1	+1	+1	+1	+1	+1	+1	+1	+1	+1	+1	+1	+1	+1	+1	+1	+1	+1	+1	+1
	0	0	0	0	0	0	0	0	0	0	0	0	0	0	0	0	0	0	0	0	0	0	0	0	0	0	0	0	0	0	0
	-1	-1	-1	-1	-1	-1	-1	-1	-1	-1	-1	-1	-1	-1	-1	-1	-1	-1	-1	-1	-1	-1	-1	-1	-1	-1	-1	-1	-1	-1	-1
	-2	-2	-2	-2	-2	-2	-2	-2	-2	-2	-2	-2	-2	-2	-2	-2	-2	-2	-2	-2	-2	-2	-2	-2	-2	-2	-2	-2	-2	-2	-2
	-3	-3	-3	-3	-3	-3	-3	-3	-3	-3	-3	-3	-3	-3	-3	-3	-3	-3	-3	-3	-3	-3	-3	-3	-3	-3	-3	-3	-3	-3	-3

Reprinted with permission from Psych-Media. Originally printed in article by Sovner , R. & Des Noyers Hurley, A. (1990). Assessment tools which facilitate psychiatric evaluation and treatment. *Habilitative Mental Healthcare Newsletter, 9(11).*

Certain medications can influence behavioural symptoms. For example, the relationship of medication to drug-induced disorders presenting with physical aggression has been shown in numerous studies (e.g., propranolol induced psychosis; Gershon et al., 1979) or viabatrin induced mood disturbance (Aldenkamp, Vermeulen, Mulder, & Overwerg, 1994). Clinicians completing a comprehensive assessment for this population will need to rely on a psychopharmacology reference guide to check potential effects and side-effects of the medications. Sovner and Hurley (1992) developed a user-friendly worksheet that can be used by caregivers to document the following types of information to assist with a medication review:

- current medications, dosages and administration schedule
- discontinued medications
- current behavioural and psychosocial interventions
- physical signs and symptoms
- global impression of the individual's behaviour problems

A tool that has been recently developed to assist clinicians in identifying biomedical factors that may be influencing the onset or aggravation of behavioural symptoms is the *Behavioral Diagnostic Guide for Developmental Disabilties* (Gedye, 1998). Gedye (1998) has compiled an exhaustive guide of potential biomedical issues that may relate to presentation of behaviours such as physical aggression, self-injury, screaming, sleep disturbance, eating disturbances, dementia and unwitnessed or unusual falls. She clearly demonstrates that each non-specific behavioural symptom can have a variety of potential factors that could be influencing the behaviour.

Screening for genetic disorders

In recent years, significant progress has been made in identifying the genetic factors that are involved in many syndromes in which developmental disability is also present. This information is important because individuals with a specific genetic syndrome often have associated medical conditions that require identification and treatment. As well, they frequently show a characteristic pattern of behavioural challenges. Thus, knowledge of an underlying syndrome is useful from an assessment and treatment perspective (See Appendix A). Since it is not feasible or advisable to perform genetic testing for most people with a developmental disability, it is important to be able to identify particular individuals who may be at risk for a syndrome, and to refer them for more thorough assessment. A screening tool can be helpful in this regard. As an example, a checklist for screening males with developmental disability for fragile x syndrome has been developed (Butler, Mangrum, Bupta & Singh, 1991). A rater determines whether each item on the checklist is present or absent. Items on the checklist include:

- large ears and testes
- plantar crease
- family history of developmental disability or autism
- tactile defensiveness
- hyperextensible finger joints

The following case provides an excellent example of the need for a full biomedical workup.

The Case of Johnny

Johnny is an 18-year-old male with Down syndrome who lives at home with both parents and his two brothers. Until recently, Johnny was always affectionate, pleasant, co-operative and interested in his schoolwork and friends.

Sixteen months prior to his first assessment at a psychiatric unit, Johnny's behaviour became slowly but progressively worse. He became unable to show any pleasure, was uninterested in his environment, and withdrew more and more to the point of losing all social skills. Johnny also stopped using his limited vocabulary and showed problems eating and sleeping. On interviewing his parents, it became apparent that there were two significant changes that coincided with Johnny's behavioural and social changes:

i) Father, due to work obligations, had to be away from home for lengthy periods of time (up to a month at a time) repeatedly for the six months prior to Johnny's noticeable changes. It is worth noting that Johnny has always been very close to his father.
ii) The family had to move across the country because of father's new employment. This move took place two months prior to the onset of the most serious observed behaviours.

Parents, at that time, tried to cope with Johnny's changes, and did not seek any professional advice. Four months following the social withdrawal and severe loss of social skills, he became extremely preoccupied with construction toys and trucks. Any intervention or attempt to disengage Johnny from these activities would escalate into a major tantrum with physical abuse and extreme protestation. Simultaneously, he started wetting himself, checking doors and whispering. At this time, his parents sought professional help. When seen by staff from a developmental clinic, he was diagnosed as suffering from Childhood Disintegrative Disorder. Following a neurological evaluation, a rare form of epilepsy was suggested but not substantiated by EEG and other tests (i.e., CAT scan, MRI).

At a final attempt to disentangle this problem, Johnny was referred to a dual diagnosis clinic. By this time, he was totally uncommunicative and withdrawn, but showed a "peculiar" preoccupation for the construction toys present in the clinic. On parents' account, Johnny's regression was "total". They were devastated and fearful of future consequences to Johnny and his family. Following the initial interview and the use of questionnaires and scales relevant to ADHD and OCD, it was felt that Johnny had suffered from a trauma that initially resulted in an episode of depression, and subsequently in the emergence of an Obsessive-Compulsive Disorder. He was treated with an SSRI (Fluoxetine) and Respiridone to which he responded very favorably. Family support and specialised academic programmes were also offered. Nine months later, Johnny feels, looks and behaves like his "old self". He is demonstrative, happy, pleasant, verbal and able to follow his scholastic programmes and activities as prior to the devastating events.

B. Psychological Factors

<u>Gathering a Psychological History</u>

A history is important to evaluate the path of the individual's life in relation to social/emotional and medical life events. Often clinicians will engage in an analysis to show these events in a temporal manner.

Important events might include:

- History of emotional/physical or sexual abuse
- Significant medical procedures (especially involving hospitalisation or invasive procedures)
- Family disruption (violence/divorce/remarriage/birth of siblings)
- Educational milestones
- Environmental changes (moves, significant changes in living arrangements or socio economic status)
- Grief or loss [due to death, abandonment, or change (i.e., change of a caregiver)]
- Change of jobs

Let's take a look at the following example in Figure 3 of a young man who has been accused of sexual interference with a child, and see how his history may be helpful in understanding his past.

Figure 3: An Historical Perspective of Challenging Behaviour

Observed death of brother	*Parents separated in violent dispute*	*Began school*	*Sexually abused by mother's cousin*	*Institutionalized*	*Sexually Abused by Sex Education Instructor/ no counseling provided*	*Placed in a community setting with minimal supervision*
4 years	41/2 years	5-6 years	5-7 years	7-10	10 -15 years	17 years
Began to show anxiety reactions	Became withdrawn	First signs of cognitive challenges	Began to show aggression	Adjusted well; no symptoms noted	Became sexually indiscriminate with other children	Anxiety reactions returned/ sexually abused a child

Psychological Testing

This section will focus on psychological tests, their uses and limitations. These tests are designed to measure various aspects of an individual's psychological functioning, often within the context of assessing learning, developmental, behavioural and/or emotional problems. By using them, psychologists are able to arrive at a better understanding of an individual's strengths and weaknesses, which aids in the diagnostic process and development of service plans.

Standardised psychological tests differ in several ways from informal tests that are often used by non-psychologists. Standardised tests are carefully developed and systematically tested before they can be made available for clinical use. They must meet established standards regarding their psychometric characteristics, such as their reliability (consistency and precision), and validity (the extent to which they measure what they are designed to measure). They must be administered and interpreted by individuals who are qualified to do so by virtue of their educational background, training and experience. Often, this is a person with a Master's degree, or a Doctoral degree in psychology.

Standardised tests are administered in a uniform manner and are scored according to objective criteria. These procedures help to minimise subjective bias and outside influences on the test scores. Tests yield numerical scores that are not inherently meaningful. In order for this to happen, the scores of the individual being assessed need to be compared to scores that are obtained by individuals in a norm group or standardisation sample. This process results in "derived" scores (such as standard scores, age-equivalent scores and percentile ranks), which indicate how well the individual being assessed performed in relation to the individuals in the norm group. It is these derived scores that are typically presented and interpreted in psychological assessment reports.

Inventories or rating scales are often used to measure aspects of an individual's personality, emotional or behavioural functioning, and can assist with identifying clinical disorders. These measures rely on information that is provided by the individual ("self-report"), or another person who is knowledgeable about him or her ("informant").

Psychological tests have limitations as well as advantages. First, they can't provide a definitive answer about the cause of an individual's learning, developmental, behavioural or emotional problems. Second, their strength lies in assessing an individual's current functioning rather than predicting his or her future performance with complete accuracy. Third, many tests are very specific and their findings may not be applicable to different psychological functions. Nonetheless, psychological tests yield information that is invaluable when deciding upon a course of action to assist an individual with learning, developmental, behavioural and/or emotional problems.

Psychological Tests

While the process of assessing the psychological functioning of individuals with developmental disabilities will vary in accordance with factors such as the referral issues that need to be addressed, the complexity of the case and/or the availability of clinically relevant information, it is customary to start with an assessment of the individual's intellectual and adaptive functioning. Additional tests may be used to assess his or her language functioning, academic or vocational performance, and to identify behavioural, emotional and personality problems.

Commonly used assessment instruments

Intelligence Tests: used to measure an individual's thinking, reasoning and problem-solving ability with verbal and/or non-verbal material, as well as his or her perceptual and spatial/mechanical ability

- Wechsler Adult Intelligence Scale – Third Edition **(WAIS-III)** (Wechsler, 1997)
- Stanford Binet Intelligence Scale - Fourth Edition **(SB-IV)** (Thorndike, Hagen & Sattler, 1986)
- Leiter International Performance Scale - Revised **(Leiter-R)** (Roid & Miller, 1997)
- Test of Nonverbal Intelligence - Third Edition **(TONI-3)** (Brown, Sherbenou & Johnsen, 1997)

The last two tests are used to assess an individual's IQ in special circumstances (e.g., when he or she comes from a non-English speaking background, or has a hearing impairment, or when there are social/cultural differences)

Hurley (1989) suggests that intelligence tests are an important part of a clinical assessment for psychiatric purposes. She notes that persons with schizophrenia, for instance, may show a significant lowering of verbal IQ and other language related functions, and may show bizarre responses to testing. Persons with anxiety disorder may show disproportionately lower scores on digit span subtests; persons who are depressed may show overall lower scores on performance tests which require quick eye-hand coordination and timing of responses (Hurley,

1989).

Measures of Adaptive Functioning: used to assess the degree to which the individual is able to cope effectively with (i.e., has mastered) the demands of his or her environment. This includes: communication, self-care, home and community living, social skills, work and leisure, and functional academics.

- AAMR Adaptive Behavior Scales- Residential and Community **(ABS-RC:2)** (Nihira, Leland & Lambert, 1993)
- Scales of Independent Behavior-Revised **(SIB-R)** (Bruininks, Woodcock, Weatherman & Hill, 1996)
- Vineland Adaptive Behavior Scales **(VABS)** (Sparrow, Balla & Cicchetti, 1984)

Language Tests: can be used to supplement verbal tasks from IQ tests

- Peabody Picture Vocabulary Test – Third Edition **(PPVT-III)** (Dunn & Dunn, 1997)
- Expressive Vocabulary Test **(EVT)** (Williams, 1997)

Academic Achievement Tests: used to assess an individual's academic skills in the areas of reading, writing and arithmetic

- Peabody Individual Achievement Test - Revised **(PIAT-R)** (Markwardt, 1998)
- Wide Range Achievement Test – Third Edition **(WRAT-3)** (Wilkinson, 1993)

Instruments for Assessing Psychopathology and Behaviour Problems:

There are many common psychiatric conditions associated with developmental disabilites (see Appendix B). However there are a number of non specific behavioural challenges that may be presented by persons who are developmentally disabled; these symptons may or may not be related to a psychiatric   condition. A careful process of differential diagnosis is required.

In the past two decades, a number of caregiver and client-rated inventories have been developed to assist in the assessment of emotional and behavioural challenges in adults and children with developmental diabilities. Hurley and Sovner (1992) identified that these symptom inventories can be very beneficial in: a) establishing a tentative or provisional psychiatric diagnosis; b) verifying a diagnosis for mental health services; c)   assisting with placement decisions, d) measuring responses to treatment; and/or e) establishing competency.

In Table 1, the most common inventories have been described. It should be noted that these instruments are not meant to stand on their own, but are to be used in conjunction with other tools and methods of gathering assessment information.

Table 1: Inventories for Assessment of Emotional and Behavioural Challenges

Instrument	Purpose	Format	Information it provides
Aberrant Behavior Checklist - Community (Aman & Singh, 1994)	-evaluate impact of pharmacological interventions on maladaptive behaviours -assess behaviour problems in children, adolescents and adults with mild to profound developmental disabilities	-58 item questionnaire, rating behaviours on a scale of 0 (not a problem) to 3 (severe problem)	-scores on 5 factors – irritability, lethargy, stereotypy, hyperactivity and inappropriate speech
Assessment for Dual Diagnosis (Matson, 1997)	-screen for psychopathology in individuals with mild to moderate developmental disability	-79 item questionnaire, rating behaviours on dimensions of frequency, severity and duration -scale scores range from a low of 0 to a high of 2 -higher scores indicate greater problem	-scores on 13 subscales - mania, depression, anxiety, posttraumatic stress disorder, substance abuse, somatoform, dementia, conduct disorder, pervasive developmental disorder, schizophrenia, personality disorders, eating disorders, sexual disorders
Developmental Behaviour Checklist - Parent/ Carer or Teacher version (Einfeld & Tonge, 1994)	-assess emotional and behavioural disorders in children and adolescents with developmental disabilities	-96 item questionnaire, rating behaviours on a scale of 0 (item is not true) to 2 (item is very true or often true)	-scores on 6 subscales - disruptive, self-absorbed, communication disturbance, anxiety, autistic relating & antisocial
Diagnostic Assessment for the Severely Handicapped - II (Matson, 1995)	-screen for psychopathology in individuals with severe to profound developmental disability	-84 item questionnaire, rating behaviours on dimensions of frequency, severity and duration -scale scores range from a low of 0 to a high of 2 -higher scores indicate greater problem	-scores on 13 subscales – anxiety, mania, depression, schizophrenia, stereotypies, self-injurious behaviour, PDD/autism, elimination disorders, eating disorders, sleep disorders, sexual disorders, organic syndromes, impulse control and miscellaneous problems

(table continues)

Instrument	Purpose	Description	Scores
Emotional Problems Scales - Self-Report and Behavior Rating Scales (Prout & Strohmer, 1991)	-help identify psychopathology and emotional problems in individuals 14 years of age and older with a mild developmental disability	-self-report inventory is made up of 147 behavioural items that require a yes or no response -behavior rating scale is made up of 135 items; behaviors are scored on a scale of 0 (almost never reported or observed) to 3 (often reported or observed)	-self-report inventory – scores on 5 clinical scales-- (thought/behavior disorder, impulse control, anxiety, depression, low self-esteem -behavior rating scales – scores on 12 clinical scales – thought/behavior disorder, verbal aggression, physical aggression, sexual maladjustment, noncompliance, distractibility, hyperactivity, somatic concerns, anxiety, depression, withdrawal, low self-esteem
Psychopathology Instrument for Mentally Retarded Adults (Matson, 1988)	-help identify psychopathological behaviours for treatment in adults with mild-moderate developmental disability	-two forms - self-report and ratings-by-others -items require a yes or no response	-self-report and ratings-by-others – scores on 8 subscales – schizophrenia, affective disorder, psychosexual disorder, adjustment disorder, anxiety disorder, somatoform disorder, personality disorder, inappropriate adjustment
Reiss Scales for Children's Dual Diagnosis (Reiss & Valenti-Hein, 1990)	-screen for dual diagnosis in children aged 4-21 years with mild - severe developmental disability	-60 item questionnaire, rating behaviours on a scale of 0 (no problem) to 2 (major problem)	-scores on 10 subscales – anger/self-control, anxiety, attention-deficit, PDD/autism, conduct disorder, depression, poor self-esteem, psychosis, somatoform, withdrawn/isolated, as well as other significant behaviours
Reiss Screen for Maladaptive Behavior (Reiss, 1988)	-screen for dual diagnosis in individuals above the age of 12 years with mild, moderate or severe developmental disability	-38 item questionnaire, rating behaviours on a scale of 0 (no problem) to 2 (major problem)	-scores on 8 scales - aggression, autism, psychosis, paranoia, depression - behavioural signs and depression - physical signs, dependent and avoidant personality disorder, as well as special maladaptive behaviour items

C. Social-Environmental Factors

Many psychiatric disorders present as non-specific behaviour challenges (Gardner & Sovner, 1994). In Chapter 3 of this book, we explained that a non-specific behaviour means there is a symptom that we see (i.e., a behaviour challenge), but until there is an assessment, we do not know why it occurs.

Behavioural Assessment:

The first step in a behavioural assessment is to clearly determine what is the behaviour of concern. It is important to determine a clear description of the challenging behaviour. Just knowing that John is aggressive is not descriptive. Does he hit, bite, punch, destroy property? How often does the behaviour occur? How severe is the behaviour? Does the behaviour occur randomly or certain times of the day, week, month or year? Does it occur with certain people or in certain situations more often than with others? Are there certain times and with certain people where the behaviour never occurs? Does the behaviour occur more likely when the person is alone or with others?

In behavioural assessment it is important to identify the "FIDD" characteristics of the behaviour (Griffiths & Hingsburger, 1991):

- *Frequency-* how often does the behaviour occur?
- *Intensity-* how severe or intensive is the behaviour?
- *Duration-* how long does the behaviour last?
- *Discrimination-* where, when and under what conditions does the behaviour occur?

The most common behavioural strategy for evaluating the

FIDD characteristics of behaviour is to conduct a functional assessment or analysis.

Functional or Motivational Assessment/Analysis

Functional assessment is a process of gathering information about antecedents and consequences that are functionally related to the occurrence of a problem behaviour (Miltenberger, 1997).

There are three types of functional assessments: indirect assessment, direct observation and functional analysis or analogue assessment)

a) Indirect assessment (interviews and questionnaires)

There are a number of interview formats and questionnaires available to conduct a functional assessment. For example the Motivational Assessment Scale-MAS (Durand & Crimmins, 1992) is a 16 item other-report questionnaire, through which the motivation of a specific behaviour is determined to be sensory (i.e., to gain stimulation), escape (i.e., to avoid an unpleasant activity or interaction), attention (i.e., to gain interaction), and tangible (i.e., to gain a desired item).

One of the most commonly used and commercially available formats is the Functional Assessment Interview (FAI) developed by O'Neil, Horner, Albin, Storey, and Newton (1997). This interview format provides an easy to conduct and quick method of gathering behavioural data. The FAI is divided into 11 major sections:

1. Description of the behaviour

2. Potential ecological setting events
3. Immediate antecedents (predictors) for the occurrence or nonoccurrence of the problem behaviour
4. Consequences for the problem behaviour
5. Efficiency of the problem behaviour
6. Existing functional alternative behaviours
7. Communication
8. Approaches that do and do not work
9. Things that are reinforcing
10. History of the undesirable behaviour and previous programmes
11. Summary of major predictors and consequences

b) Direct observation

A more accurate but more time consuming way ot gathering functional information is through direct observation.The ABC observation, observation cards, scatterplot, and functional assessment observation form are four methods of completing direct functional assessments. Although the types of assessment forms vary among behaviour analysts, they are universally designed to gather information on the interaction between the behaviour and factors in the environment. From this, a working hypothesis, on which intervention can be based, is developed.

The data method should provide information that allows the clinician to (i) redesign the environment to reduce or eliminate or alter antecedents to the problem behaviour, and to introduce or increase antecedents for competing alternative behaviours; (ii) identify behaviours that can be taught or increased which could act as functional alternatives to the challenging behaviour; (iii) alter the consequences to provide the functionally-related reinforcement for appropriate means of gaining the desired outcome, and reducing the reinforcement for the challenging behaviour.

ABC plus chart: The ABC sheet is a standard recording tool that is used for collecting data that are used for analysing the contextual relationship of behaviour. A stands for Antecedent, or the events that occur before the problem behaviour, and which set occasion for the behaviour to occur. **B** is the behaviour, and **C** is the consequence that followed the behaviour.

A standard ABC chart looks like the following:

Staff: Alice Smith   Date: July 20, 6:20 p.m.   Client: Paul Brown

A=ANTECEDENT (what happened before)	B=BEHAVIOUR (what happened)	C=CONSEQUENCE (what happened after)
Jane, the new staff, asked Paul to do the dishes	Paul sat on the couch and refused to move	Jane came closer and gave him a second instruction
Jane came closer and gave a second instruction	Paul threw the ashtray at the staff member	Jane told him to go to his room if he could not behave; Jane did the dishes

These data tell a very clear story. Paul was able to avoid doing the dishes by throwing an ashtray. However, sometimes the data are not so clear for some of the following reasons:

- The behaviours may occur at a very high frequency such that it is difficult to record each incident.
- The behaviours may occur for different reasons at different times.
- There may be patterns to the behaviour that are difficult to assess.
- The antecedents may be a stimulus complex, and as such

depend on a combination of certain triggering events, as well as the presence of some other factors.

Hurley (1997) has developed a training guide for using the ABC Sheet to collect and analyze data. She recommends an expanded ABC chart that includes describing as antecedents not just the event immediately preceding the behaviour, but other setting events or contributing events that could be observed. Additionally, she teaches staff to provide expanded information on the behaviour and the consequences. For example she suggests recording:

- *Antecedents* including where it was occurring, what was occurring, what activity or interaction was present, who was present, and were there any indications of body language or of a physical state that could be observed.
- *Behaviours* including what happened, to whom, where, for how long, and to what intensity or frequency.
- *Consequences* including who responded, and how (verbally and nonverbally) and to what end (what changed in the person or for the person).

Data Recording Card: Gardner and Sovner (1994) describe a procedure for obtaining more systematic observational data. A small index card is used by an observer to record each incident of the problem behaviour as it occurs, or shortly after it occurs. The observer records the *Date and Time* of the occurrence, the *Situation* (e.g., lunch, gym), antecedent *Triggering Events* (e.g., Tom asked Jane to pick up her coat), *Challenging Behaviour* (e.g., Jane began to yell), *Consequences* (e.g., Jane was ignored), and *Possible Contributing Instigating Influences* (i.e., anxiety, eye rolling, rocking motion prior to incident, room was extremely noisy)

Scatterplot: The scatterplot is a recording method developed by Touchette, MacDonald and Langer (1985). Using this sheet, someone in the person's natural environment records during predetermined intervals whether the behaviour occurred during the previous interval (1/2 hour is a typical interval). A single chart contains seven days of data. Severity and frequency are delineated as solid blocks (severe or high frequency) versus a stroke (mild or low frequency). The severity and frequency are clearly defined. The block is left unmarked if no behaviour occurred. After a week the data sheet can reveal patterns for the behaviour (i.e., time of day, days of the week), which can lead to additional analysis of the factors that may be influencing the behaviour.

Functional Assessment Observation Form: The Functional Assessment Observation Form (i.e., O'Neill et al., 1997) has become a standard data sheet for gathering multiple points of information on a single data sheet. This sheet is used to collect data in intervals. As such, the day is divided into daily intervals along the left side of the page. Across the top, data are gathered on the following: various behaviours, predictors (demands/requests, difficult tasks, transitions, interruption, alone), perceived functions to obtain or get (attention, desired item or activity, self-stimulation, other), or to escape/avoid (demands/requests, an activity or person), and the actual consequences. Multiple behaviours and multiple incidents can be recorded on a single sheet that can be analysed for frequency, trends and functions.

c) *Experimental manipulations/ Functional Analysis*

The most controlled approach to functional assessment is experimental manipulation of the antecedents and consequences, to isolate the antecedents, setting events and consequences that influence the behaviour. This is called a Functional Analysis. Traditionally, this method has been conducted with carefully orchestrated repeated sessions (i.e., Iwata, Duncan, Zarcone, Lerman & Shore, 1994). However, less time consuming approaches have been described by Derby et al. (1992), in which a single 90 minute evaluation session is employed. Although a functional analysis is considered more methodologically sound compared to the methods of functional assessment described previously, research has shown that a comparison of the two approaches in an applied setting (children in home setting) produced comparable results (Amdorfer, Miltenberger, Woster, Rortvedt & Gaffaney, 1994). This finding is important for clinicians working within applied community settings where the use of highly controlled analogue functional analysis would be difficult to implement.

d) Specialised screening and assessment

Sociosexual testing and assessment: One area of specialised assessment that is often requested is a sociosexual assessment. Several measures are available for sociosexual evaluation. Three will be discussed below. The most comprehensive socio-sexual assessment is the Sociosexual Knowledge and Attitude Test-SSKAT (Wish, McCombs, & Edmonson, 1980). It has been criticised as being out-of-date, value-laden, time consuming, requiring a high level of skill to administer, overly complicated in parts and lacking in detail in others. However, it appears to be still the most widely used measure in this area. A revised Socio-sexual Knowledge and Attitude Assessment Tool (SSKAAT-R) (Griffiths & Lunsky, in press) is currently being field tested.

Less complicated questionnaires (i.e., Timmers, DuCharme & Jacob, 1981; Ousley & Mesibov, 1991) have been developed, but they lack psychometric evaluation. A more recent evaluation is the Sexual Knowledge, Experience, Feelings and Needs Scale (SexKen-ID) by McCabe (1999). This is not commercially available, and has been criticised for use as an assessment tool because it goes beyond knowledge and attitudes into personal experiences.

Violence and Sexual Risk Assessments: An important challenge for mental health professionals is the assessment and treatment of persons with intellectual disabilities who have committed a sexual offense. The reader is referred to Chapter 13, Sexuality and Mental Health Issues for a description.

Issues in Assessment of Persons who are Nonverbal or Profoundly Challenged

As covered in Chapter 17, Mental Health Issues in Clients with Severe Communication Impairments, a number of formidable challenges are encountered when assessing individuals who do not communicate verbally. These challenges are due to a number of factors, including:

- the lack of firsthand information from the individual and the need to rely on information from other sources (e.g., interviewing others, direct observation of behaviour).
- the co-existence of medical or sensory conditions which can further complicate the picture.
- the finding that psychiatric illness may manifest differently in these individuals and that diagnostic criteria for specific disorders may need to be translated into "developmental disability equivalents" (e.g., Pary, Levitas

& Hurley, 1999).

Putting it Together: The Comprehensive Biopsychosocial Assessment

The following multi-factorial case illustrates the point that, while it is not always possible to arrive at a definitive clinical diagnosis, a biopsychosocial assessment results in a more thorough understanding of the individual's needs and provides a solid basis upon which to make more reasoned decisions about treatment.

The Case of Bill

Bill is a 21-year-old male who was diagnosed with autism at the age of two years. He is non-verbal, but uses augmentative forms of communication (signs, gestures, vocalisations, pointing to picture communication symbols). He rarely initiates activities or makes spontaneous requests, but relies instead on staff to prompt him to do so. He does not have any major health concerns, although there is a family history of migraine headaches.

Bill moved from his family home into a group home one year ago. He is the only non-verbal resident who lives there and staff did not know initially how to use sign language. Many of them have never worked with anyone with autism. Bill graduated from a modified high school programme 6 months ago. While attending the programme, Bill was involved in several community work placements, and was described as a model student.

Until 9 months ago, Bill's behaviour was very stable. He was gentle, cooperative and easy going. He had a long history of compulsive or ritualistic behaviours, such as putting things in order, or pushing in chairs. However, he did not become upset when his rituals were interrupted except when he was anxious. He would at times display signs of anxiety or agitation in the form of pacing, loud humming, and occasional head hitting. There was no clear pattern associated with these periods of agitation, and they would not last longer than a day or two.

Staff started to notice a major change in Bill's behaviour about 3 months ago. Whereas he was formerly happy and eager to please, he started to display high levels of anxiety and agitation. He also became aggressive toward a particular roommate in his group home. There were no changes in his appetite, energy level or sleep habits. He appeared to be in pain occasionally, and pointed to his head as if to indicate the presence of a headache. A support plan was developed which focused on helping him to communicate his needs and wants through the use of picture communication symbols and training staff to use sign language; reducing his level of stress by taking him for a walk or to a quiet place; allowing him to complete his rituals when he was anxious; avoiding crowded or noisy settings; involving him in structured activities; and preparing him for changes in his routines or activities through the use of calendars and picture schedules. He was also given medication for pain relief when he showed signs of having a headache.

Bill's behaviour improved considerably about 2 weeks after the support plan was introduced, and was stable until one month ago when he again started to display signs of intense anxiety, and aggressed toward several staff and roommates. Staff continued to follow his support plan, but his anxiety did not lessen. Bill's family physician prescribed Ativan as a PRN, but this only made him more anxious and ritualistic. Staff were forced to call an ambulance one day when his behaviour went out of control. Bill was taken to the local emergency room, and kept in 4-point restraint for several hours. He was given Haldol and Ativan, and was sent home with orders for Chlorpromazine, Valium and Cogentin. These medications made him extremely drowsy, but the anxiety and aggression continued. Several days later, his family physician discontinued all his other medication and started him on Risperidol twice daily. His agitation disappeared within two days and only recurred again periodically; when it did occur, it was short-lived and usually related to physical ailments (e.g., GI problems). Bill's dosage of Risperidol was decreased in response to concerns that he was sedated and "spaced out". For the first time in months, Bill is back to his formerly happy and easy-going self. Staff continue to implement his support plan, and he is being eased slowly into community work placements.

Bill recently underwent an interdisciplinary assessment in regard to his behavioural difficulties. The consensus of the team was that Bill had reacted to the cumulative effects of a number of stressors in his life, but they were unable to offer a definitive diagnosis regarding the etiology of his anxiety and aggression. They were encouraged by the improvement in his behaviour, and urged staff to continue to implement his support plan, and to maintain him on his current level of medication.

Table 2: Summary of biopsychosocial factors that were hypothesised to be operating in Bill's case

	Instigating Factors	Vulnerabilities	Reinforcing Conditions
Biomedical	-anxiety in response to series of life stressors -migraine headaches(?)	-autism -family history of migraines -anxiety disorder(?) -obsessive compulsive disorder(?)	Negative reinforcement –offered medication for pain relief -reduction in anxiety when allowed to complete rituals
Psychological	-frustration over wanting/needing something and having to wait for prompt from staff -frustration over staff inability to understand his augmentative communication forms -confusion or distress over end of school placement and loss of long-time friends	-rarely initiates requests or performs tasks without prompting from staff -lacks verbal skills -need for routine and structure	Negative reinforcement – reduction in frustration when he is able to perform a task or obtain a desired object after a prompt Differential reinforcement – when staff understand his signs or gestures and can meet his needs (in the absence of aggression)
Social	-crowded, noisy environments -programmes that focus on sedentary activities -programmes that do not have clearly defined tasks	-over-stimulated by too much noise or too many people -need for high levels of physical activity -need for structured programmes	Negative reinforcement – removed from noisy or crowded environments; taken for a walk; given small jobs to perform

Summary

This chapter contains a review of instruments that are used during the biopsychosocial assessment of mental health problems in individuals with developmental disabilities. Uses and limitations of various assessment tools were discussed. Practical information regarding how to conduct an assessment was provided along with specific examples to illustrate the content and format of different assessment instruments. Differences between screening and in-depth assessment were highlighted. Finally, case examples were used to draw the points together.

Do You Know?

1. Why are screening and assessment so important in understanding the presenting behaviours in a person with developmental disabilities? Name two reasons.
2. What are the most common biomedical conditions that influence such behaviours?
3. Name a few common psychological events that can present with excessive behaviours.
4. How the psychological assessment/s contribute to the screening process?
5. What FIDD stands for?
6. What are the most common elements of a behaviour assessment?
7. What are some of the challenges in assessing and treating persons with developmental disabilities that have committed a sexual offence?

Resources

The following list can help the reader to obtain more information regarding the psychological assessment instruments that were identified in the chapter. Access to many of these instruments is restricted to professionals with specific training and expertise; details are available from the companies or test publishers.

PSYCAN, Unit 12, 120 West Beaver Creek Road, Richmond Hill, ON L4B 1L2; Phone: 905 731-8795; Fax: 905 731-5029; Email: mail@psycan.com; Website: www.psycan.com (EVT; PIAT-R, PPVT-III; TONI-3; VABS; WRAT-3) .

Psychological Corporation, 55 Horner Avenue, Toronto, ON M8Z 4X6; Phone: 800-387-7278 or 416 255-4491; Fax: 800 665-7307 or 416 255-6708; E-mail: cs_canada@harcourt.com; Website: www.hbtpc.com/tpccanada (WAIS-III; WRAT-3)

Psychological Assessment Resources, Inc. P.O. Box 998, Odessa, FL 33556; Phone: 800-331-8378; Fax: 800 727-9329; E-mail: custserve@parinc.com; Website: www.parinc.com (ABS-RC:2)

Riverside Publishing , 425 Spring Lake Drive, Itasca, IL 60143-9921; Phone: 800-323-9540; Fax: 630-467-7192; Website: www.riverpub.com (SB-IV, SIB-R)

Stoelting Co., 620 Wheat Lane, Wood Dale, IL 60191; Phone: 630 860-9700; Fax: 630 860-9775; Website: www.stoeltingco.com (Leiter-R)

References

Aldenkamp, A.P., Vermeulen, J., Mulder, O.G., Overwerg, J., Van Parys, A.P., Beun, A.M., Va'tSlot, B. (1994). Gammavinyl GABA (Vigabatrin) and mood disturnbances. *Epilepsia, 35,* 999-1004.

Aman, M.G., & Singh, N.N. (1994). *Aberrant Behavior Checklist-Community. Supplementary manual. E. Aurora, NY: Slosson Educational Publications.*

Armdorfer, R.A., Miltenberger, R.G., Woster, S.H., Rortvedt, A.K., Gaffaney, R. (1994). Home-based descriptive and experimental analysis of problem behaviors in children. *Topics in Early Childhood Special Education, 14,* 64-87.

Brown, L., Sherbenou, R., & Johnsen, S. (1997). Test of Nonverbal Intelligence Third Edition. Austin, TX: PRO-ED.

Bruinicks, R.H., Woodcock, R.W., Weatherman, R.F., & Hill, B.K. (1996). Scales of Independent Behavior-Revised: Comprehensive Manual. Itasca, IL: Riverside Publishing Co.

Butler, M.G., Mangrum, T., Gupta, R., & Singh, D.N. (1991). A 15-item checklist for screening mentally retarded males for the Fragile X syndrome. *Clinical Genetics, 39,* 347-354.

Carr, E.G., Neuman, J.K., & Darnell, C.L. (1998). The clinical importance of sleep data collection: A national survey and case reports. *Mental Health Aspects of Developmental Disabilities, 1,* 39-43.

Derby, K.M., Wacker, D.P., Sasso, G., Steege, M., Northup, J., Cigrand, K., & Asmus, J. (1992). Brief functional assessment techniques to evaluate aberrant behavior in an outpatient setting. *Journal of Applied Behavior Analysis, 25,* 713-721.

Down Syndrome Medical Interest Group (1999). Health care

guidelines for individuals with Down syndrome. *Down Syndrome Quarterly, 4*, 1-36.

Dunn, L.M. & Dunn, L.M. (1997). Peabody Picture Vocabulary Test Third Edition. Circle Pines, MN: American Guidance Service.

Durand, V.M. & Crimmins, D.B. (1992). The motivation assessment scale (MAS) administration guide. Topeka, KS: Monaco and Associates.

Einfeld, S.L., & Tonge, B.J. (1994). Manual for the Developmental Behaviour Checklist. School of Psychiatry, University of New South Wales, and Centre for Developmental Psychiatry, Monash University.

Feldman, M. & Griffiths, D. (1997). Comprehensive assessment of persons with developmental disabilities In N.N. Singh (Ed.), *Treatment of Severe Behavior Problems: Models and Methods* (pp. 23-48). Pacific Grove, CA: Brooks/Cole.

Gardner W.I. & Sovner, R. (1994). *Self-injurious behaviours, diagnosis and treatment, a multimodal approach.* Willow Street, PA: VIDA Publishing.

Gedye, A. (1998). *Behavioural Diagnostic Guide for Developmental Disabilities.* Vancouver: Diagnostic Books.

Gershon,W.S., Goldstein, R.R., Moss, A.J., & van Kammen, D.P. (1979). Psychosis with ordinary doses of propranolol. *Annals of Internal Medicine, 90.* 938-939.

Griffiths, D. (2001). Strategic behavioral interventions in aggression. In A. Dosen, & K. Day (Eds.), *Treating Mental Illness and Behavior Disorders in Children and Adults with Mental Retardation* (pp. 305-322). Washington, DC: American Psychiatric Press.

Griffiths, D., & Hingsburger, D. (1991) *OPTIONS.* Richmond Hill, Ontario: York Central Hospital.

Griffiths, D., & Lunsky, Y. (in press). *Socio-sexual Knowledge and Attitude Assessment Tool.* Wooddale, Ill.: Stoelting.

Griffiths, D., Richards, D., Fedoroff, P., & Watson, S. (2002) Sexuality and Mental Health in Persons with Developmental Disabilities. In D. Griffiths, C. Stavrakaki, & J. Summers (Eds.), *An introduction to the mental health needs of persons with developmental disabilities.* Sudbury, ON: Habilitative Mental Health Resource Network.

Hurley, A.D. (1997). Using the ABC sheet to analyze behavior: A training guide. *The Habilitative Mental Healthcare Newsletter, 16,* 81-89.

Hurley, A.D. (1989). Clinical use of intelligence testing. *Psychiatric Aspects of Mental Retardation Reviews, 8,* 49-55.

Hurley, A.D. & Sovner, R. (1992). Inventories for evaluating psychopathology in developmentally disabled individuals. *The Habilitative Mental Healthcare Newsletter, 11,* 45-49.

Iwata, B.A., Vollmer,T.R., & Zarcone, J.R. (1990). The experimental (functional) analysis of behavior disorders: Methodology, applications, and limitations. In C. Repp & N.N. Singh (Eds.), *Perspectives in the use of non-aversive and aversive interventions for persons with developmental disabilities* (pp. 301-330). Sycamore IL: Sycamore Publishing Co.

Iwata, B.A., Duncan, B.A., Zarcone, J.R., Lerman,D.C., Shore, B.A. (1994). A sequential test-control methodology for conducting functional analyses of self-injurious behavior. *Behavior Modification, 18,* 289-306.

Loschen, E.L. & Osman, O. (1992) Self-injurious behavior in the developmentally disabled: Assessment techniques. *Psychopharmacology Bulletin, 28,* 433-437.

Lowry, M. & Sovner, R. (1991). The functional significance of problem behaviour: A key to effective treatment. *The Habilitative Mental Healthcare Newsletter, 10,* 59-63.

Markwardt, F.C., Jr. (1998). *Peabody Individual Achievement*

Test-Revised. Circle Pines, MN: American Guidance Service.

Matson, J.L. (1995). *The Diagnostic Assessment for the Severely handicapped– Revised (DASH-II).* Baton Rouge, LA: Scientific Publishers.

Matson, J.L. (1988). *The Psychopathology Instrument for Mentally Retarded Adults: Test Manual.* Orland Park, IL: International Diagnostic Systems.

Matson, J.L. (1997). *The Assessment for Dual Diagnosis (ADD).* Baton Rounge, LA: Scientific Publishers.

McCabe, M. (1999). Sexual knowledge, experience, and feelings among people with disabilities. *Sexuality and Disability, 17(2),* 157-170.

Miltenberger, R. (1997). *Behavior modification: Principles and procedures.* Pacific Grove, CA.:Brooks/Cole Publishing.

Murphy, W.D., Coleman, E.M., & Haynes, M. (1983). Treatment and evaluation issues with the mentally retarded sex offender. In J. Greer & I Stuart (Eds.), *The sexual aggressor: Current perspectives on treatment* (pp. 22-41). New York: Van Nostrand Reinhold.

Nihira, K., Leland, H., & Lambert, N. (1993). *Adaptive Behavior Scale - Residential and Community Second Edition.* Austin, TX: PRO-ED.

O'Neill, R.E., Horner, R.H., Albin, R.W., Storey, K., & Newton, J.S. (1997*). Functional assessment and program development for problem behavior: A practical handbook.* Pacific Grove, CA.:Brooks/Cole Publishing

Ousley, O.Y. & Mesibov, B.G. (1991). Sexual attitude and knowledge of high functioning adolescents and adults with autism. *Journal of Autism and Developmental Disorders, 21,* 471-481.

Pary, R.J., Levitas, A.S., & Hurley, A.D. (1999). Diagnosis of bipolar disorder in persons with developmental disabilities. *Mental Health Aspects of Developmental Disabilities, 2,* 37-49.

Prout, H.P. & Strohner, D.C. (1991). *Emotional Problems Scales: Professional Manual for the Behavior Ratings Scales and the Self-Report Inventory.* Odessa FL: Psychological Assessment Resources.

Reiss, S. (1988). *Reiss Screen for Maladaptive Behavior: Test manual (2nd ed.)* Orland Park, IL: International Diagnostic Systems.

Reiss, S. & Valenti-Hein, D. (1990). *Reiss Scales for Children's Dual Diagnosis: Test manual 2nd edition.* Worthington, OH: International Diagnostic Systems.

Roid, G., & Miller, L. (1997). *Leiter International Performance Scale-Revised.* Wood Dale: IL: Stoelting Co.

Ryan, R. & Sunada, K. (1997). Medical evaluation of persons with mental retardation referred for psychiatric assessment. *General Hospital Psychiatry, 19,* 274-280.

Quinsey, V.L., Harris, G.L. Rice, M.E., & Cormier, K. (1998). *Violent offenders: Appraising and managing risk.* Washington, DC: American Psychological Association.

Sovner, R. & Hurley, A.D. (1990). Assessment tools that facilitate psychiatric evaluation and treatment. *Habilitative Mental Healthcare Newsletter, 9,* 91-99.

Sovner, R., & Hurley, A.D. (1992). The psychiatric followup visit worksheet. *Habilitative Mental Healthcare Newsletter, 11,* 1-6.

Sparrow, S.S., Balla, D.A., & Cicchetti, D.V. (1984). *Vineland Adaptive Behavior Scales: Interview edition, Expanded form manual.* Circle Pines, MN: American Guidance Service.

Thorndike, R.L., Hagen, E.P., & Sattler, J.M. (1986). *Guide for administering and scoring the Stanford-Binet Intelli-*

gence Scale: Fourth Edition. Chicago, IL: Riverside.

Timmers, R.L., DuCharme, P., & Jacob, G. (1981). Sexual knowledge, attitudes, and behavior of developmentally disabled adults living in a normalized apartment setting. *Sexuality and Disability, 4,* 27-39.

Touchette, P.E., MacDonald, R.F. & Langer, S.N. (1985). A scatterplot for identifying stimulus control of problem behavior. *Journal of Applied Behavior Analysis, 18,* 343-351.

Wechsler, D. (1997). *Wechsler Adult Intelligence Scale-Third Edition.* San Antonio, TX: Psychological Corporation.

Wilkinson, G.S. (1993). *Wide Range Achievement Test 3.* Wilmington, DL: Wide Range, Inc..

Williams, K.T. (1997). *Expressive Vocabulary Test Manual.* Circle Pines, MN: American Guidance Service.

Wish, J.R., McCombs, K.F. & Edmonson, B. (1980). The Socio-Sexual Knowledge and Attitude Test. Wood Dale, IL: Stoelting Co.

Chapter 6

Person-Centred Approaches to Services and Supports

Sandra Gahan, Len Dykstra and Jane Summers

Learning objectives

Readers will be able to:

1. Understand the reasons why person-centred approaches were developed
2. Identify key elements of a person-centred plan
3. Identify two differences between person-centred planning and conventional planning approaches

Introduction

The purpose of this chapter is to outline the underlying principles and key elements of person-centred planning. Differences between person-centred planning and conventional planning approaches will be highlighted. Challenges to implementing person-centred plans will be discussed. Finally, a case example will be used to illustrate some of these points.

History of person-centred planning

In recent years, increasing emphasis has been placed on improving the quality of life for people with developmental disabilities. This growing trend is related to findings that these individuals are treated differently and have fewer opportunities for positive growth and development than people without disabilities. Issues of reduced quality of life are even more problematic among individuals with a dual diagnosis, as their mental health problems further heighten the disparity of their situation. Also, deinstitutionalization has been accompanied by the transfer of institutional patterns of service into community settings (Smull, 1989). For these reasons, an approach to planning individualized services and supports was called for that targeted the very things that most people without disabilities take for granted – a pleasant and safe home environment; enriching and satisfying personal relationships; acceptance by the community; opportunities for work and leisure activities; freedom to make effective choices and decisions; and attainment of hopes and dreams. Person-centred planning approaches were conceptualized as a way to reorganize and reorient the service system to achieve these global, long-range positive outcomes as well as to respond creatively to pressures in relation to dwindling resources and increasing demand. In the words of Todd Risley (1996), the intent of these approaches is to assist the person with a developmental disability to "get a life!"

Elements of person-centred planning

Life plans, lifestyle planning, essential life plans, personal futures planning and functional life planning are all examples of approaches to person-centred planning. Despite some differences, most approaches have several key elements in common. First, they bring together a group consisting of the individual with a dual diagnosis ("focus person") and the people who play an important role in his or her life. For instance, this group may consist of family members, friends, housemates, co-workers and service providers. The activities of the group are governed by principles that include *community integration, normalization, increasing competency, and empowerment.* Specific goals or outcomes are based on *operationalizing* these principles. For instance, the principle of community integration may be defined in concrete terms as "the person (with a dual diagnosis) will be supported to eat in a restaurant or to take swimming lessons at the local recreational center". The principle of empowerment or self-determination may be translated into goals that "the person will be assisted to make decisions about "little things" (e.g., what to wear or where to go to dinner) and "big things" (e.g., choice of roommates) in his or her life" (Kincaid, 1996).

A general format for person-centred planning

Under the guidance of a facilitator, the planning group typically gathers the following kinds of information:

- People and relationships – e.g., who are the most important individuals in the focus person's life and how much time is spent with each person
- Places – e.g., where the focus person spends his or her time
- Important life events – e.g., home, family and school history; changes in living arrangements; serious illnesses and hospitalizations; service history
- Current health – e.g., indicators of good health and poor health; whether the indicators reflect a temporary or permanent situation; current medications and their positive and negative effects on the person's functioning
- Effective choices — e.g., whether the focus person makes decisions/choices in day-to-day matters and matters of ma-

jor significance or whether these decisions are controlled by others
- Preferences, hopes and dreams – e.g., in regard to people and relationships; things to do or to have; physical, spiritual and emotional health
- Acceptance and respect – e.g., aspects of the focus person's behaviour that promote acceptance and inclusion and behaviours that interfere with or prevent these things from happening
- Fears and concerns – e.g., in regard to the implications of supporting the focus person to make major life decisions
- Challenges and opportunities – e.g., things about the focus person or the system that act to enable or discourage change.

(Adapted from Kincaid, 1996; Smull & Harrison, 1992)

The process of categorizing this information into overall themes which can be used to develop plans to bring about positive lifestyle changes can be enhanced with the use of graphics and diagrams to delineate and explore different factors and outcomes. The group continues to meet to review how much progress has been made toward reaching these goals and to rework the goals and plans as needed. In actuality, the process is never finished since successes fuel new goals and create other opportunities for positive outcomes.

How do you know you are doing person-centred planning?

If there is no commonly accepted approach to person-centred planning, how can you be sure that this is what you are doing? In order to lend some clarity to this issue, Holburn et al. (2000) developed a list of core principles that are integral to the person-centred planning process (see Box 1).

Box 1- Core principles for person-centred planning

1. Services and supports are based on the individual's prefer-
    ences, interests and skills
2. The individual and important others are involved in the
    planning process
3. The individual makes real choices and decisions
4. Services and supports promote social inclusion
5. The plan incorporates natural community supports
6. Planning is collaborative and involves a long-term commit-
    ment
7. Opportunities are created and non-traditional solutions are
    considered
8. The individual is satisfied with the changes in his/her life-
    style

(Adapted from Holburn et al., 2000)

These authors have also identified a number of factors or conditions that result in positive planning outcomes (see below).

Box 2- Examples of factors or conditions that are related to positive outcomes

1. The group is lead by a skilled facilitator
2. The focus person's positive qualities are emphasized
3. The group has members that are skilled at building com-
    munity relationships and are able to access community re-
    sources
4. The group has a way to influence decision makers

5. There is administrative support for an individualized planning approach
6. Supports are flexible and portable
7. The group meets regularly to review and refine its plan

(Adapted from Holburn et al., 2000)

How does person-centred planning differ from conventional planning approaches?

Some of the differences between person-centred planning and conventional planning approaches are summarized below:

Table 1- Key differences between conventional and person-centred planning

Elements/ Factors	Conventional Approaches	Person-Centred Approaches
Language	Clinical/technical	Plain language
Units of Intervention	Micro level (e.g., discrete behaviours)	Macro level (e.g., life arrangements)
Options	Limited; usually a fixed menu of services and interventions (fitting the person into pre-existing "slots")	Potentially limitless (best fit between person and service options)
Membership of Team	Typically professional/paid	Mixture of professional/ paid, nonprofessional and volunteer
Roles	Clearly defined roles	Step outside of roles
Time frame	Usually time-limited	Life long
Decision-making process	Top down; driven by systems or organizations	Bottom up or individually driven

Problems with implementing person-centred planning approaches

The acceptance and implementation of person-centered planning approaches may present significant challenges at both a personal and a system level. These difficulties can encompass a range of practical and conceptual issues, such as:

- involving people in the planning process who aren't sufficiently familiar with the focus person or don't play a significant and ongoing role in his or her life
- underestimating the time and resources that are required
- maintaining the group's enthusiasm and commitment
- lack of adequate or portable funds to bring about significant lifestyle changes
- mixed or uncertain feelings due to differences in philosophies and role confusion

Holburn and Vietze (1999) caution that failure to acknowledge and address these factors may undermine the process and its ultimate success.

Bringing it together: A case example

The Case of John

John is a thirty-year-old man who has lived in a residential group home operated by the local Association for Community Living for the past two years. He has a mild developmental disability and a controlled seizure disorder. Before moving to the group home he lived with his mother and younger sister. John's parents are divorced and he has not had contact with his father for several years. John's move to a group home was prompted by frequent angry outbursts in which he became verbally abusive and damaged property around the home. His mother was unable to cope with these outbursts due to her own declining health. After moving into the group home, John was referred for a comprehensive biopsychosocial assessment. The assessment yielded a diagnosis of bipolar disorder. His angry outbursts were found to be related to sleep and mood disturbances as well as poor strategies for coping with stress. In terms of his strengths and needs, the assessment revealed that John is primarily a visual learner and has a good memory. He has strong interest in people and is mostly pleasant and sociable. He has good money management skills but requires help to plan and cook healthy meals.

In conversations with his family and primary worker, John revealed several wishes regarding his future: (1) to find a job he liked, (2) to live in his own apartment with support, and (3) to find a friend, preferably a female companion.

Steps in the person-centred planning process for John

1. Forming the planning group.

John's primary worker coordinated a meeting to initiate the planning process. John was asked to give input into who the participants should be, and he identified his mother and sister, primary worker, and a long-time friend of the family. The group also decided it would be helpful to invite his social worker to participate. A staff person from John's agency agreed to facilitate the planning meetings.

2. Developing guidelines for the group process.

With the assistance of the facilitator, the following "ground rules" were worked out.

- The group would work toward assisting John to become an accepted and productive member of his community and support him to develop and maintain social relationships with people from his community.
- They would build upon John's strengths and positive qualities.
- They would commit to long-term involvement in the process.
- They would step outside their traditional or professional roles and be willing to consider a variety of creative options.

3. Identifying goals and priorities.

With the assistance of the group, John decided that his immediate priority was to be able to live in his own apartment with support.

4. Establishing an action plan.

Several "success" factors were identified with respect to supporting John to achieve his goal of living in his own apartment:

(1) He needed to take his medication regularly to control his seizures and his moods
(2) He needed to learn and use strategies to better manage his

anger and response to stressful situations
(3) He needed to get at least 8 hours of sleep at night
(4) He needed help with meal preparation and shopping

The group developed a detailed plan to address these issues.
The plan outlined specific roles, tasks and timeframes.

5. Specifying an evaluation plan.

The group chose to evaluate the success of their plan in relation to three factors: the target goal (i.e., John is able to live in
his own apartment with support), John's satisfaction with this
lifestyle change (e.g., John is pleased about living in his own
apartment), and whether the principle of community integration was met (e.g., John is accepted by the other tenants in his
apartment building, and is invited to their monthly social
events). They agreed to meet monthly to review John's progress toward achieving these goals, and to problem solve
around any difficulties that came up along the way.

Summary of the planning process for John

A planning group was formed that consisted of John, his
mother and sister, a close friend of the family, agency staff and
mental health professionals. The meetings were facilitated by
a staff person from the agency. During lifestyle planning
meetings, John revealed three long-range personal goals:

1. to find a job he liked,
2. to live in his own apartment with support, and
3. to find a friend, preferably a female companion.

The case management role was filled by John's primary

worker. She agreed to coordinate services among John's support circle, consisting of his family, family physician, psychiatrist, social worker and job coach.

In the course of working together, the group identified the following obstacles that prevented John from achieving his goals:

- instability of his moods
- noncompliance with medication
- lack of experience with decision making
- need for monitoring of sleep, moods and medication
- need for emotional support and assistance to implement anger management strategies
- lack of familiarity with community transportation
- lack of opportunities for social outings

John's goal of living in his own apartment was prioritized. In addition to the other services he was already receiving, several new elements were added to the support plan:

- responsibility for monitoring his sleep, moods and medication was shared among his primary worker, a staff person from the local mental health agency, and family members
- assistance around meal planning and preparation was provided by his sister and a visiting homemaker
- support to follow through on anger management strategies; also, informal counseling to review and problem solve after an outburst had occurred, provided by his case manager, social worker, job coach and a "buddy" with whom John was paired who lived in the same building

Summary

In this chapter, person-centred approaches to services and supports were presented. The rationale for and context underlying the development of these approaches was discussed. Despite their growing popularity and usage, many issues regarding these approaches remain to be resolved. However, they show great promise and serve to remind us of the critical importance of working toward a positive and inclusive vision for

---

Do You Know?

1. The differences between person-centred planning and conventional planning approaches?
2. Some of the key principles and concepts underlying these approaches?
3. Some of the challenges to implementing these approaches?

General Reading

Forest, M. & Pearpoint, J. (1992). Commonsense tools: MAPS and circles. In J. Pearpoint, M. Forest & J. Snow, (Eds.) *The inclusion papers: Strategies to make inclusion work* (pp. 52-57). Toronto: Inclusion Press.

Institute on Community Inclusion (1993). *Whole life planning: A guide for organizers and facilitators*. Boston, MA: Institute on Community Inclusion.

Mount, B., Ducharme, G., & Beeman, P. (1991). *Person centered development: A journey in learning to listen to people with disabilities*. Manchester, CT: Communitas.

the future of people with a dual diagnosis.

Mount, B., & Zwernick, K. (1988). *It's never too early, it's never too late: An overview of person centered planning*. St. Paul, MN: Governor's Council on Developmental Disabilities.

O'Brien, J. & Forest, M. (1989). *Action for inclusion*. Toronto: Inclusion Press.

O'Brien, J., Mount B. & O'Brien, C.L. (1990). *The personal profile*. Lithonia, GA: Responsive Systems Associates.

Resources

Circles Network
Website: www.circlesnetwork.org.uk
This is the home page for the Circles Network. It describes the organization's mission, and provides information about building inclusive communities for individuals with disabilities.

Inclusion Press International
Website: www.inclusion.com
This site provides information on material regarding full inclusion in school, work, and community.

Pacer Centre
Website: www.pacer.org
This is the home page for the Pacer Center. It describes the organization's mission and includes links to person-centred planning websites and other planning resources.

References

Holburn, S., Jacobson, J.W., Vietze, P.M., Schwartz, A.A., & Sersen, E. (2000). Quantifying the process and outcomes of person-centered planning. *American Journal of Mental Retardation, 105*, 402-416.

Holburn, S., & Vietze, P. (1999). Acknowledging barriers in adopting person-centered planning. *Mental Retardation, 37*, 117-124.

Kincaid, D. (1996). Person-centered planning. In L.K. Koegel, R.L. Koegel, & G. Dunlap (Eds.), *Community, school, family and social inclusion through positive behavioral support* (pp. 439-465). Baltimore, MD: Brookes.

Risley, T. (1996). Get a life! Positive behavioral intervention for challenging behavior through life arrangement and life coaching. In L.K. Koegel, R.L. Koegel, & G. Dunlap (Eds.), *Community, school, family and social inclusion through positive behavioral support* (pp. 425-437). Baltimore, MD: Brookes.

Smull, M.W. (1989). *Crisis in the community*. Baltimore, MD: Applied Research and Evaluation Unit, University of Maryland at Baltimore.

Smull, M.W., & Harrison, S.B. (1992). *Supporting people with severe retardation in the community*. Alexandria, VA: National Association of State Mental Retardation Program Directors.

Chapter 7

Collaborative Treatment Approaches

Integrating medication with nonpharmacological treatments

Robert King and Robert Carey

Learning Objectives

Readers will be able to:

1. Appreciate the value of a collaborative, interdisciplinary approach to challenging behaviours in individuals with developmental disabilities.
2. Understand the role of objective monitoring of the signs and symptoms of mental illness in the treatment process.
3. Appreciate the need to combine behavioural, environmental, counselling and medication interventions to address complex challenging behaviours.
4. Be introduced to various types of psychiatric medication.

Introduction

The biopsychosocial model, introduced by Engel in 1977, emphasizes the effects that events within systems and between systems have upon each other. In understanding the onset and course of mental illness in individuals with developmental disabilities (DD), this model endorses the identification of illness vulnerabilities, precipitants, perpetuants and protective factors in multiple domains of an individual's life. This information is then utilized to best support individuals in times of crisis and emotional distress. Treatment support plans often require co-ordination of pharmacological, behavioural, psychotherapeutic and habilitative (environmental) interventions. This chapter will explore this concept.

The prevalence of mental illness in individuals with DD is very high, 24-40% (Pyles, Muniz, Cade, & Silva, 1997). The use of psychiatric medication has been reported as also ap-proaching 26-40% in community residential placements, and 35-50% in institutions in North America (David et al., 1997). Unfortunately, these percentages attest to a historical overuse of a particular class of medication (neuroleptics or antipsy-chotic drugs). In the absence of a behavioural diagnostic proc-ess examining all domains of an individual's life, the prescrip-tion of these drugs may result in behavioural toxicity (impaired learning, skill acquisition and response to reinforcement con-tingencies) rather than improve quality of life.

Aggression, self-injurious behaviour, overactivity and sleep disturbance are all common changes in behaviour creating con-cerns amongst family members and support staff in the lives of individuals with DD. As illustrated on the following page, these behavioural changes are often linked to underlying cog-nitive (thinking) changes, and mood changes occurring in the context of:

1. adverse reactions to prescribed medications
2. distress arising from a physical illness
3. distress arising from mental illness

This algorithm highlights the fact that challenging behaviours in and of themselves are not disorders or illnesses, but rather potentially overt, symptomatic expressions of a variety of un-derlying etiologies. Myers (1998) has explored this relation-ship in affective disorders, documenting the risk of aggression in the context of an irritable or dysphoric mood. Disinhibition during hypomanic or manic phases of a bipolar disorder in in-dividuals with DD has been described. Attempts to avoid or

Figure 1- Decision Tree for Selecting Psychopharmacological Intervention in Adults with Developmental Disabilities Presenting with Aggression

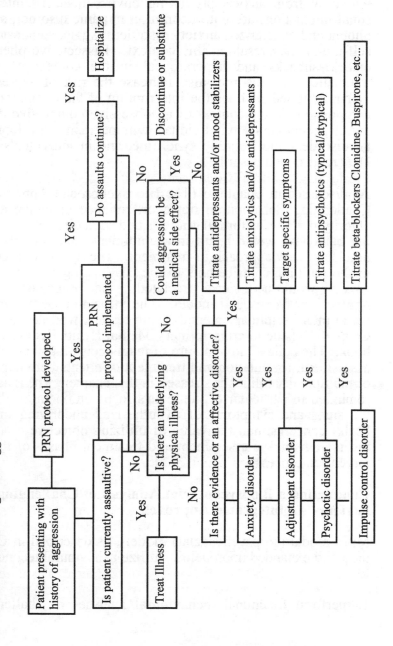

withdraw from anxiety-provoking environments or interpersonal interactions are not uncommon in panic disorder, social phobia and generalized anxiety disorder. Again, aggression or self-injury may result in this context. Dissociative phenomena, flashbacks and hyperarousal in the context of posttraumatic stress disorder also increase the risk of aggression being exhibited, as does the interruption of the completion of compulsions in the context of an obsessive compulsive disorder. Rage outbursts in individuals with pervasive developmental disorders and Tourette syndrome, and in individuals with DD are also well described.

As discussed in Chapter 3 (The Biopsychosocial Approach to Challenging Behaviours), however, reliance upon the above algorithm alone in formulating an understanding of challenging behaviour would result in a unidimensional, and at times unidisciplinary approach to treatment. The dynamic interplay of the multiple contributants to the challenging behaviours of concern would be under-appreciated in the absence of an integrative biopsychosocial model. The utilization of this model by an interdisciplinary mental health team is well described in Chapter 10 (The Interdisciplinary Mental Health Team) of this book. The collaborative nature of team decision making in the assessment, formulation and treatment of clients with complex or multiple disabilities is stressed in this chapter. The reader is reminded in particular of the team's focus on operationalizing the signs and symptoms of hypothesized underlying mental health concerns, and the value of utilizing objective monitoring systems in the assessment and treatment phases of the intervention process.

Conducting a Biopsychosocial Analysis of Challenging Behaviour- An Integrated Approach

Multi-modal (biopsychosocial) models, as described in Chapter 3 and expanded upon below, utilize behavioural technology to:

1. perform functional, behavioural analyses of challenging

behaviours.

2. support specifically the testing of hypotheses that mental illnesses act as instigating, vulnerability, and maintaining conditions in the context of challenging behaviours.
3. translate signs and symptoms of mental illnesses into observable behaviours that can be recorded and measured.
4. utilize the above measures to assist in determining the efficacy of prescribed interventions.

State-of-the-art models strive to:

1. improve quality of life as defined by an individual's goals.
2. teach appropriate and useful interpersonal, social, coping and self-management skills.
3. minimize or eliminate in a positive and non-intrusive manner individually unique biochemical and psychosocial conditions that contribute to challenging behaviour.

Examples of two of these multi-modal models are: (1) *Gardner's Multi-Modal Contextual Behavioural Analytic Model* (Griffiths, 1998), and (2) *Carey's Positive Systems Approach* (Carey, 1983).

Gardner's model is well described and illustrated with case examples in Chapter 3.

An example of a case which describes **Gardner's model** is presented below:

The Case of Peter

Peter was a 40-year-old man who was assessed as being at the mild range of developmental handicap. He had a long history of sexual assault towards female children, ranging in age from 9 to 18. Peter had been repeatedly charged for his offenses and had spent some time in jail - usually placed in isolation because of his vulnerability to attack from other prisoners. Peter's sexual offenses included: exhibiting himself in public to young children; touching adolescent females in a sexual manner; making lewd remarks and threats to young females while staring at them in a very obvious and threatening manner. Peter was living in his own apartment with some Supported Independent Living (SIL) support (eight hours/week).

Instigating Conditions:

A Functional assessment of his behaviours revealed that the behaviour:

a) occurred in specific situations - namely, out in public places where he could enter into close, physical proximity with young pre-pubescent and adolescent girls;

b) usually occurred during unstructured free time - mostly during evenings and weekends, when he had no staff supervision;

c) were most likely to occur following the viewing of certain sexually explicit video tapes that were in his possession;

d) could also occur towards female staff - usually following a situation where they had made a request for him to do something to which he did not wish to comply.

Vulnerability Conditions:

Psychological assessment of Peter showed:

a) that his cognitive deficits were such that he had very poor abstract reasoning abilities, with short-term memory, and poor sequential reasoning and problem-solving skills - suggesting poor social comprehension, and lack of ability to anticipate consequences;

b) a family history marked by sexual abuse when he was a child (perpetrated by an older female relative), as well as by a former employee of the agency that was supporting him when he was in his early 20's;

c) that he was diagnosed by a psychiatrist to have a Narcissistic Personality Disorder (DSM IV code: 301.81) with passive-aggressive features.

An analysis of his support system also revealed some problems that increased his vulnerability and predisposition to reoffend, and repeatedly engage in these behaviours. These included:

a) inadequate staffing resources to monitor his behaviours during the times when he was most likely to engage in them;

b) no medical involvement to evaluate factors related to testosterone levels and elevated libido;

c) poor choice of location for his residence (e.g., - located near a high school, shopping mall and several coffee shops);

d) family support system that tended to engage in denial regarding his potential to offend, and to create conflict for support staff as well as expose him to high risk situations when he came home to visit.

Consistent with Gardner's Multi-Modal Contextual Behavioural Analytic Model, the treatment approach that was devised for Peter encompassed behavioural, educative, biomedical and ecological interventions. Behavioural strategies were put into place for staff/family, providing firm limits to specific behaviours that were carefully operationally defined to ensure consistent recording and intervention. In addition, Peter was taught pro-social communication, greeting skills, and he was provided with heavy positive reinforcement when these skills were displayed during the training sessions, as well as when there was evidence that they had generalized to daily living situations. Staff and family were educated with respect to the nature of the development of his sexually deviant behaviours, as well as to the nature of his personality disorder.

A psychiatrist was also involved, and diagnosed him with a Narcissistic Personality Disorder and Pedophilia. After an extensive medical work-up, Peter was placed on Depo-Provera medication (medroxyprogesterone acetate) to control his sexual urges and obsessional thinking.   Peter was identified as a Type IV offender - or "paraphiliac" - these are individuals who associate sexual arousal, fantasy and fulfillment with unacceptable stimuli such as children. It is reported that only Type IV offenders (paraphiliacs) will respond to Depo-Provera treatment because the other three types either deny their behaviour (Type I), project blame for their behaviour (Type II), or enjoy exercising violent urges (Type III), and will not admit that their behaviour is out of control or inappropriate. Depo-Provera is an antiandrogen drug that lowers the blood serum testosterone levels in males by restricting the release of luteinizing hormones (LH) from the pituitary gland. The reduction of testosterone triggers a corresponding reduction in sexual interest and, therefore, helps to reduce recidivism. Furthermore, the drug works to effectively reduce the frequency of erotic imagery, and normally causes a temporary form of "impotence" (or interference with erections) which also helps to reduce recidivism. The drug was prescribed for Peter because it takes effect quickly, and positive results generally appear within six months of treatment.

In addition to the medical approach, Peter's entire support system (ecological intervention) was drastically overhauled as well. This included changing his residence, adding staff complement to the times of the week when he was most vulnerable, and building an alarm monitoring system into his residence so that he could not leave without alerting staff. Social work involvement was also important in terms of helping his family learn to accept the nature of his disorder, and to agree to cooperate with his programme in a consistent fashion.

Peter's incidence of sexual acting out dropped from an average of over twenty episodes per month to less than two per month within six months. He still requires a structured environment with sufficient staffing resources to be able to effectively monitor his behaviour 24 hours per day.

Carey's Positive Systems Approach is described by its author as "an amalgamation of different aspects of the major approaches that are currently in popular use" (in supporting individuals with DD and challenging behaviours) (Carey, 1998). These approaches include:

- **applied behavioural analysis**
- **behaviour communication theory**- acknowledging that challenging behaviours are often attempts to communicate needs, and advocating teaching more acceptable methods of self-expression
- **systems theory**- advocating the belief that systems are sets of components, which when coupled together, interact and influence each other to form a whole.
- **gentle teaching**- a concept developed by McGee based on the psychology of interdependence (seeing change as being mutual and bringing about a feeling of companionship in

the community). This philosophy advocates (a) teaching individuals to feel safe with caregivers, (b) teaching individuals to feel engaged, (c) teaching individuals to feel unconditionally valued, and (d) teaching individuals to return unconditional valuing.

Six individual factors are identified in this model in supporting individual growth and care:

1. *Identification* - understanding behaviour in the context in which it occurs. Similar to Gardner's model, this factor includes an evaluation of biomedical and mental health issues as instigators or perpetuants to challenging behaviour.
2. *Communication* - looking at an individual's behaviour as a form of communication that has function and meaning.
3. *Stimulation* - heightening exposure to fun and stimulating activities not contingent on behaviours.
4. *Reinforcement* - advocating intense non-programmatic and non-contingent reinforcement that occurs on a frequent basis.
5. *Redirection* - changing aspects of the individual's environment and interaction pattern; capitalizing on stimulus change opportunities.
6. *Coping* - teaching methods and skills to handle stressors and friction.

Carey has also identified six systemic factors which must be addressed in understanding and treating challenging behaviours. These are listed as:

1. *Flexibility* - the system must offer as much flexibility as possible in areas such as: staffing credentials, staffing scheduling, living arrangements, and day programme requirements.
2. *Perseverance/Tolerance* - support programmes must demonstrate strong agency commitment towards maintaining individuals in their community - rather than having indi-

viduals "fit" into a prescribed environment, a commitment requires service providers to establish an environment that is fluid, and can best fit individuals and their presenting needs and desires.

3. *Consistency* - one cannot implement a PSA approach on a part-time, haphazard basis. Protocols of support should be established to promote a positive, methodical response to the problematic behaviour.

4. *Portability* - the support plan must have the ability to move with persons in the various settings in which they interact - staff and family in all locations must be trained in the interactional approaches.

5. *Intensity* - this has to do with the frequency and quality of interactions with individuals during the course of the day.

6. *Change* - refers to rearranging the environment or teaching staff/caregivers to become sensitized to stimuli or triggers that cue behaviours, with a focus on prevention of these behaviours manifesting themselves.

An example of a case which describes Carey's approach is presented below:

The Case of Sally

Sally was 22 years of age and was being removed from a facility for children, and placed into the community. Sally was placed into the community, not because she was ready, but because she was over the age of 18. Sally had resided in the children's facility since the age of 2, placed by her schizophrenic mother, who could no longer deal with her. Sally's history further included severe self-abuse dating back to admission - head banging, head slapping with both her hands and objects. During adolescence, self-injury was so severe that Sally was considered for neurosurgery as the only means of controlling her dangerous behaviours.   Despite Sally's behavioural challenges, she still presented as an individual who was personable and quite bright (high functioning autism). Sally was able to operate a photocopier, and to collect money for copies made for workers at the facility.   She was able to make change, and could relay amounts owing.   When she was discharged into the community residence, which was a large core residence in a rural setting, she had high rates of self-injurious behaviour (SIB), and the recommended approach was to use a strong verbal reprimand procedure, followed by brief, contingent physical restraint (holding hands down at her side).   The community agency was instructed to continue using this procedure, or else the behaviour would soon escalate to an 'out of control' state.

The behaviour gradually started to escalate - probably due to inconsistent administration of the procedure/ approach.   There were 28 different staff personnel who worked with Sally over the course of any given week, all interpreting and implementing the procedure in a variant manner.

Sally's self-abuse continued to escalate to the point where her face frequently looked quite swollen and red.   The many years of head slapping had also caused one of her retinas to become detached. Surgery was required. Sally's regular physician was away on vacation, and an unfamiliar doctor who witnessed Sally's self-injury in the office interpreted her behaviour to be indicative of suicidal behaviour, and immediately had an ambulance dis-

patched to take her involuntarily to a local psychiatric hospital. Sally's psychiatric admission included the use of a straight jacket. Her medications were significantly changed, and the incidence of her self-injury had risen to 2000 per day. Her hospital stay lasted 6 months. The old verbal reprimand and hands down procedure no longer worked. The case had escalated to a crisis point and the agency was considering a referral to a facility where shock treatment would have been used as a means of decreasing Sally's behaviours (even though previous shock treatment had not worked). Out of frustration and desperation, management decided to go with a Positive System Approach being recommended by one of the authors (Carey). The emphasis was to view Sally's behaviour as a form of communication, and to try to address her wants/ needs, using behavioural assessment, as well as providing staff with positive types of interaction strategies, designed to prevent the occurrence of the behaviour, and re-direct inappropriate behaviours while reinforcing alternative coping skills.

The PSA approach for Sally included:

a) Interpreting behaviour as communication - providing appropriate forms of stimulation - using re-direction, stimulus change, teaching more appropriate form of communication-understanding that Sally was communicating that she did not like the workshop and the task expectations. More choices needed to be available to Sally around her daily activities. Leisure and recreational activities needed to be incorporated into Sally's life. As staff became more aware and in-tune with the early warning signs of Sally's agitation and behaviour, redirection and stimulus changes were employed to break the cycle of self-injury, and to bring about change. Staff also encouraged Sally to communicate verbally, and to convey her wants and needs in a more appropriate manner. Sally was provided opportunity to express herself, and to have control over her day to day activities.

b) Focusing on the relationship Sally had with her caregivers - the relationship was not to be one of power, control and compliance. A core team of five people who truly enjoyed and liked Sally was established, and they received special training in the new interactional style/approach. One of them was placed on each shift to facilitate the consistent implementation and modeling of the desired manner of how to respond and to interact with Sally.

c) Changing Sally's living environment - constructing a self-contained apartment in the large core residence so that Sally could have her own space, and was not disrupted by outside noise and chaos. This respected the fact that Sally has autism. Her residence was further adapted to include increased insulation to reduce noise and distractions.

d) Involving a psychiatrist who was well-versed in the field of autism to incorporate all elements of a biopsychosocial approach. After a complete medical, Sally's medications were changed. First, it was acknowledged that the most appropriate diagnosis for her was autism, and this suggested that her present regimen of heavily sedating drugs was likely ineffective. Sally was placed on Risperidone, and although this drug does not have an indication for the treatment of autism, recent studies suggest that it can improve the behaviour of individuals with autism (McDougle et al., 2000). Neurobiological research has implicated the dopamine and serotonin systems in the pathogenesis of autism. We decided to go with this medication, as reports suggested that the serotonin 2A, and dopamine D2 antagonist Risperidone may be safe and effective in reducing the interfering symptoms of persons with autism.

e) Probing family history and considering re-establishing contact with Sally's mother. Contact was established and positive outcomes were reported by both parties.

Overall, to the surprise of many, Sally's self-injury dropped from 2000 incidents per day to 200 per day within the first 6 months of implementing the new approach. A year later, self-injury was at zero frequency. This progress had never been achieved since Sally was admitted into a facility at 2 years of age. The behaviour remained at zero for several years and the case was closed.

Case Formulation

These models, which allow for implementation of state-of-the-art therapeutic modalities, including pharmacological support to individuals with challenging behaviour, base recommendations for multi-modal interventions on a *case formulation* process. An interdisciplinary team approach involving professionals with both mental health and behavioural analytic expertise allows the incorporation of these formulations into a unified process. An example of such a process is illustrated on the following page.

To participate in this interdisciplinary process, it is important for all members of the interdisciplinary team to have an understanding of the principles of pharmacological approaches to mental health concerns in individuals with DD.

Figure 2- Case Formulation Process

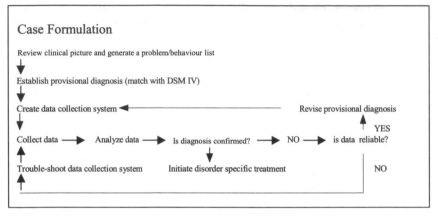

The Integration of Pharmacological Processes

The identification of a mental illness as an instigating, vulnerability or reinforcing condition to challenging behaviour has historically been hindered by the failure of clinicians to create a valid diagnostic and treatment formulation, invoking an absence of forethought regarding expected response to treatment, and a lack of established prospective outcome criteria. Again, it is important to remember that a psychiatric diagnosis is more than a label. Rather, it represents a hypothesis for the cause of the challenging behaviours observed, based on neurochemical (and potentially many other) variables (Sovner 1992).

The accuracy of the diagnosis of a specific DSM-IV disorder in individuals with DD, in the absence of an integrated biopsychosocial approach, is challenged by:

1. *behavioural overshadowing* - the attribution of an increase in the intensity or frequency of maladaptive behaviour to 'learned behaviour', rather than overt behavioural expressions of an underlying disorder.
2. *diagnostic overshadowing (*Reiss, Levitas, & Szyszko, 1982*)* - identifying maladaptive behaviour as being a direct outcome of the individual having a developmental disabil-

ity.
3. ***baseline exaggeration*** - failing to recognize that an increase in the frequency or intensity of a maladaptive behaviour may be signaling the onset of an underlying mental or physical illness, or an adverse effect of a medication.
4. failure to account for the impact of impoverished life experiences and communication deficits on the expression of signs and symptoms of mental illness.
5. failure to recognize that complex, concurrent disorders may occur at the same time.
6. misidentification of non-specific, stress-induced loss of adaptive functioning as an indication of a psychotic disorder (Sovner & Hurley, 1983).

It is important to remember that mental illnesses have natural histories with prodromal or early warning signs, acute episodes, possibly with critical periods of crisis, chronic episodes, and partial and complete remissions. All major psychiatric illnesses also carry risk, as illustrated below in Figure 3 using depression as an example of relapses (the return of symptoms in the first six months after remission) and recurrence (a second episode of the disorder beyond six months from the initial period of remission).

Figure 3– The Natural History of Depression

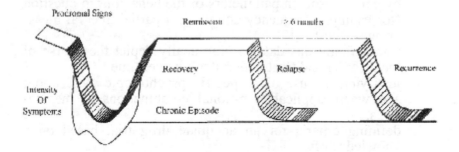

Four broad categories of pharmacological treatment are available to address psychiatric disorders:

1. *acute treatment* to treat acute signs and symptoms of illness.
2. *crisis management* or the utilization of PRN medication to address crises during acute phases.
3. *continuation treatment* to decrease the risk of relapse.
4. *maintenance treatment* to decrease the risk of recurrence.

The treatment formulation should ideally:

1. present evidence that the diagnosis is valid.
2. identify target symptoms which can be measured objectively to determine response to treatment - this concept has been advanced by Lowry (1997) through his model of *An Assessment of Symptomatic Behaviours.*

Although focusing on mood disorders, Lowry's recommendations, as follows, are generalizable to all psychiatric disorders. He recommends:

1. establishing operational definitions of each symptomatic behaviour to allow caregivers to participate in the development of an objective monitoring system.
2. choosing an appropriate data collection system as dictated by existing known parameters of the behaviour in question (for example, frequency counts or a partial interval measuring system).
3. summarizing this data to graphically depict the course of the disorder and treatment outcome over time.
4. justifying the use of a specific psychotropic medication; and where applicable, rational combinations of medications.
5. defining criteria for an adequate drug trial based on a knowledge of:
    (a) the natural history of the disorder
    (b) knowledge of the properties of the drug as illustrated on the following page.

All psychotropic medications share the following properties depicted in Figure 4:

Figure 4– Psychotropic medication properties

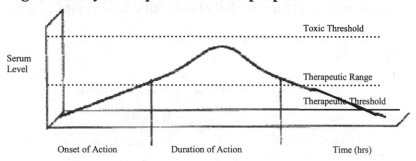

- *onset of action* - the time required for medication to have an optimal effect. This is the time frame in which efforts to support the individual non-pharmacologically are particularly important.
- *duration of action* - this property determines appropriate dosing intervals (the minimum time between doses of medication).
- *therapeutic range* - the level of medication in the blood and brain achieved over a period of time by the prescription of a specific dose of a medication. This range is characterized by:

  a. *a therapeutic threshold* below which the drug has a suboptimal effect.

  b. *a toxic threshold* above which adverse effects increase in the absence of any further positive effects.

6. Establish expected goals of treatment - these can include:

- behavioural suppression - a goal in crisis situations only.
- behavioural stabilization - to induce quantitative rather than qualitative changes in chronic disorders.
- normalization - achieving remission and minimizing the risk of relapse and recurrence.

The following Table 1 illustrates the work of a behavioural therapist and residential counsellors in translating signs and symptoms of hypomania and depression in a non-verbal individual with a developmental disability, an autistic disorder, and a bipolar disorder into daily observable behaviours.

Table 1– Signs and Symptoms of Hypomania and Depression

Signs and Symptoms of Hypomania and Depression	
Mania	**Depression**
Nonstop hyperactivity (e.g., pacing, rocking)	Hand biting leaving mark on skin
Knocking over or throwing objects repeatedly	Crying
Bringing same object to staff repeatedly	Public masturbation three or four
Disrupted sleep (<4 hours sleep at night time)	times
New words, almost sentences, improved expressive speech	Laying in fetal position in unusual place
Euphoric, loud and intense "eehing", pronouced laughing	Inactivity– remained in one place for extended periods >1 hour

Physical aggression (e.g., hitting and/or pushing), urinating in odd places (e.g., laundry basket), and incontinence, are also followed but seem to be present in both phases.

(King & McCartney, 1999)

In crisis situations (times when an individual's coping skills are insufficient to deal with the increased stress brought about by the crisis), acute psychotropic medication and *PRN (pro re nata medication as needed) protocols* are necessary to minimize risk of harm to the individual in crisis, to peers and caregivers, and to minimize property destruction (King, Fay, & Croghen, 2000). Potential scenarios representing the time courses of crisis intensity are illustrated below. Again, it is critical to utilize an interdisciplinary team, and a biopsychosocial model in developing crisis plans which include the use of medication. The identification of instigating, vulnerability and maintaining conditions can assist in developing recommendations to reduce the frequency of crises (this is primary prevention). In turn, this will reduce the need for behavioural suppression with PRN medications.

Figure 5- Potential scenarios representing the time course of crisis intensity

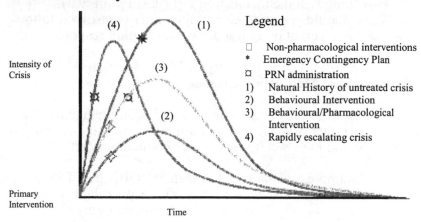

Figure 5 illustrates that:

1. Observable periods of onset, periods of peak intensity, and eventual spontaneous resolution characterize the natural history of crises (natural history).
2. Non-pharmacological interventions established in advance through team consensus, and a review of previous intervention outcomes, may well minimize crisis intensity and duration (behavioural interventions).
3. A historical review of previous crises may assist in decision-making regarding the timing of the use of PRN medication, thereby reducing crisis intensity.
4. A rapid escalation of challenging behaviours may necessitate urgent use of PRN medication concurrent with the implementation of an emergency contingency plan

It is important as advocates to ask medication prescribers:

1. Do we have the time to safely use this medication in the environment (onset of action)?
2. What can be done to support the individual in the interim until the medication begins to help?

3. What are the expected positive and negative effects of the medication (therapeutic and toxic thresholds)?
4. How long will the medication last (dosing interval)?
5. What should we do to ensure the crisis is resolved following the observation of a sedative or calming response to the drug?

Psychotropic Medication Classes

1. ***Benzodiazepines*** - as anxiolytic and sedative agents, these drugs target psychomotor agitation, anxious and fearful affects, and have a calming or sleep-inducing effect.

    Examples include: Lorazepam (Ativan), Diazepam (Valium), Oxazepam (Serax), Alprazolam (Xanax), Clonazepam (Rivotril) and Midazolam (Versed)

2. ***Antipsychotics*** - these drugs target psychomotor agitation and aggressive behaviour, particularly in the presence of psychotic symptoms (hallucinations, delusions and disorganized behaviour). There are two classes of antipsychotic medication:
    (a) traditional antipsychotics - examples include Haloperidol (Haldol), Chlorpromazine (Thorazine), Thioridazine (Mellaril), Methotrimeprazine (Nozinan), Trifluoperazine (Stelazine), Loxapine (Loxapac) and Perphenazine (Trilafon)
    (b) atypical antipsychotics - examples include Clozapine (Clozaril), Risperidone (Risperdal), Olanzapine (Zyprexa) and Quetiapine (Seroquel)

Their relative properties categorized as advantages and disadvantages, both in crisis situations and in the treatment of psychotic and other disorders, are listed in Table 2:

Table 2- Advantages and Disadvantages of Traditional Neuroleptics

Advantages of Traditional Neuroleptics	Disadvantages of Traditional Neuroleptics
1. The ideal neuroleptic should have: a. A rapid onset of action. b. An initial sedative effect. c. Few neurological adverse effects. d. A longer duration of action to minimize administration frequency. e. Good local tolerability if given intramuscularly or intravenously (Carey, 1998). *As a recent advance, intramuscular Zuclopenthixol Acetate (Clopixol Acuphase) offers a duration of action of 48 - 72 hours.	1. A risk of paradoxical response secondary to over sedation and akathesia. 2. Acute neurological adverse effects (including dystonia, spasmodic torticollis, oculogyric crisis) each with a potential negative impact on subsequent compliance. 3. Exacerbation of seizure disorders. 4. Sedative and anticholinergic adverse effects which may produce a delirium. 5. Exacerbation in post traumatic stress disorder of dissociative phenomena.

Atypical antipsychotics as a group provide fewer acute and long-term adverse effects compared to traditional neuroleptics. These adverse effects are illustrated in Table 3.

An expanding list of use of atypical neuroleptics in individuals with DD includes:

- Acute and maintenance treatment of schizophrenia and other psychotic disorders.
- Adjunctive mood stabilizers in bipolar disorder (BD).
- Acute treatment of hypomania and mania in BD.
- Tic suppression and treatment of oppositional behaviour in Tourette's Syndrome (TS).
- Adjunctive treatment in obsessive compulsive disorder (OCD).
- Symptomatic treatment of aggression, self-injury and agi-

tation in pervasive developmental disorders (PDD).
- Conversion strategy - switching from previously pre-scribed traditional neuroleptics to atypical antipsychotics to reduce the life-time risk of TD.

Table 3- Advantages and Disadvantages of Atypical Antipsychotics

Advantages of Atypical Antipsychotics	Disadvantages of Atypical Antipsychotics
1. A decreased propensity for extrapyramidal adverse effects and tardive dyskinesia.	1. A risk of agranulocytosis, particularly in the first six months of treatment with Clozapine.
2. Decreased risk of hyperprolactinemia (except Risperidone).	2. A theoretical risk of respiratory depression with combined use of Lorazepam and Clozapine.
3. Improved impact on the negative symptoms of schizophrenia.	3. Dose related risk of seizures with Clozapine.
4. Interaction with both Dopamine and Serotonergic systems.	4. Significant weight gain.

Antidepressants

- *Selective serotonin reuptake inhibitors* - through altering the transmission of the neurotransmitter serotonin, this class of medication also is used in the treatment of (i) panic disorder, (ii) OCD, (iii) social phobia, and (iv) bulimia.

These drugs are generally well-tolerated in individuals with DD. Adverse effects include sexual dysfunction, nausea, vomiting, headache, insomnia, and a paradoxical increase in anxiety.

- *Novel antidepressants* -Venlafaxine (Effexor), Nefazodone (Serzone), Moclobemide (Manerix), Bupropion (Wellbutrin).

These drugs differ in the manner in which they influence specific neurotransmitters in the brain and fail to respond to one or more SSRI's.

- *Tricyclic antidepressants* - Examples include Amitriptyline (Elavil), Imipramine (Tofranil), Sinequan (Doxepin), Clomipramine (Anafranil).

As older medications with multiple influences on neuro-transmitters, these drugs are generally poorly tolerated in individuals with DD. Common adverse effects include sedation, tremor, constipation, dry mouth, blurred vision and orthostatic hypotension. These adverse effects often prevent the attainment of a therapeutic dose of the drug.

Mood Stabilizers

These drugs are used in the acute, continuation and maintenance phases of BD. They include Lithium Carbonate, Carbamazepine and Valproic Acid. Recent work suggests that newer anticonvulsants, Gabapentin (Neurontin) and Lamotrigine (Lamictal), also have mood stabilizing properties. Lithium, Carbamazepine and Valproic Acid can be monitored through serial assessments of blood levels to individualize doses, to minimize adverse effects, and to optimize treatment response. (See Table 4)

Stimulants

Methylphenidate (Ritalin) and Dexamphetamine Sulfate (Dexedrine) are used in the treatment of attention deficit disorder with hyperactivity (ADDH).

Anti-Parkinson or Anticholinergic Agents

This class of medication includes Benztropine Mesylate (Cogentin), Trihexyphenidyl Hydrochoride (Artane), Amantadine (Symmetrel) and Procyclidine (Kemadrin), amongst others. These medications are used primarily to counteract the neurological adverse effects of antipsychotic medications.

Table 4- Mood Stabilizers

	Dosage Range (mg)	Serum Level Range	Target Symptoms	Common Adverse Effects
Valproic Acid	750-3000 mg/d	350-700 μmol/L	Acute Mania and Long term control	GI complaints, changes in appetite and weight, alopecia, ataxia, asymptomatic hepatic transaminase elevation
Car-bamazepine	300-1200 mg/d	17-54 μmol/L	Acute Mania and long term control	Dizziness, drowsiness, blurred vision, diplopia, ataxia, headache, chills, tremors, dry mouth, nausea, fever
Lithium	900-2400 mg/d (acute) 300-1200 mg/d (maintenance)	0.8-1.2 mmol/L (acute) 0.6-1.0 mmol/L (maintenance)	Long term control and prevention or diminution of the intensity of subsequent episodes of mania and depression	GI irritation, muscular weakness, restlessness, slurred speech, blurred vision, dazed feeling, vertigo

Beta Blockers

Used primarily as antihypertensive agents, these medications, for example Propranolol, are also used for:

- the symptomatic relief of performance anxiety
- the treatment of neuroleptic-induced akathisia
- the treatment of Lithium-induced tremor
- the treatment of aggression, self-injury or other challenging behaviours in the context of states of overarousal, such as PDD

Clonidine

Indications include:

- tic suppression in TS
- ADHD
- symptomatic treatment of states of overarousal

Opiate Blockers

Example: Naltrexone.

Indications include:

- alcohol dependence
- self-injurious behaviour

Buspirone

Buspirone is a non-benzodiazepine antianxiety agent.

Indications include:

- agitation in dementia and head injury
- generalized anxiety disorder

Conclusion

This chapter has reviewed various state-of-the-art biopsycho-social approaches to dealing with the challenging behaviours exhibited by some individuals with a DD. An inter-disciplinary process is critical to understanding the full nature and complexity that is frequently inherent in these cases. The principles of psychiatric diagnosis combined with the functional analysis of behaviour is a powerful combination of therapeutic traditions to apply to these challenging individuals. It is equally important that the consumers of these approaches are familiar with the basic principles of safe and effective pharmacotherapeutic treatment as well as the ethical, moral and legal dilemmas that are often involved in behavioural treatments. This chapter highlighted two of the more popular multi-modal approaches being used today - Gardner's Multi-Modal Contextual Behavioural Analytical Model, and Carey's Positive Systems Approach. Both of these conceptual models of behaviour analysis focus on the more positive and least intrusive aspects of behavioural and systems interventions. These collaborative treatment approaches value and recognize the importance of understanding and working within systems, and it should be noted that systems theory originated in the traditional biological sciences, and has in recent years, been applied to the human sciences (Clarke & Crossland, 1985). It has become clear that clinicians can no longer work in an isolated fashion without considering that the human mind and body are part of a highly complex system (biological and social), and a thorough understanding of a problem affecting an individual can only be arrived at through the study and consideration of the whole system, and the interrelationships of the parts of that system, and how they impact on each other. The treatment approaches that were presented in this chapter are all grounded within a sound empirical, theoretical framework, and they represent effective and humane approaches to solving the puzzle that underlies many of the challenging behaviours presented by individuals with a DD.

Future interdisciplinary alliances between psychiatry and behavioural analysis can reap positive rewards. One of these areas currently being explored is the use of detailed behavioural assessment/recording/evaluation procedures to monitor and chart common side effects to psychotropic medications that are frequently used on persons with Developmental Disabilities.

This will permit careful analysis of the "cost-benefit" of such medications, and track any potential side effects for quicker response to medication adjustment.

Do You Know?

1. The manner in which medication treatment can be incorporated into a biopsychosocial model of challenging behaviour in individuals with DD?
2. Examples of state-of-the-art multimodal treatment approaches?
3. The names of the major classes of psychotropic medications?
4. How members of an interdisciplinary team can support the safe and efficacious use of psychotropic medication?

Resources

Crabbe, H.F. (1995). *A Guidebook for the use of psychotropic medications in persons with mental illness and mental retardation.* Second Edition. New London, CT: OmniCare Consultants Inc.

Reiss, S., & Aman, M.G. (1998). *The International Consensus Handbook: Psychotropic medications and developmental disabilities.* Ohio State University: Nisonger Center.

Tsiouris, J.A., & Adelman, S.A. (1997) *Guidelines and general Information on the use of psychotropic and antiepileptic drugs for individuals with developmental disabilities .* New York State office of Mental Retardation and Developmental Disabilities.

Mental Health Aspects of Developmental Disabilities
    Telephone: 336-581-3700

Website: http://www.mhaspectsofdd.com
NADD Bulletin
Telephone: 914-331-4336
Website: http://www.thenadd.org
The University of Western Ontario Clinical Bulletin of the Developmental Disabilities Program
Telephone: 519-661-3804
Website: http://www.psychiatry.med.uwo.ca/ddp
Habilitative Mental Health Resource Network
Website: http://www.nbpsych.on.ca/HMHRN.HTM
Quality of Life of People with Developmental Disabilities
Website: http://www.utoronto.ca/qol/projpwdd.htm
Mental Retardation – A Journal of Policy, Practices, and Perspectives
Telephone: 301-604-1340
Website: http://www.aamr.org
OACL – Accreditation Ontario Newsletter
Telephone: 705-356-2782
Website: http://www.acl.on.ca
Dr. Bob Carey – PSA article/manuals
Website: http://www.members.home.net/bobcarey

References

American Psychiatric Association (1994). *Diagnostic and statistical manual of mental disorders (4th edition)*. Washington, DC: Author.
Carey, R. (1983). *Positive systems approach.* Unpublished manuscript.
Carey, R. (1998). *Positive systems approach.* Unpublished manuscript.
Clarke, D.D., & Crossland, J. (1985). *Action systems: An introduction to the analysis of complex behaviour.* New Fetter Lane, London: Mehuen & Co. Ltd.

Engel, G.L. (1977). The need for a new medical model: A challenge for biomedicine. *Science, 196*, 129-136.

Griffiths, D., Gardner, W., & Nugent, J. (1998*). Behavioral supports: Individual centered interventions: A multimodal functional approach.* Kingston, NY: NADD Press.

King, R., & McCartney, J. (1999). Charting for a purpose: Optimal treatment of bipolar disorder in individuals with developmental disabilities. *Mental Health Aspects of Developmental Disabilities, 2(2)*, 1-9.

King, R., Fay, G., & Croghan, P. (2000). Pro Re Nata: Optimal use of psychotropic PRN medication. *Mental Health Aspects of Developmental Disabilities, 3(1)*, 8-16.

Lowry, M. (1997). Unmasking mood disorders: Recognizing and measuring symptomatic behaviors. *The Habilitative Mental Healthcare Newsletter, 16(1)*, 1-6.

McDougle, C.J., Scahill, L., McCracken, J.T., Aman, M.G., Tierney, E., Arnold, L.E., Freeman, B.J., Martin, A., McGough, J.J., Cronin, P., Posey, D.J., Riddle, M.A., Ritz, L., Swiezy, N.B., Vitiello, B., Volkmar, F.R., Votolato, N. A., & Walson, P. (2000). Research units on pediatric psychopharmacology (RUPP) Autism Network. Background and rationale for an initial controlled study of Risperidone. *Child and Adolescent Psychiatric Clinics of North America, 9(1)*, 201-224.

Meyers, B. (1998). Major depression in persons with moderate to profound mental retardation: Clinical presentation and case illustration. *Mental Health Aspects of Developmental Disabilities, 1*, 57-68.

Pyles, D.A.M., Muniz, K., Cade, A., & Silva, R. (1997). A behavioral diagnostic paradigm for integrating behavior-analytic and psychopharmacological interventions for people with a dual diagnosis. *Research in Developmental Disabilities, 18(3)*, 185-214.

Reiss, S., Levitas, G., & Szyszko, J. (1982). Emotional distur-
    bance and mental retardation: Diagnostic overshadowing.
    American Journal on Mental Deficiency, 86, 567-574.
Sovner, R., & Hurley, A.D. (1983). Do the mentally retarded
    suffer from affective illness? *Archives of General Psy-
    chiatry, 40,* 61-67.
Sovner, R., & Hurley, A. (1992). The diagnostic treatment
    formulation for psychotropic drug therapy. *The Habilita-
    tive Mental Healthcare Newsletter, 11(12),* 81-85.

Chapter 8

Psychopharmacological Treatments in Persons with Developmental Disabilities (DD)

Chrissoula Stavrakaki, Ruxandra Antochi, Jane Summers, and Judy Adamson

Learning Objectives

Readers will be able to:

1. Identify the categories of psychotropic medications
2. Learn how to use psychotropic medications in order to minimize their side effects
3. Identify an appropriate monitoring system to determine the effect of the medication
4. Learn the protocols on how to use PRN medications:
   - The reason for PRN medication
   - Know at what stage of behaviour it should be used
5. Learn what staff need to know about the psychotropic medications being prescribed:
   - Why the medication is being prescribed
   - How long before it becomes effective
   - Under what conditions the medication should be stopped
   - How long it is necessary to take the medication
   - The adverse effects of the medication

Introduction

Try to recollect how frequent the use of medications is in clients with developmental disabilities. Can you understand the multiple uses of these medications? Have you ever wondered what they are for? Professionals and caregivers dealing with persons with developmental disabilities, frequently have tried to use pharmacological treatments (prescribed medications) to treat:

- mental health disorders (i.e., anxiety, depression, schizophrenia) and
- prevent negative cycles from occurring, such as in Bipolar mental illness.

These medications have also been used to manage :

- maladaptive behaviours whilst definitive and active treatment is taking place and
- extreme anxiety when rehabilitative intervention is not available or practical.

In many instances, different types of medications are used in an attempt to improve outcome, and to enable the person with a developmental disability and mental disorder to lead a productive and peaceful life.

However, the state of our medical knowledge on medication uses, although better than it has been, is still crude, and in many cases imprecise. During the past ten years, our knowledge in assessing, diagnosing and treating persons with mental health problems has improved tenfold. Despite this immense expansion of our database, there are situations where the use of medication is not the optimal, or the combinations used (polypharmacy) are less effective, or even detrimental.

In this chapter, an attempt has been made to:

1. Present the various medication categories mostly used in persons with a dual diagnosis.
2. Discuss possible side effects and how you evaluate them in this group.
3. Create efficient strategies of assessing the needs for medication use and the different ways of prescribing them (i.e., continuously; on a per needed basis; in crisis/emergency care.

What are psychotropic medications?

Psychotropic medications include any prescribed drugs that are given to stabilize or improve mood, mental status or behaviour. The following categories of medications are commonly used in persons with developmental disabilities:

- Antidepressants
- Antianxiety medications
- Sedative/hypnotics
- Mood stabilizers
- Antipsychotic agents
- Stimulants

How to use psychotropic medications in order to minimize their adverse effects

Individuals with DD have risks similar to the general population with respect to developing the same spectrum of side effects from psychotropic drugs. However, there are a few situations in which these drugs seem to cause adverse effects that are specific to this population, such as epileptic attacks. Moreover, individualized response to the medications' effects is probably higher in people with DD. Thus, their adverse effects may be more unexpected. Presently, for the majority of psychotropic drugs, it is difficult to predict, based on scientific evidence, which patients are at risk of experiencing clinically significant side effects.

Nevertheless, people with DD may have side effects which may go undetected due to three main factors:

- The patient's functional handicap may mask some signs of medication toxicity.
- The individual may experience difficulty in informing caregivers regarding adverse effects. On one hand, people with a lesser degree of impairment may have the ability to report problems, but they may not be able to understand or appreciate adverse effects as being secondary to medication. On the other hand, patients with more serious difficulties may be unable to report adverse effects due to speech or language impairments. For these people, adverse reactions may manifest as behavioural changes, such as increased aggression or self-injurious activity.
- Stereotypic behaviours, which are common in people with DD, may make the recognition of adverse effects very challenging. Differentiating between these behaviours and drug-induced abnormal movements may be difficult. In addition, it is problematic to distinguish between the adverse effects of some psychotropic medications, and co-morbid psychiatric or medical conditions (Sovner & Des Noyers Hurley, 1985; Pary, 1993).

It is best to start at low dose when initiating pharmacological treatment, in situations where there is no psychiatric emergency and slowly titrate the dose to the lowest optimally effective dose to achieve therapeutic effect. By implementing this approach, the likelihood of experiencing adverse effects may be significantly diminished. Furthermore, it is advisable to avoid frequent medication dose changes in response to the identified target behaviours, which may vary on an ongoing basis. Administration of medication at certain daytime events, such as breakfast or before bedtime, is a good strategy, geared towards promoting compliance with medications used. In addition, use of multiple concomitant medications may significantly contribute to patient's problems with compliance and side effects. Thus, it is advisable to minimize them or avoid them if possible (Bregman, 1996; Santosh & Baird, 1999).

Rapid discontinuation of most psychotropic drugs may lead to withdrawal reactions. Generally speaking, these medications should be gradually tapered off. In addition, people with DD may be more susceptible to developing withdrawal symptoms secondary to rapid discontinuation of psychotropic medication. However, frequent monitoring during tapering will minimize the occurrence of withdrawal symptoms. Furthermore, patients with DD may present with behavioural changes due to withdrawal symptoms. In some cases, it may be challenging to distinguish between decrease suppression of maladaptive behaviours or frank symptoms of mental illness or a combination of the two. However, in these cases, giving an immediate dose of the medication being withdrawn may lead to relief of withdrawal symptoms, but with a lack of substantial improvement of the relapse of behavioural problems. In these circumstances, restarting of the last dose of medication, and a more gradual decrease of dosage may facilitate successful discontinuation of the medication (Madrid, State, & King, 2000; Sovner & Des-Noyers Hurley 1985).

Table 1- Physical checkup prior to the use of
         Psychopharmacological agents in Persons with
         Developmental Disability

Category	Class	Checkup
Benzodiazepines	Antianxiety	Complete blood count, blood chemistries with attention to liver function tests
Tricyclics	Antidepressants	Blood chemistries, electrocardiogram
SSRIs	Antidepressants	Blood chemistries, electrocardiogram
Typical/Atypical Neuroleptics	Antipsychotics	Blood chemistries, electrocardiogram
Anticonvlusants	Mood stabilizers	Complete blood count, platelet count, blood chemistries with attention to liver function
Lithium	Mood stabilizer; anti mania	Thyroid test, blood chemistries, electrocardiogram
Propranolol	Antihyperactive Antianxiety	Blood pressure, pulse, electrocardiogram, blood chemistries

Note: When pharmacological intervention is established, regular 3-6 months monitoring of the same functions is necessary.

Drug monitoring inactive treatment and or management is necessary for medications such as mood stabilizers but not so helpful in antianxiety medications, SSRI's and antipsychotics excluding Clozapine.

How to evaluate for adverse effects

It is important to keep in mind the following strongly advised guidelines:

- Baseline physical assessment and laboratory screening should occur prior to initiation of medication.
- Baseline behavioural assessment is important *prior* to initiating drug therapy. Target behaviours, signs or symptoms, and quality of life parameters must be defined and quantified. Quantification should be based on empirical measurement methods (e.g., frequency count, duration recording, rating scales, time sample, interval recording). Data should be collected over two to four weeks prior to initiating non-emergency medication, and also after the initiation of any psychotropic medication, especially before and after any dose or drug change.
- Anticipate side effects; an increase in behavioural problems may reflect the adverse effects of a medication.
- Follow-up assessments and laboratory monitoring at regular intervals (during the initial phase weekly and at least once every three to six months in maintenance).
- Patient, parents and caregivers should be informed about the potential side effects of the medication and instructed to report immediately any change in behaviour.
- Use open-ended questions when screening for side effects.
- Use rating scales.

There are three different types of rating scales used to detect adverse drug reactions: medication-specific, general purpose, and side effect-specific. However, standardized, user-friendly rating scales for monitoring drug-induced side effects are still needed (Reiss & Aman, 1998).

Medication-specific scales are based on the most frequently occurring symptoms described in the Physicians' Desk Reference. They lose their utility when polypharmacy is employed. General-purpose rating scales provide an in-depth review of all body parts, and contrary to medication-specific scales, can be used in patients who take multiple medications.

Side effect-specific scales were developed to evaluate the acute and chronic extrapyramidal symptoms secondary to most antipsychotics. Examples include:

• Abnormal Involuntary Movement Scale (AIMS) (Guy, 1979) is the most widely recognized and utilized rating scale for routine screening and early detection of tardive dyskinesia. However, this scale is unable to detect tardive dystonias or tardive akathisia.
• Extrapyramidal Symptom Rating Scale (ESRS) (Choinard, Ross-Choinard, Annabelle, & Jones, 1980) is monitoring for the presence or absence of acute and chronic extrapyramidal side effects (EPSE). On the downside, this scale does not register the severity of symptoms.

Protocols and Guidelines on how to use PRN Medications

Medications are prescribed to be taken in a certain way (See Table 2). At other times, medications are prescribed to be taken as required (PRN). PRN medications are best used as follows:

Table 2: Abbreviations for Medication and PRN Orders

od	to be given once a day
bid	to be given twice a day (usually at 9 a.m. and 6 p.m.)
tid	to be given three times a day (usually at 9 a.m., 1 p.m. and 6 p.m.)
qid	to be given four times a day (usually at 9 a.m., 1 p.m., 6 p.m., and 10 p.m.)
hs	to be given at bedtime
qh	to be given every hour
qH	to be given every 2 hours
q4H	to be given every 4 hours
a.c.	to be given prior to meals (usually 1 hour before meals)
p.c.	to be given 1 hour after meals
tid a.c.	to be given three times a day, prior to meals
tid p.c.	to be given three times a day, after meals

Note: Medications given regularly during the day could be given at times which are adjusted to accommodate an individual's schedule.

PRN medications:

PRN	to be given when required
PRN bid	can be given up to twice a day
PRN tid	can be given up to three times a day
PRN q3h	can be given every 3 hours
PRN q3h tid	can be given every three hours up to three times a day

- Management of extreme anxiety when rehabilitative intervention is not available or practical. For example when a person requires urgent medical attention and is not capable of allowing the medical examination and or treatment to occur. A destinction can be made when a person requires a preplaned intrusive intervention such as a visit to the dentist. In this case a rehabilitative approach can be more appropriate if practical. In situation when this is not available or practical PRN medication can be used.
- Management of an individual's maladaptive behaviours while definitive and active treatment of a specific mental disorder is taking place.

The categories of medications used as management strategies in such crises are primarily:

- Antianxiety medications/Benzodiazepines. (Please refer to the text)
- Antipsychotic medications. (Please refer to the text)
- Sleep inducing medications. (Please refer to text)

Other medication groups have occasionally been used to prevent a crisis, but to a much lesser extent, and their usefulness is far more limited. Examples include SSRIs and Beta-Blockers.

What we want to achieve when we use medications in crises:

- Primarily and preferably to prevent the crisis from occurring.
- To settle already existing escalation of behaviours.
- Minimize damage to self/others and/or property.

- Maintain a less disturbing environment for the wellness and stability of the other clients.

These medications are usually prescribed by psychiatrists, family physicians, dentists, anesthetists, and other relevant disciplines. It has been commonly accepted that environmental, medical and social changes can lead to crises. In any crisis, if time allows, the caregivers have to make an attempt to disentangle the reasons and causes for the crisis. In certain situations, however, the escalation of behaviour is so fast and so unpredictable, or it is so extreme in severity, that analysis of causes becomes impossible. In these instances, the clear guidelines and use of PRN protocols are very useful so that any staff/caregiver, familiar or unfamiliar with the person in crisis can respond adequately and appropriately to resolve the problematic situation.

An attempt is made to present the reader with certain examples of protocols/guidelines in order to facilitate an appropriate and speedier response in these very traumatic and traumatizing situations.

The Case of John

This case describes individual signs of agitation that can lead to major crisis.

John is a *40* year-old male who is diagnosed with developmental disability and Bipolar illness. John lives in a high support group home, and is treated with a mood stabilizer in titration.

During the titration process John remains excessively
overactive and over reactive to environmental stimuli.
In this process John's behaviour can escalate to becoming extremely physically and verbally abusive to himself
and others. PRN medication is used in order to safe-
guard John and others

The protocols/guidelines for John are as follows:

Name: John J.
Date: 2/4/2002
Psychiatrist/Family Physician: Dr. M. Peterson

Medication: Haloperidol 0.5 mg PRN up to 3 mg per 24 hrs

Descriptions of Behaviours:

Mild Anxiety: Signs of tension occur when John bites his lip,
pinches his arm, scratches excessively, or paces and bangs his
head. Try to divert John's attention and lead him to a quiet
area. Allow 15 minutes for John to settle. If this fails, then
PRN medication is administered.

Severe Anxiety/Agitation: Signs of severe anxiety include: yelling, threatening staff or clients, obsessing, muttering under his
breath. PRN medication is administered immediately.

Aggression: Procedure to be followed:
         Quiet time, restraint if necessary, PRN as soon as it is
         possible
         Behaviour/Timeout/Mat restraint Guidelines.
         PRN medication should be given when John is able to

receive it.

Dosages:

- For mild Anxiety: Haloperidol 0.5 mg stat to be repeated within 45 minutes if necessary.

- For Severe Anxiety/Agitation: Haloperidol 1 mg to be repeated within 30 minutes if necessary.

- For Aggression: Haloperidol 1mg to be repeated if necessary every 30 minutes up to 3 mg.

Note: Any of the above combinations must not exceed 3 mg per 24 hours.

The Case of David

This case presents David, a *47* year old male, who is developmentally disabled and experiences recurrent depressive disorder. Four years prior David was treated successfully and medication was withdrawn. David did well for several years. However, in the past several months he has recurrent symptoms of his depressive condition. Whilst his antidepressant medication is being titrated and to insure David's safety PRN medication is being used.

In addition to his regular medication, David is given occasionally PRN medication to prevent behavioral escalation.

The protocol/PRN guidelines for David are as follows:

Name: David L.
Date: 6/5/2002
Psychiatrist/Family Physician: Dr. M. Peterson

Medication: Lorazepam 1 mg , 3 mg/24 hours.

Description of Behaviours:

David's signs of severe anxiety are banging head, yelling, pacing, whining noises, and frequent visits to the washroom.

The following steps should be taken prior to the administration of this medication:

1. Establish verbal communication, and suggest that David try to relax. Allow him time and a quiet area to do so. Allow 15-20 minutes time lapse. If David relaxes, please praise him.
2. If above fails, then administer medication.
3. Continue to encourage him to relax. Repeat PRN administration if the behaviours continue over 30 minutes. Do not exceed recommended maximum.

Note: All PRN administrations must be documented and accompanied by a behaviour report.

The Case of George

This case presents George, a *35* year old male with Down Syndrome, who experiences generalized anxiety disorder. Despite adequate trial of anti-anxiety medication, George continues to manifest interrupted sleep as well as rapid changes in mood state with periods of both excessive smiling and crying. Whilst the team is awaiting to have George reassessed PRN medication is used to prevent self injury or injury of others. .

The protocols/guidelines for George are as follows:

Name: George T.
Date: 5/4/2002
Psychiatrist/Family Physician: Dr. M. Peterson

Medication: Risperidone 0.5 mg

Maximum Dosage: 2 mg/24 hours

Description of Behaviours:

1. Inability to relax
2. Intense staring
3. Loud and repeated screaming
4. Physical aggression against another person or property

The following steps should be taken prior to the administration of medication:

1. Ask George to relax. Allow him time and a quiet area to relax.
2. If this fails, try to redirect him to a quiet area.
3. If he chooses to stay in this area, allow sufficient time to relax.
4. If behaviours continue for more than 20 minutes, or are severe and intense in nature, then administer PRN.

 Note: All PRN medication must be accompanied by a behaviour report.

As is evident, PRN protocols/guidelines are very important so that:

- medication is used to assist in the management of maladaptive behaviours which cannot otherwise be managed safely
- staff/caregivers that are unfamiliar with the person concerned are still able to manage acute behaviour without jeopardizing anyone's health or safety.
- maximum amounts used per 24 hours are always a must in order to prevent unwanted side effects or prolonged periods of sedation of the individual client.

It is our hope that the outlined guidelines, as well as the case scenarios, will assist the reader to maximize effectiveness of the PRN medication with minimal risk to health and safety of the individual client and his/her environment.

Description of Psychotropic Medications

A. Antidepressants

Why the medication is being prescribed?

Management of psychiatric states such as:

- Major Depression and other depressive disorders
    SSRI's
- Anxiety Disorders
    SSRI's
- Body Dysmorphic Disorder and Trichotillomania
    May respond to SSRIs
- Eating Disorders
    High doses of SSRIs are effective in reducing bingeing
    and purging behaviours.
- Smoking cessation
    Bupropion (Zyban) has been shown to be effective in
    smoking cessation when used as a component of an
    overall therapeutic program.
- Functional Enuresis
    Often is treated with Imipramine.
- These states influence occurrence and severity of behaviours, such as aggression, impulsive behaviour, self-injurious behaviour and possibly stereotypy.

How long before antidepressants become effective?

Antidepressants are used for treatment of major depression and other depressive disorders. Over 50% of depressed patients will fully recover when an appropriate amount of any antidepressant is used for at least 6 weeks; whereas, 10-15% will experience some improvement and 20-30% will not improve significantly.

How long is it necessary to take the medication?

SSRIs have a better side effect profile than do other antidepressants. Therefore, they are usually used as the first line of treatment. If there is no improvement after four weeks of the initial dosage, three weeks on a higher dosage should be attempted. If no improvement is noted, the diagnosis of depression needs to be re-evaluated. Then, in case the diagnosis is reconfirmed, other antidepressants should be tried, such as Manerix, Trazodone, and Venlafaxine.

After a first episode of major depression, treatment is recommended for at least 6 months with an antidepressant at the therapeutic dose to which the patient showed response. Thereafter, the antidepressant should be gradually reduced to diminish the risk of relapse, or the discontinuation syndrome.

What are the classes of antidepressants?

1.   Selective Serotonin Reuptake Inhibitors (SSRI)

As persons with developmental disability have lower seizure threshold, caution should be exersized at the speed of titration of the anti-depressant medication used. Caution should be also exersized when a long acting anti-depressant medication is used such as Fluoxatine in case the diagnosis is incorrect as the adverse effects will be felt for longer periods of time.

Table 3– SSRIs and Recommended Doses

Generic Name	Brand Name	Initial Dose (mg/d)	Maintenance Dose (mg/d)
Fluoxetine	Prozac	20 od	20-40
Fluvoxamine	Luvox	50 od	50-300
Paroxetine	Paxil	20 od	20-50
Sertraline	Zoloft	50 od	50-200
Citalopram	Celexa	20 od	20-40

*These are guidelines. Doses may vary on individual basis.

What are the SSRIs' adverse effects?

- Nausea, reduced appetite, vomiting, diarrhea, and gastrointestinal discomfort. These side effects may be dose limiting, or require therapy changes during treatment with SSRIs. It is possible to minimize these side effects by administering the medication with or after meals.
- SSRIs (especially Fluoxetine) may lead to agitation and restlessness at the start of the treatment. SSRIs occasionally may cause akathisia (sudden onset of inner restlessness, irritability, increased energy and insomnia), lasting from a few hours to a day; lowering the initial dose may be beneficial for the patient.
- When agitation associated with SSRIs causes sleep disturbance, many clinicians add Trazodone (Desyrel), a sedating anti-depressant, in low doses to alleviate insomnia.
- Other common side effects include excessive sweating, headache, insomnia, sedation, dizziness, and sexual dys-

function (changes in libido, impotence, ejaculatory or orgasmic disturbances).

- Other adverse effects include rash, dry mouth, urinary retention, weight gain (during long-term treatment).
- Abnormal lab results may occur with SSRIs.
- SSRIs have the benefit of being safe on overdose.
- SSRI withdrawal symptoms include influenza-like symptoms, dizziness, nausea, and insomnia; these symptoms may appear even with slow tapering of dosage.
- Serotonin syndrome is usually triggered by the use of multiple serotonergic drugs, and can be potentially lethal, but resolves with discontinuation of the medications.
- Red flags include: tremor, hypertension, tachycardia, diarrhea, myoclonus, ocular oscillations, and in a severe form, may lead to convulsions and even coma.

2. Tricyclic and Tetracyclic Antidepressants

Table 4– Tricyclic and Tetracyclic Antidepressants and

Generic Name	Brand Name	Initial Dose (mg/d)	Maintenance Dose (mg/d)
Amitriptyline	Elavil	25 tid	75-200
Clomipramine	Anafranil	25 od	75-300
Doxepin	Sinequan	25 tid	75-200
Imipramine	Tofranil	25 tid	75-300

Recommended Doses
* These are guidelines. Doses may vary on individual basis.
**ECG should be done prior to the commencement of TCA's and during their use.
***Slow titration is advisable unless otherwise indicated as persons with DD cannot communicate the adverse effects of these medications.

What are TCAs adverse effects?

- Common side effects: nausea, vomiting, and gastrointestinal discomfort.
- Anticholinergic effects include dry mouth, blurred vision, constipation, urinary hesitancy, tachycardia, and may impair memory.
- Most patients develop some tolerance to the dry mouth side effect over time. However, ongoing dry mouth may lead to problems with chewing, swallowing, speaking, increased risk of dental carries, denture fit and oral thrush. Treatment includes either stopping these medications, or changing with other medications that have a lower anticholinergic profile. In addition, other strategies include chewing sugarless gum or using sugarless candy, as both stimulate saliva production. For symptomatic relief, artificial saliva (e.g., Moi-Stir, Salivart or Oral Balance) may be beneficial for some patients. Finally, to diminish the risk of dental carries, use of sugarless food preparations is recommended.
- Constipation is a commonly occurring problem in people with DD. Constipation and bowel distention are significant side effects due to potentially severe complications such as obstruction. Therefore, patients taking drugs with anticholinergic properties need adequate monitoring. If constipation develops, dietary fiber, bulk laxatives, stool softeners, and osmotic agents are helpful strategies to use. Fluid intake is also very important in preventing constipation, with eight to ten glasses of water per day being recommended.
- Other adverse effects include sedation, carbohydrate craving, weight gain, orthostatic hypotension, cardiac effects, tremor, and seizure induction.

- TCAs may cause sexual dysfunction including changes in libido, impotence, or priapism (prolonged, painful erection) especially with Amitriptyline and Desipramine.
- TCA withdrawal may cause nausea, vomiting, diarrhea, abdominal cramps, chills, cold sweats, headache, and insomnia within two weeks of abrupt discontinuation.
- Red flags of TCA toxicity include dilated pupils, blurred vision, dry skin, hyperpyrexia, ileus, urinary retention, confusion, seizures, arrhythmias, and hypotension.
- TCAs overdose can be lethal.

3. Monoamine Oxidase Inhibitors (MAOI)

Table 5– MAOIs and Recommended Doses

Generic Name	Brand Name	Initial Dose (mg/d)	Maintenance Dose (mg/d)
Moclobemide	Manerix	100 tid	300-600

*These are guidelines. Doses may vary on individual basis.

What are MAOIs adverse effects?

- Most common are: postural hypotension (which may not appear until the third to sixth week of treatment), insomnia, agitation, sedation, and sexual dysfunction (impotence).
- Other adverse effects include weight change, dry mouth, constipation, and urinary retention.
- MAOIs may cause liver damage.
- MAOIs are the most likely to lower sezure threshold and should be only considered for truly resistant cases.

B. Antianxiety Medications

Table 6– Antianxiety Medications and Recommended Doses

Generic Name	Brand Name	Short Acting/ Long Acting	Initial Dose (mg/d)	Maintenance Dose (mg/d)
Alprazolam	Xanax	Short	0.25-0.5	0.5-1
Clonazepam	Rivotril	Long	0.25	0.5-1
Diazepam	Valium	Long	2.5	5-20
Lorazepam	Ativan	Short	1	1-4
Oxazepam	Serax	Short	10	15-60
Temazepam	Restoril	Short	15	15-30

*These are guidelines. Doses may vary on individual basis.

1. Benzodiazepines (BDZ)

How long before BDZs become effective?

There is a rapid onset of effects within hours. However, the full range clinical response may take several days.

Why is it being prescribed?

Management of psychiatric states, such as:

- Anxiety disorders
- Depression
- Bipolar type I illness
- Akathisia
- Alcohol withdrawal
- Insomnia

BDZ alone should only be used for a maximum of three weeks.
Long-term treatment of insomnia includes behavioural modification, relaxation techniques, and sleep hygiene.
May consider Trazodone as a non-addictive alternative to BDZ for treatment of insomnia.

How long is it necessary to take this medication?

It is recommended to minimize the use of long-acting BDZ beyond three months. In addition, short-acting BDZ should not be used for more than fourteen days.

What are BDZs side effects?

- All benzodiazepines can produce sedation and decrease available cognition.
- The use of benzodiazepines may lead to some impairment in memory and even impair new learning.
- Cautious use in elderly is advocated given increased sensitivity to sedation, memory impairment, ataxia, risk of falls.
- Hostility, disinhibition, self-injurious behaviour, and aggression are occasionally seen as paradoxical reactions to benzodiazepines, especially in people who exhibit evidence of stereotypical, self-injurious behaviours prior to starting treatment with BDZ.
- In case these paradoxical effects occur, close monitoring is advisable during discontinuation of the BDZ.
- BDZs may cause sexual dysfunction (changes in libido).
- BDZs can cause urinary retention.
- Abuse, tolerance and dependence potential
- Abnormal lab results may occur: thrombocytopenia.

- Discontinuation syndrome

  Discontinuation of BDZ should be done on a gradual basis, because rapid taper or abrupt discontinuation may lead to a withdrawal syndrome with symptoms such as rebound anxiety, insomnia, and weakness. In addition, the discontinuation syndrome may present with seizures, confusion, and psychotic symptoms. Furthermore, there is a higher likelihood of occurrence of these symptoms after discontinuation of shorter-acting agents. In these cases, one of the strategies used to decrease withdrawal symptoms is to switch a short-acting agent to a longer acting BDZ prior to starting the tapering. Finally, relapse of anxiety disorder need to be considered should symptoms continue for more than two weeks after stopping the medication.

- BDZ overdose.

  Overdose with BDZ alone has a favorable outcome; however, it may be fatal in association with alcohol, antidepressants, or antipsychotics.

  Flumazenil may be used to treat BDZ overdose.

2. Other Agents

(i) Buspirone

Generic Name	Brand Name	Initial Dose (mg/d)	Maintenance Dose (mg/d)
Buspirone	BuSpar	5 bid	10-30 bid

Table 7– Buspirone and Recommended Doses
*These are guidelines. Doses may vary on individual basis.
**Caution should be excersized when treating symptoms of anxiety when other mental disorders are involved.

Why is it being prescribed?

Management of psychiatric states, such as:

- anxiety disorders, in particular generalized anxiety disorder which may influence occurrence and severity of agitation and behavioural problems, including aggression and self-injury.

How long before it becomes effective?

- It takes two to three weeks to achieve its therapeutic effects.

What are its adverse effects?

- Headache, nausea, dizziness, and rarely insomnia.

(ii) <u>Beta-blockers</u>

Generic Name	Brand Name	Initial Dose (mg/d)	Maintenance Dose (mg/d)
Propranolol	Inderal	10-20 bid	20 bid-tid
Pindolol	Visken	5 bid	10 bid

Table 8– Beta-blockers and Recommended Doses
*These are guidelines. Doses may vary on individual basis.
** Caution Beta-blockers can aggravate depression in persons at risk.

Why is it being prescribed?

- Anxiety disorders, in particular social phobia-performance type (propranolol), or
- Lithium-induced postural tremor (propranolol)
- Neuroleptic-induced acute akathisia (propranolol); which may influence occurrence and severity of behaviours, such as impulsivity, aggression (propranolol, pindolol)

How long before it becomes effective?

- Beta-adrenergic blockers act within one hour of administration.
- For treatment of chronic disorders, the therapeutic effects may not be seen until four to eight weeks of treatment.
- Treatment should never be discontinued abruptly.
- Beta-blockers need to be discontinued if heart rate is less than 50, systolic blood pressure is less than 90, or if symptoms such as dizziness, ataxia, and wheezing occur.

C. Sedatives/Hypnotics

These agents fall into several pharmacological categories:

- Antihistamines (e.g., Hydoxyzine, Dyphenhydramine)
- Barbiturates (e.g., Phenobarbital, Amobarbital sodium)
- Benzodiazepines
- Chloral derivatives (e.g., Chloral hydrate, Paraldehyde)
- Cyclopyrrolone derivatives (e.g., Zopiclone)
- Imidazopyridine agent (e.g., Zolpidem)
- L-Tryptophan

Mood Stabilizers

Generic Name	Brand Name	Initial Dose (mg/d)	Maint Dose (mg/d)
Lithium Carbonate	Carbolith, Lithane	300 bid-tid	1200-1800
Lithium Carbonate Long Action	Duralith	300 bid	600-1800

Table 9– Mood Stabilizers and Recommended Doses
**These are guidelines, doses may vary on individual basis (mg/kg body weight)

Why is it being prescribed?

Management for psychiatric states such as:

- Acute mania and prophylaxis of bipolar illness type I
- Cyclothymic disorder
- Cycloid psychosis (especially in Prader-Willi syndrome
- These states may influence occurrence and severity of be-haviours such as aggression

How long before it becomes effective?

- Response to lithium alone can take 1 to 3 weeks of treat-ment at therapeutic concentrations.

How long is necessary to use mood stabilizers?

Mood stabilizer maintenance treatment is indicated in several circumstances:

- after the first episode in patients who are adolescents or 30 years or older;
- male gender;
- positive family history of bipolar disorder;
- poor support network;
- history of severe first episode;
- high suicide risk.

What are lithium's adverse effects?

- Nausea, vomiting, and gastrointestinal discomfort may occur. It is possible to significantly reduce these adverse effects by taking the medication with meals, by using sustained-release preparations (e.g., Lithobid), or by giving smaller doses more often.
- Diarrhea may occur in patients treated with lithium, particularly during the first six months of treatment, and when serum lithium levels exceed 0.8. This side effect is important because dehydration may lead to accumulation of lithium with potential intoxication.
- Weight gain may occur. It is difficult to treat, and it may be partially reversible if lithium is stopped.
- Sexual dysfunction such as priapism may be experienced.
- Intention tremor of upper extremities may be present.
- Lithium-induced hypothyroidism increases with increasing duration of treatment. People with developmental disabilities may not be able to report the symptoms of hypothyroidism. Therefore, the thyroid functioning should be adequately monitored.
- Nephrogenic diabetes insipidus (NDI) are frequently caused by lithium treatment.
- People with developmental disabilities should be carefully monitored for polyuria. Increased urine volume may be

problematic to recognize in patients who are incontinent, and wear diapers. In addition, patients with developmental disabilities may have difficulties communicating increased thirst or adequately increasing their liquid intake to counteract the effects of polyuria. Moreover, these people may be at higher risk for developing dehydration and severe lithium intoxication. It is essential to address the misconception that polyuria results from excessive fluid intake because restricting liquids may lead to potential intoxication. Therefore, people with lithium related polyuria should be encouraged to have free access to liquids.

- Cardiac dysrhythmias may occur with lithium. Usually lithium must be discontinued.
- Dermatological effects can include worsening of eczema, acne, and psoriatic lesions.
- Cognitive effects are reported by some patients, including impaired memory, slowed reaction times, and sedation.
- Abnormal lab results may be observed.
- Lithium toxicity red flags include coarse tremor, speech difficulty, ataxia, confusion, myoclonus, seizures. Lithium toxicity is a medical emergency; management includes discontinuation of lithium, and rehydration; hemodialysis is required in most serious cases.

D. Anticonvulsants

Table 9– Anticonvulsants and Recommended Doses

Generic Name	Brand Name	Initial Dose (mg/d)	Maint Dose (mg/d)	Blood Level (mmol/L)
Valproic Acid	Depakene	250 bid	1000-3000	350-700
Divalproex Na	Epival	250 bid	1000-3000	350-700
Carbamazepine	Tegretol	100 bid	800-1200	17-50
Lamotrigine	Lamictal	12.5-25 hs	50-250 bid	Nil
Gabapentin	Neurontin	300 od	600-1200	Nil
Topiramate	Topamax	25 bid	200-400	Nil

**These are guidelines, doses may vary on individual basis (mg/kg body weight)

1. Carbamazepine

Why is it being prescribed?

Management of psychiatric states such as:

- Acute mania and maintenance treatment of bipolar disorder, mixed states and rapid cycling, or
- Seizure disorders.
- Treatment for these can influence the occurence and severity of outbursts and aggression; however, carbamazepine has been reported to produce hyperactivity, self-injury, or aggression.

How long before it becomes effective?

- The anticonvulsant and anti-pain effects have a rapid onset. However, the antimanic effects take longer to develop.

What are Carbamazepine's side effects?

- Common side effects include: dizziness, ataxia, dysarthria, clumsiness, sedation, and nausea
- Cardiac effects: conduction delay
- Cognitive effects: may impair memory in some people with DD.
- Liver damage
- Abnormal lab results may occur.

2. Valproic acid

Why is it being prescribed?

Management of psychiatric states such as:

- Acute mania; many clinicians consider valproic acid to be a first line antimanic agent for all ages except children under 10 due to its potential hepatotoxic side effects in this age group.
- Maintenance treatment of bipolar illness rapid cycling and mixed states (Valproic acid is the treatment of choice), or
- Seizure disorders.
- Treatment of these states may affect occurrence and frequency of associated behavioural outbursts.

How long before it becomes effective?

- The antimanic therapeutic effects may appear within one to two weeks of treatment.

What are its adverse effects?

- Similar to Carbamazepine

3. Gabapentin

Why is it being prescribed?

Management of medical/psychiatric states such as:

- Seizure disorders
- Anxiety disorders, in particular panic disorder and social phobia
- May be used to alleviate irritability

What are its adverse effects?

- Common side effects include sedation, ataxia, dizziness, dry mouth, and fatigue.

4. Lamotrigine

Why is it being prescribed?

Management of biomedical/psychiatric states, such as:

- Seizure disorders
- Maintenance treatment of bipolar illness, rapid cycling

What are its adverse effects?

- Common side effects include headache, dizziness, ataxia, blurred vision, fatigue, nausea
- Dermatological effects include a rash which may occur in up to 40% of patients, especially when initial doses are high. Severe rashes, which may lead to Stevens-Johnson syndrome, usually occur during the first eight weeks of treatment.

E. Antipsychotic Agents (Neuroleptics)

Table 11– Neuroleptics and Recommended Doses

Generic Name	Brand Name	Initial Dose (mg/d)	Maintenance Dose (mg/d)
Chlorpromazine	Largactil	50-100	200-400
Thioridazine	Mellaril	30-150	75-400
Metho-trimeprazine	Nozinan	25-100	100-200
Loxapine	Loxapac	10-50	60-100
Perphenazine	Trilafon	4-12	12-24
Trifluoperazine	Stelazine	2-15	6-20
Fluphenazine	Moditen	2.5-10	1-5
Haloperidol	Haldol	1.5-3	4-12
Pimozide	Orap	2-4	2-12

**Caution should be exercised in using high doses of neuroleptics because of possible severe side effects especially in persons with Developmental Disability who may not be able to communicate these side effects.

F. Atypical Antipsychotics

Table 12– Atypical Antipsychotics and Recommended Doses

Generic Name	Brand Name	Initial Dose (mg/d)	Maintenance Dose (mg/d)
Clozapine	Clozaril	12.5	200-600
Olanzapine	Zyprexa	5-10	10-20
Risperidone	Risperdal	0.5-1	1-6
Quetiapine	Seroquel	50	300-750

Why are they being prescribed?

Management of psychiatric states such as:

- Psychoses, including schizophrenia, schizoaffective disorder, delusional disorder, acute mania, and secondary psychoses occurring in the context of dementia, brain tumors, Huntington disease, substance abuse.
- Movement disorders such as Huntington disease and Tourette's disorder.
- Management of acute, uncontrollable, severe agitation and violent behaviour, or stereotypical and self-injurious behaviour.

How long is it necessary to take this medication?

- The duration of therapy with neuroleptics varies with the nature of the targeted diagnosis, or behaviour for which medication was initiated. In patients who are suffering from schizophrenia, antipsychotics are recommended to be continued for two years for the first episode, five years for the second relapse, and may require indefinite maintenance after the third relapse. When anti-psychotics are used to manage severe maladaptive behaviors, attempts should be made to treat the underlying causes if identifiable and discontinue them as soon as possible.

What are antipsychotics' adverse effects?

- Convulsant effects may occur.
- Endocrinological effects may occur.
- Cardiac effects may occur especially with low potency neuroleptics (e.g., Thioridazine).
- Orthostatic hypotension occurs especially with low potency neuroleptics during the first few days of treatment; however, tolerance usually develops rapidly.
- It is important to monitor the blood pressure (lying and standing) during the first few days.
- Sexual side effects such as impotence or ejaculatory and orgasmic disturbances ay be experienced with antipsychotics, expecially Thioridazine. Clozapine and Risperidone may cause priapism.
- Most neuroleptics may lead to weight gain.
- Other side effects may include liver damage, urinary retention and dysphagia.
- Neurological effects may include acute, dose-related neuroleptics-induced movement abnormalities, described as extrapyramidal side effects (EPSE). EPSE occur in approximately one third of people with developmental disabilities receive neuroleptics. Symptoms usually appear relatively early in the course of therapy with neuroleptics,

especially with more frequent or larger doses, are reversible with discontinuation of medication, and respond to treatment with anticholinergic, anti-Parkinson medications. The EPSE include acute dystonia, neuroleptic- induced Parkinsonism, and acute akathisia (Marsden et al, 1981; Bodfish et al, 1997).

- Tardive dyskinesia (TD) is a movement disorder presenting with frequent, repetitive, involuntary movements of the lips, tongue, jaw, face, trunk, or limbs. These abnormal involuntary movements may be exacerbated by emotional stress. In addition, repetitive motor activities or fine motor tasks may worsen TD. On the other hand, trying to voluntarily control these symptoms may either relieve or accentuate the abnormal movements. However, TD symptoms may diminish with relaxation, and are absent during sleep. The prevalence of TD in the population with DD is quite high. Up to one third of children and adults receiving neuroleptic medication have been reported to develop TD. Risk factors for TD include length and degree of neuroleptic exposure, dosage and age. However, TD may appear in persons without histories of neuroleptic exposure.

- Neuroleptic malignant syndrome (NMS) is a rare, but potentially fatal adverse effect of all antipsychotics. NMS symptoms include muscle rigidity (lead pipe rigidity) or catatonia, instability of the autonomic nervous system (hypertension or labile blood pressure, arrhythmias, dilated pupils, sweating, and incontinence), rapid onset of fever, and altered mental status (confusion, agitation, stupor). (Boyd, 1993).

    Treatment involves stopping the causative medication, adequate hydration, and possibly using a dopamine agonist (Bromocriptine), or a muscle relaxant (Dantrolene)

- Antipsychotic overdose:

  Signs and symptoms of overdose include dilated pupils, EPSE, increased heart rate, and low blood pressure. The overdose usually has a favorable prognosis
  except for Thioridazine and Mesoridazine due to their
  cardiotoxic side effects. In addition, the outcome of
  neuroleptic medication overdose is more guarded in the
  presence of alcohol and benzodiazepines; complications include delirium, respiratory depression, and seizures.

- Neuroleptic withdrawal symptoms:

  Nausea, vomiting, decreased appetite, behavioural
  changes, decreased sleep, sweating, abnormal move
  ments, and seizures have been reported. These
  symptoms usually occur after long-term treatment, and
  an abrupt discontinuation of therapy.

  A gradual reduction of 10% to 25% of the original dose
  every two to four weeks may be helpful in avoiding or
  minimizing these withdrawal symptoms. Low-dose
  Lorazepam or Propranolol may be helpful in managing
  these side effects.

- Atypical antipsychotics have less side effects than do typical neuroleptics.

G. Stimulants

Table 13– Stimulants and Recommended Doses

Generic Name	Brand Name	Initial Dose (mg/d)	Maintenance Dose (mg/d)
Methylphenidate	Ritalin	2.5 am & noon	5-40
Methylphenidate	Ritalin SR	20 am	20-40
Dextro-amphetamine	Dexedrine	2.5-5 od	5-40
Dextro-amphetamine	Dexedrine Spansules	10od	10-40

Why are they being prescribed?

- Attention deficit hyperactivity disorder (ADHD)

What are their adverse effects?

- Stimulants may exacerbate tics, obsessions, compulsions, epilepsy, anxiety, or psychotic features.
- Growth delay, anorexia and weight loss in children
- Difficulty falling asleep, nightmares
- Irritability, anxiety
- Hair loss and hematological side effects are rare.
- Potential for abuse and tolerance
- Stimulants withdrawal may lead to symptoms of dysphoria, depression, fatigue, hypersomnia, and hyperphagia.

Summary

This chapter provides the reader with a list of prescribed medications (pharmacotherapy) used in persons with dual diagnosis - (developmental disability and mental disorders). An attempt has been made to encourage clinicians, caregivers, and families to use psychotropic medications only when a psychiatric diagnosis is supported. It is understood that from time to time these medications may be used to manage acute and violent behaviours. In these instances, however, every effort has to be made to initiate other rehabilitative interventions whenever possible. The various categories of these pharmacological treatments are outlined in groups that are addressing different mental health/behaviour problems. This chapter also offers a list of desirable/ undesirable (side-effects) effects of all medications listed. An attempt has been made to provide the severity and malignancy of the side effects in an effort to assist the reader in his/her clinical decisions as to the subsequent steps necessary to be followed in the resolution of the medical/ mental crises resulting from the medication used. Guidelines for use of medications in various ways (i.e., continuous, on an as per needed basis, in crisis) are also provided.

The most important steps to be followed in a situation where a client is thought to be suffering from mental disorder/s is the following Axis:

1. Think of mental disorder as a possible explanation of certain behaviour changes.
2. Assess the problem behaviour.
3. Diagnose the problem as a mental disorder.
4. Treat the problem with medication whenever appropriate.
5. Follow-up to determine:
    - efficacy of medication used.
    - explore the side-effects, if any.
    - treat the side-effects.
    - maintain a minimal level of medication necessary to address the problems.
    - physical checkup re other physiological functions that can become affected by the prolonged use of medication.

It is to be remembered that the client is in the centre of our caring, and that various pieces of the puzzle of wellness/disease are necessary to be in place in order to maximize the beneficial effects of all of the parts, and enhance the quality of life of persons with a dual diagnosis.

Do You Know?

1. What are the categories of psychotropic medications?
2. For each category of medication, describe indications, mechanism of action, duration of treatment, side effects, and conditions under which the drug should be discontinued.
3. How would you use psychotropic drugs in order to minimize their adverse reactions?
4. How would you monitor for side effects?
5. What are the protocols on how to use PRN medications?

Resources

Bezchlibnyk-Butler, K.Z. & Jeffries, J.J. (Eds.) (1998). **Clinical handbook of psychotropic drugs**, Eighth Revised Edition. Seattle, WA: Hogrefe & Huber Publishers.

Kaplan, H.I. & Sadock, B.J. (1997). **Synopsis of Psychiatry**, 8th edition, Baltimore, MA: Williams & Wilkins Company

Kutcher, S.P. (1997). **Child and adolescent psychopharmacology**. Philadelphia: W.B. Saunders Company

References

Bergman, J.D. (1995). Psychopharmacologic treatment of neuropsychiatric conditions in mental retardation. **Pediatric Psychopharmacology: Child and Adolescent Psychiatric Clinics of North America,** *4(2)*, 401-433.

Bergman, J.D. (1996). Pharmacologic interventions: Mental retardation. **Child and Adolescent Psychiatric Clinics of**

North America, *5(4)*, 853-880.

Bezchlibnyk-Butler, K.Z. & Jeffries, J.J. (Eds) (1998). **Clinical handbook of psychotropic drugs** (8th Revised Ed.) Seattle, WA: Hogrefe & Huber Publishers.

Bodfish, J.W., Newell, K.M., Sprague, R.L., Harper, V.N., & Lewis, M.H. (1997). Akathisia in adults with mental retardation: Development of the akathisia ratings of movement scale (ARMS). **American Journal on Mental Retardation, 101*(4)*,** 413-423.

Boyd, R.D. (1993). Neuroleptic malignant syndrome and mental retardation: Review and analysis of 29 cases. **American Journal on Mental Retardation, 98*(1)*,** 143-155.

Chouinard, G., Ross-Chouinard, A., Annagelle, L., & Jones, B. D. (1980). Extrapyriamidal symptom rating scale. **Canadian Journal of Neuroscience,** *8,* 164-166.

Dorland's Medical Dictionary (24th Ed.) Philadelphia: W.B. Saunders Company.

Guy, W. (1976). **Abnormal involuntary movement scale.** In ECDEU assessment manual for psychopharmacology (Revised). PHEW publication ADM 76-338 (pp. 534-537). Washington, DC: US Government Printing Office.

Kaplan, H.I. & Sadock, B.J. (1998). **Synopsis of psychiatry** (8th Ed.) Williams & Wilkins Company

Kutcher, S.P. (1997). **Child and adolescent psychopharmacology.** Philadelphia: W.B. Saunders Company

Kutcher, S. (2000). Practical clinical issues regarding child and adolescent psychopharmacology. **Child and Adolescent Psychiatric Clinics of North America, *9(1)*,** 245-260.

Madrid, A.L., State, M.W., & King, B.H. (2000). Pharmacologic management of psychiatric and behavioral symptoms in mental retardation. **Psychopharmacology: Child and Adolescent Psychiatric Clinics of North America, *9 (1)*,** 225-243

Marsden, C.D. & Schachter, M. (1981). Assessment of extrapyramidal disorders. **British Journal of Clinical Pharmacology, 11** *(2)*, 129-151

Medical Economic Date. (1966). **Physician's desk reference.** Monvale, NJ: Author.

Pary, R. (1993). Psychoactive drugs used with adults and elderly adults who have mental retardation. **American Journal on Mental Retardation,** *98(*1), 121-127

Reiss, S. & Aman, M.G. (1998). Psychotropic Medications and Developmental Disabilities. In S. Reiss & M.G. Aman (Eds.), **Psychotropic medications and developmental disabilities: The International Consensus Handbook** (pp. 45-72). Ohio State University: Nisonge Centre.

Santosh, P.J. & Baird, G. (1999). Psychopharmacotherapy in children and adults with intellectual disability. **LANCET,** *354*, 233-242

Sovner, R. & DesNoyers Hurley, A. (1985). Assessing the quality of psychotropic drug regimens prescribed for mentally retarded persons. **Psychiatric Aspects of Mental Retardation Reviews,** *8/9*, 31-38.

Silka, V.R. & DesNoyers Hurley, A. (1999). When do you decide to use an antipsychotic medication? **Mental Health Aspects of Developmental Disabilities,** *2(*1), 33-35

Acknowledgements

Special thanks to Steven Weisblatt for his invaluable contribution to this chapter.

Chapter 9

Building Responsive Service Systems

Laurie Dart, William Gapen, and Susan Morris

Learning Objectives

Readers will be able to:
1. Describe how ideology, culture and philosophy have influenced the development of services and systems for individuals with dual diagnosis;
2. Identify creative ways in which the gaps and barriers in service delivery have been addressed globally, with particular reference to Ontario;
3. Identify strategies for building a community support network and promoting ongoing participation of all stakeholders; and
4. Describe future challenges to bridging service sectors and building service delivery systems.

Introduction

Much work has been done in the past decade that focuses on the context or "system" within which individuals with complex needs are served. What has been learned is that attention to issues in the service delivery system is essential for successful outcomes. This chapter provides an overview of the evolution of this system's focus, and summarizes current thinking regarding effective systems of care for individuals with a dual diagnosis. A review of systems and service models in various jurisdictions provides the context for building systems. Key concepts are defined, service gaps and barriers are identified, the ideal continuum of service is described and, strategies for building networks and partnerships are reviewed. The chapter concludes with a discussion of future challenges.

Historically, services and supports for individuals with a dual diagnosis have been fragmented due to a lack of coordination and communication. One agency or service sector cannot meet all the needs of a person with a dual diagnosis. To be effective, service planning and delivery must be coordinated at the individual (consumer), programme, and system levels. By creating a responsive delivery system, service gaps can be addressed effectively, and in a timely manner. In addition, various community stakeholders can establish formal partnerships, building a community support network that results in better outcomes for individuals who present the most challenging difficulties.

This systemic approach to service planning and delivery promotes an integrated service system for individuals with a dual diagnosis, and in turn, provides a range of comprehensive supports involving a number of service providers and sectors. The goal is to build a *network* based on a continuum of integrated services and supports. Such a network can offer a wide range of options to a consumer, with specific services being provided by agencies working in partnership within the network.

The Context for Building Systems

For purposes of comparison and learning, we have chosen to describe briefly the evolution of service models for persons with a dual diagnosis in other countries and in Canada. This contextual framework is based on the assumption that culture, philosophy and economics influence system development and change. This overview provides a context for what is happening in Ontario. It should also alert us to the future challenges we may face as we better understand the factors impinging on the development of these systems and policies, and their implementation within the community.

The Metro Agencies' Treatment Continuum for Health (MATCH, 1996) document *Creating a Continuum of Supports and Services* describes community and government responses to the needs of persons with a dual diagnosis as dependent upon three broad factors:

- the degree of acknowledgement or denial of developmental disabilities;
- the degree of acknowledgement or denial of mental health needs for individuals with a developmental disability; and
- a community's response to the normalization and social integration movements.

These three factors provide a starting point from which to consider the evolution of services in various countries.

Service system change and development for vulnerable persons with complex needs can arise out of a variety of contexts or trends. Human rights movements, initially focussed on the oppression of specific racial or cultural communities, have often broadened to include other groups of people who are recognized as being marginalized or neglected. Any advocate must first name the group of individuals whose rights are being ignored or abused so that they become visible to mainstream society. By drawing attention to such individuals and the circumstances of their lives, advocacy efforts can then begin to shape the emerging service system on their behalf.

In most countries, the services and community supports for individuals with developmental disability, and people with mental health issues, emerged and grew separately as two discrete areas of concern. The challenge has been to further identify and create an understanding of those individuals with the dual diagnoses of both developmental disability *and* mental health issues. As the knowledge base and understanding of the needs of dually diagnosed individuals grew, along with the recognition that traditional ideologies were not useful in meeting their needs, communities have been challenged to rethink their systems of care in order to provide services to those with the most complex needs. Creating opportunities to learn through research and training, and funding of dedicated clinical resources has emerged in countries where the core values include the creation of a safety net for vulnerable people.

Frequently, the widely held community values that formed the basis for the original advocacy initiative are in conflict with the complex needs presented by people with a dual diagnosis. Jurisdictions that have been more successful in addressing the needs of persons with a dual diagnosis have first had to re-examine their core values as they relate to all persons with special needs. It is important to ensure that the service systems that have been created do not just comply with the policy or ideological framework, but that they operate to actually meet the range of needs for which they are designed. The concepts of normalization and integration as core values surrounding the development of services for individuals with developmental disabilities, therefore, must be massaged to fit the needs of individuals with a dual diagnosis. These factors provide a starting point from which to consider the evolution of services in various countries.

United States

In the United States the *Community Mental Health Retardation Facilities Construction Act* was established in 1963. This formed the origin of the development of systems of care based upon normalization and community integration principles. Social change agendas, founded upon the belief that individuals with a developmental disability should no longer be hidden away in institutions, but rather, included in the life of communities. They resulted in community living alternative care environments, and began the ongoing downsizing of public institutions. However, until the 1990's, many of the individuals with a developmental disability and accompanying mental illness continued to be housed in institutional care settings.

As community integration became the norm for individuals with a developmental disability, legal avenues (e.g., class action suits) were sought to improve the care of those with more complex needs both within institutional facilities and in the community. Despite efforts to ensure that entitlement agendas included those with the most complex needs, access to appropriate, individualized care is still uncertain for individuals with a dual diagnosis, since community agencies serving persons with developmental disabilities continue to screen out the clients with more complex needs. However, efforts are being made to create a diverse array of service options within the community, and in institutional settings that can accommodate those with higher needs.

It is interesting to note that in the United States, the services for persons with a dual diagnosis have emerged primarily out of the service system for mental retardation. This has meant that policy and community initiatives for serving individuals with a dual diagnosis must grapple with how to effectively meet the needs of this group within the context of normalization and community integration values, while, at the same time, recognizing that some individuals do need more intensive and specialized care. Being rooted in the developmental service system also creates challenges for individuals with a dual diagnosis who require access to appropriate mental health services. Menolascino (1994) notes that, despite apparent legislative entitlement to services for persons with a developmental disability, the services that are actually publicly funded are limited. Such examples of conflict arising between values and funding realities appear to be closely related to the fact that other mainstream needs drive political agendas. Conversely, the needs of more vulnerable populations that go beyond safe and protective care models of service, are more difficult to address, since they require the populace to understand complex concepts, and to support a range of service options that may require sophisticated funding structures. The result seems to be what has been called a "cobbled together" funding package (from private insurance, base funding, *Medicaid* and federal grants) to create the individualized services needed.

Sweden

In Sweden, the law clearly articulates that persons with a developmental disability are entitled to the same rights as other members of society (Dosen, 1993). However, by assuming fair and appropriate access to the mental health system for persons with a developmental disability, a service gap has actually been created, in that there is no recognition that specialized services are needed. A well-intentioned commitment to entitlement can effectively become a barrier to the creation of much needed services for those with complex needs. Similar to the challenges faced in the United States, creating specialized services for persons with a dual diagnosis appears to fly in the face of normalization principles upon which all other developmental services are based.

United Kingdom

Alternatively, in the United Kingdom, developmental disability is a psychiatric speciality; hence, a strong clinical base has been created for research and mental health intervention for those with a dual diagnosis. Education and training are enshrined within various professional schools (e.g., psychiatry, nursing). The challenge arises again, however, with the influence of normalization ideology, but in this case, from a different perspective and sector. How should services for persons with a dual diagnosis be organized – within the mainstream of psychiatric services, or as specialized services (i.e., separate from either sector)? How can successful community integration best be supported for people who have very specialized needs?

Italy

In Italy a long-standing influence on the development of services for persons with a dual diagnosis has been a cultural difficulty in accepting the diagnosis of developmental disability. With this as a back-drop to policy and community directions, the shift from institutional care of persons with a developmental disability to community care actually became a shift to family-based care models with minimal organized government-funded supports, and mental health interventions only for those with the most severe needs. In this case, the gap in government-sponsored supports due to a lack of public outcry led to the existence of several private institutions and clinics run by religious organizations (Dosen, 1993).

Other Countries (e.g., Germany, Belgium, Switzerland)

Other countries (e.g., Germany, Belgium, Switzerland, and, to some extent, Canada) until very recently, have failed to integrate in any meaningful way the psychiatric with the developmental or behavioural perspectives. The reasons are varied but some similar themes emerge as follows: benign neglect (usually supported by continued institutional care models); a lack of political will to challenge the extent to which ideologies (e.g., normalization) can actually reduce services for some individuals even though they are intended to provide improved access and support; economic constraints; and/or competing priorities.

The Netherlands

Dosen (1993) notes that in the Netherlands, deinstitutionalization combined with the adoption of normalization principles in

the 1970's, brought attention to the shortage of psychiatric resources for people with a developmental disability. Traditional community psychiatric services were directed towards
individuals with higher intellectual levels, many of whom
could effectively access services on their own, thus reinforcing
the service gap.

Canada (Ontario in particular)

Canada has traditionally had a well-articulated commitment to
a publicly funded health care system. Programme delivery responsibilities are assigned to the provinces. Services for individuals with developmental disabilities and mental health
needs are designed and delivered on a provincial level, with
the result that there is no national vision or approach for persons with a dual diagnosis. Ontario provides a vivid example
of the impact of culture, ideology, economic challenges and
priorities upon the development of models of care for individuals with a dual diagnosis (Puddephatt & Sussman, 1994).

In the 1800s, institutional care in Ontario was established to
shelter and protect both individuals with mental illness and
with a developmental disability (both conditions were viewed
as untreatable). Later, these same settings were seen as places
to keep these "undesirables" from being a "danger" to the rest
of society. Also at that time, with the growth in the field of
psychiatry and insight-oriented interventions, individuals with
a developmental disability were excluded from psychiatric settings because they "drained" resources and services needed for
the mentally ill. The resultant facilities for persons with developmental disabilities included those with a dual diagnosis who,
because of their behaviours, were often segregated into separate units, and over time were provided with some form of

treatment, depending upon the clinical will and interest of the psychiatric resources.

In 1974, the Ontario *Developmental Services Act* moved the responsibility for individuals with a developmental disability from the jurisdiction of the Ministry of Health to the Ministry of Community and Social Services. This served to affirm that individuals with a developmental disability are not "ill", but rather, are in need of appropriate supports to live as freely as possible and to the best of their abilities. Across Canada, normalization became the philosophy behind significant deinstitutionalization activity. However, typically those individuals with the most challenging behaviours and complex mental health needs continued to be served in the remaining specialized units either within the provincial psychiatric hospitals, or the institutions serving this population.

Similar to other jurisdictions already mentioned, Ontario struggled to create a useful way of understanding and meeting the needs of persons with a dual diagnosis. Defining the problem as "behavioural" or "psychiatric" created a continual shifting back and forth of service responsibility between programmes funded by the Ministry of Health, and services funded by the Ministry of Community and Social Services. This situation was exacerbated by the fact that there was no real knowledge base or expertise that integrated the various professional and community perspectives of the needs and potential for successful intervention. Individuals who were released to the community tended to be referred back and forth between the different service systems, sectors and programmes, while professionals entering either the developmental services or the mental health fields came with no training or experience in serving individuals with dual diagnosis.

In the last ten years, in many areas of Canada, there have been significant changes in the understanding of the needs of persons with a dual diagnosis, both clinically and at the service systems level. In its simplest form, we now recognize the need for a multi-systemic, integrated and comprehensive assessment of the needs of each individual and his/her environment and natural supports. We know also that, based upon this assessment, the components of the individualized service plan must fit together in a way that is flexible, creative, and seamless, virtually eliminating jurisdictional and professional barriers to appropriate service.

Today's challenge in Ontario is to create a system for serving persons with dual diagnosis based upon a well-documented and agreed-upon vision. In the early 1990's the Ministries of Health and Community and Social Services participated in an Inter-ministerial Dual Diagnosis Initiative. An outcome of this initiative was the development of the *Joint Policy Guidelines for the Provision of Services to Persons with a Dual Diagnosis, 1997*, in which this vision is articulated.

At the regional level, implementation strategies are currently in various stages of development, depending upon local organization and government commitments, competing priorities, and a willingness to work together across system boundaries. For example, in an effort to support the intent of the *Joint Policy Guidelines*, the Ontario Ministry of Health has at various times required its funded providers (e.g., hospitals, community mental health programmes) to describe in their annual operating plans how they intend to address the guidelines. As well, the guidelines have been integrated into the most recent mental health policy framework and implementation plans. The Ministry of Community and Social Services' *Making Ser-*

vices Work for People policy does not directly reference or include the *Joint Policy Guidelines*. However, at the local community level, the needs of the group of persons with dual diagnosis continue to be highlighted and identified as requiring special cross-sectoral attention. The response to the guidelines at the developmental service provider level is therefore, primarily voluntary in nature, based upon local partnerships that enhance the capacity of the providers to serve individuals with a dual diagnosis by a sharing or exchange of resources. Examples of this are described in more detail below.

Key Concepts in Understanding Service Systems

The issues and concepts underpinning responsive service systems for persons with a dual diagnosis must be understood at three levels: individual, programme, and system (see Figure 1). In the following section we discuss each of these levels.

Individual Level

A key feature of successful services for individuals with a dual diagnosis is that each person is viewed within the broader context of his or her environment (McKinnon, 1999). The environmental context includes where the person lives and works, family and friends (informal networks), and services, groups and organizations (formal networks) with which s/he interacts on a daily basis (Trainor, Pomeroy, & Pape, 1993). For individuals who require a range of services and supports, one must use a systemic approach that de-emphasizes the person as 'the problem' and considers the individual within the context of his/her total environment.

It is important to be aware of the quality of the connections an individual may have with the various components of his/her network. Are they strong? Tenuous? Weak? Understanding the impact of these connections, both on the consumer and on the other members of his/her informal and formal networks, is important in assessing the individual's social environment. Understanding the nature of these network transactions allows one to begin thinking about possible points of intervention in terms of strengthening an individual's network of support (Compton & Galoway, 1994). Viewing the person in light of his or her total environment provides a useful framework for identifying how the whole system can be strengthened in order to provide more support to different network components (e.g., family, service providers).

Figure 1– Levels of Support and Services

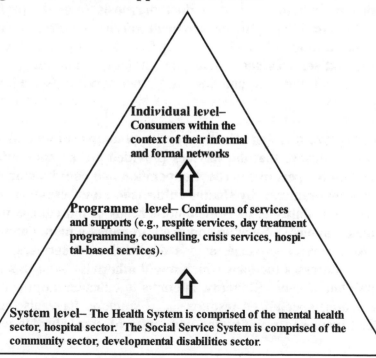

A person with a dual diagnosis who has a life threatening illness, and who is on probation, may be involved with a number of services that help support the physical, emotional and social aspects of his/her life. These might include specialized services offered through the mental health, developmental, probation and parole, and hospital service sectors. Incorporating this concept of networks with the biopsychosocial approach to assessment and intervention provides the necessary framework for examining how and where supports may work together in a cross-sector fashion, and thus, an integrated plan of care can be developed.

Programme Level

The programme level refers to the actual services that are provided to individuals with a dual diagnosis (e.g., a specific agency providing case management services). Programmes include a range of services drawn from a continuum of supports and services such as respite services, counselling, residential and day programming, and other services (see Figure 1).

The key to providing effective service planning for an individual is to ensure that the services provided are an appropriate match to the person's needs. Cooperation and coordination between programmes, by sharing information and resources, enhances the ability to meet the unique needs of individuals with a dual diagnosis. Such an approach promotes a more comprehensive service package, avoids duplication of services, and better addresses the gaps which might otherwise exist in a client's plan of care. Similarly, attempts to enhance programmes by adding specialized resources and supports have also provided increased stability and continuity of care. In this way, the continuum of supports and services includes those particular programmes that best meet the needs of the individual, while also supporting all involved with implementing the care plan.

System Level

"System" is a broad term referring to inter-connected parts, which form a complex unity (MATCH, 1996). The major components of a system are called "sectors". For example, the mental health sector (which is comprised of a range of residential, day programme, support and treatment services) is a component of the broader health system. Other sectors within the health system include hospitals and long term care. Similarly, the developmental service sector (also comprised of a range of residential, day programme, support and treatment services) is a component of the broader social service system. Other sectors within the social service system include income maintenance, and child welfare. Given the range and complexity of needs of individuals with a dual diagnosis and their families and caregivers, it is not unusual for various sectors within and across a number of systems to be involved in their care.

Service Gaps and Barriers

From the above discussions regarding the context of service system development, and individual, programme and system level perspectives, one can see how the concept of a continuum of services and supports begins to emerge. Described below is a summary of the gaps and barriers that are often identified by consumers, families and service providers regarding services for individuals with a dual diagnosis.

The Metro Agencies Representatives Council (MARC) report *A Continuum of Service for Persons with a Dual Diagnosis*, June, 1989, is an Ontario report that succinctly summarized seven key service issues or gaps. They are:

1. fragmentation of assessment and treatment;
2. knowledge gaps;
3. failure of existing community support systems to meet the needs of persons with a dual diagnosis;
4. problems with access to mental health services, and lack of resources for discharge from psychiatric units and facilities;
5. mental health services which do exist are only at the most intensive level;
6. lack of specialized treatment and care options for the fragile client; and
7. specialized psychiatric treatment programmes for the developmentally handicapped serve only those in the mild to moderate range of intellectual functioning.

The report also describes common barriers to effective treatment planning, such as the longstanding debate about behavioural vs. psychiatric problems, which can result in the denial of mental health or developmental disability treatment due to causality. Another barrier is the lack of interaction between the staff of the mental health sector and the staff of the developmental service sector; this lack of interaction impedes development of new service responses within the separate sectors.

The Ideal Continuum of Services and Supports

When considering how to build responsive service systems that will effectively address the above gaps and barriers, one has to consider both processes as well as a range of services and supports. This section will examine the service and support elements of the continuum and give examples of creative development within these areas.

For the individual with a dual diagnosis (and his or her family members and caregivers), key service elements along the continuum of supports and services can be divided into three components:

1. Prevention and Early Intervention;
2. Intervention and Treatment; and
3. Long Term Care and Support.

This continuum is fully explained in the document: *Creating A Continuum of Supports and Services: A resource Document* (MATCH, 1996). It represents an ideal model that integrates developmental and mental health perspectives as well as individual, programme and system level approaches.

Following is a summary of these three main components of the continuum, with examples from Ontario and around the world, of how these components have been implemented to address individual, programme and system level gaps and barriers. The examples are not exhaustive, and are provided only to assist the reader in thinking creatively about his or her own experience and local situation. In reflecting on these examples, one cannot over-emphasize the impact of the local culture, philosophy and existing systems. In addition, one must take into consideration that the evolution of the services and systems described is a dynamic and ongoing, ever-changing process.

Prevention and Early Intervention

Prevention and early intervention services and supports focus on the aspects of health that affect the emotional well-being of individuals with a developmental disability. This component includes activities that build on the strengths and positive aspects of the individual, her caregivers and environment. Ensuring access to generic health services for individuals with a dual diagnosis is an example of a preventative and early intervention activity. It also includes anticipating potential crisis situations (e.g., identification of high-risk groups) so that supports and services can be implemented to prevent the escalation of difficulties and longer-term mental health problems.

Early Identification and Prevention *(system level)*

In the United Kingdom, generic and specialized developmental disability services are organized into small geographic units (e.g., 100,000 population). This facilitates early identification and diagnosis through a register of people and their special needs within each area. A range of services (from respite care, in-home support, and community services to specialized services) is accessed through a central point.

Information *(programme level)*

Many dual diagnosis committees have been initiated in Ontario in the last few years. These committees have cross-sector participation, and one of the first activities often identified for joint work involves the dissemination of information and educational booklets or packages.

Support Networks (*individual level*)

In eastern Nebraska, USA, a parent support programme within the developmental service sector offers parents support from other parents by providing such services as programme information and assistance through the initial stages of diagnosis.

Education and Training

Formal educational activities are underway in many locales across Ontario. These include: courses and certificate programmes at various community colleges and universities (*individual level*); internet-based training for medical students (*programme level*); as well as local, provincial and international workshops and conferences on various aspects of dual diagnosis. An effective *system level* approach in the United Kingdom has been the inclusion of developmental disabilities as a required part of the training for both psychiatrists and nurses.

Intervention and Treatment

Intervention and treatment services and supports attempt to reduce the impact of a condition, and to help the consumer return to his or her previous level of functioning. While the focus in this component is often to address acute needs, it obviously builds upon elements in the prevention and early intervention component. Work done at the intervention and treatment level, such as assessment, will frequently overlap with long term care and support elements. For example, assessment may identify a need for ongoing recreational supports or day programming.

Some programmes in this component have evolved to integrate more than one service element (e.g., crisis services combined with a specialized multidisciplinary assessment and treatment team). The degree to which this integration of services is evolved depends upon various factors including the stage of policy, inter-agency collaboration and service development in a jurisdiction. It should be noted that programmes often start at a relatively simple level. They may offer one or two elements of service (such as case conferencing with various stake-holders from other programmes and sectors, along with the involvement of a specialist), and then evolve to shared ways of working (e.g., protocols for dealing with crisis situations), and sharing of staff to offer services to specialized groups.

Depending on the stage of policy, inter-agency collaboration and service development in a jurisdiction, some programmes have evolved to integrate more than one service element within this component (e.g., crisis services combined with a specialized multidisciplinary assessment and treatment team). It should be noted, however, that often programmes start with what they have. They may offer one or two elements of service (such as case conferencing with various stakeholders from other programmes and sectors).

Specialized Community Services *(programme level)*

Many innovations in service have been initiated in response to the identified needs of clients attending a particular programme or agency. These specialized services have included anger management groups, sexuality programmes, multidisciplinary assessment and treatment, case management, grief counselling and social skills groups being offered by forensic, developmental, mental health, behaviour management or autism services. Examples of this phenomenon abound across Ontario where such programmes are found in developmental service agencies, child and adult mental health services, and community and psychiatric hospitals.

Transitional Day and Residential Programmes *(programme and system levels)*

A programme in eastern Nebraska (ENCOR) provides transitional group home and pre-vocational services to clients with a dual diagnosis and behaviour management problems for a period of six to twelve months. The transitional nature of EN-COR's services allows for the movement of individuals between programmes and sectors, such as from an in-patient or treatment milieu in the mental health sector to a long term care placement in the developmental sector. This model also integrates other elements within the intervention and treatment component, including a range of specialized residential and day community services, to meet the needs of those with more complex behavioural difficulties. It also provides training for psychiatry residents and other professionals.

Intake, Continuum of Crisis Services and Specialized Multidisciplinary Teams *(individual, programme and system levels)*

A lot of attention has been focused in various jurisdictions on specialized crisis and multidisciplinary teams. This has likely occurred in an effort to provide help to individuals with the most complex needs while, at the same time, working with the limited availability of expert resources in areas such as psychiatry, psychology, behaviour therapy, nursing and family or systems work. As a result, a specialized team model has been identified as a key component of various systems: such teams support and build on the strengths of the network of formal and informal service providers working with an individual.

The START programme, located outside of Boston, Massachusetts, is one of the original model services addressing the crisis and specialized multidisciplinary team components of the continuum. It combines 24-hour mobile crisis and respite services with provision of an access point to specialized assessment, treatment, and time-limited inpatient mental health services for individuals with a dual diagnosis. The services are provided by a multidisciplinary team and include psychology, psychiatry and social work (with staff trained at both the Masters and Bachelor degree levels).

Similar to the START model, but with adaptations for the larger urban environment, is the Griffin Community Support Network in Toronto, Ontario. The Griffin Community Support Network was developed to provide a comprehensive response to individuals with a dual diagnosis and their families in crisis situations, and is accessed via city-wide integrated crisis service mobile teams. This network provides community and general hospital safe beds, one-to-one contract workers, and a range of coordinated services (e.g., case management, assessment) through formal cross-sector partnership agreements with over fifty organizations. Services are coordinated for the consumer by a designated agency or agencies, but there is a shared responsibility among members of the network to provide the various treatment and support components.

A recent development is the expansion of the Griffin Community Support Network through integration with the Dual Diagnosis Resource Service. The Resource Service multidisciplinary community team provides specialized assessments, consultation, time-limited treatment, education, training, facilitation services and triage to a specialized inpatient unit. Together with the Support Network, this expanded programme serves as an intake point to a network of services. The goals are to mobilize, strengthen and empower the network, to improve communication, to develop problem-solving strategies, and to increase the supportive capacity of the network for all stakeholders.

Other Treatment and Intervention Models

In British Columbia, four community-based multidisciplinary specialized teams cover specific geographic areas across the province, and are accessed through local mental health centres. Their purpose is to prevent hospitalization, and to work with community caregivers to provide specialized assessment, diagnosis, consultation, treatment, training, back-up support, and mediation between caregivers and systems.

In the United Kingdom, local community mental handicap teams provide back-up to the generic developmental and mental health services. These teams are staffed to provide a range of services, including activities of daily living, behaviour management, family, work, medication consultation and information. They also have a program and system level responsibility for identifying mental health care needs.

In Rochester, New York, crisis intervention, respite care, and clinical assessment and treatment form a continuum of service provided by a multidisciplinary team of specialists in psychiatry, behaviour therapy, and psychology. The team that provides the services is associated both with the university and the developmental service sector.

In Minneapolis/St. Paul, Minnesota, mobile crisis services are integrated across several service sectors. This community based service approach includes access to 90 day respite care, and assessment and treatment services which can provide a range of intervention recommendations in developing a plan of care for a consumer. Staffing of this service constitutes a range of multi-disciplines including psychology, psychiatry, pharmacy, nursing, social work, and behaviour specialists.

Long Term Care and Support

Long term care and support services are required to reduce the level of continuing disability, and to prevent recurrence and relapses over time. As noted above, the services and supports in this component may overlap with those offered within other components of the continuum. Thus, the long term care and support component ultimately reflects the whole system of services, and its capacity to use its resources in a flexible manner.

There are two specific areas that deserve particular focus within this component:

- a range of programmes that meet basic needs such as housing or social recreation; and

- specialized supports and services that meet special and/ or chronic needs (e.g., a dual diagnosis day treatment programme within a long term care setting, or a long-term high support living situation in the community).

Range of Case Management/Individual Supports *(individual level)*

In Ontario, there are many examples of how the system has

evolved to extend the capacity of each sector to develop informal cross-sector teams around individual cases. For example, staff of a case management or community support service in the developmental service sector, working together with a case management programme in the mental health sector, have successfully expanded the range of options available for maintaining an individual in his or her community.

Medical and Mental Health Follow-up *(individual and programme level)*

Where geography and/or a lack of resources present many challenges, such as in the areas of central and northern Ontario, some psychiatric hospitals have designated staff with specialist knowledge in dual diagnosis (e.g., nursing, behaviour therapy, psychology) to travel to various locales to provide on-site services. These specialists work with local service providers, general practitioners and family members to create a multidisciplinary team providing follow-up and back-up support. In addition to specialized assessment, this arrangement allows for the ongoing monitoring and adjustment of interventions within the individual's home community.

Transitional Programmes and Services *(programme level)*

The ENCOR model described above is one example of a transitional programme. Another example is Home Base in Toronto, a new housing and support service developed to meet the needs of individuals with a dual diagnosis who are also homeless. A five-bed residence for a one-year length of stay is provided to individuals in transition from the shelter system. Linked to the Dual Diagnosis Resource Service and Support Network (previously described), these individuals will benefit from a coordinated system of supports.

A Range of Residential and Day Programmes, Life and Social Skills Training *(individual, programme and system levels)*

The various elements of the long term care and support component described facilitate an individual's successful integration within a community environment. At the same time, the level and nature of integration should be tailored to the needs of the individual (or group of individuals). Within this component, there are a range of services that represent a variety of approaches to integration. For example, in the area of employment, there are instances of work training activities across Ontario occurring in partnership with colleges, universities and private sector businesses.

Specialized services have also been developed within the long term care and support component of the continuum. Programmes have evolved within the developmental sector to meet the specific long term needs of some individuals. Examples of this can be found in housing programmes where smaller clusters of individuals with higher needs are living together in larger spaces. These arrangements balance individual need by providing a less stressful and safer environment with the goals of community integration and adequate staffing to ensure safety. As a further example, individuals with a history of sexual offences are placed in a specialized home where staff has access to specialists for consultation and support.

An example of a fully integrated community model is found in Italy's 'Open City' (NADD, 1995). Low cost housing is available to both persons with and without disabilities, situated within an existing community. Individuals with disabilities live, work and socialize with all members of the community.

Strategies for Building Community Support Networks and Partnerships

It is important to recognize that no single service or individual alone can achieve the goal of developing a support network, nor can a network be established through any single process or method. Rather, what is needed is an approach that ensures coordination among the various stakeholders. Both formal and informal supports and services must be involved in the development of the network, with formal service agreements signed by network participants outlining the specific services that each will provide. The different services provided by each network member reflect components of the range of resources needed to develop a comprehensive continuum of supports and services as described above. A systemic approach ensures that the essential components of the service continuum are included in the development of the support network. Formal agreements among participants also help to ensure that network members have a vested interest in the success of the network, that they are clear on their roles and responsibilities, and that they are formally recognized as a "network partner" with access to the range of resources provided by the network's continuum of supports and services.

Described below is a range of strategies that can be used when beginning to identify and develop the necessary linkages between community partners that will contribute to the network, and to the development of an integrated continuum of supports and services.

Reframing the Issue: Creating Shared Solutions

Frequently, caregivers and service providers involved with individuals with a dual diagnosis experience a range of concerns and feelings in trying to respond to the complexity of needs such individuals present. At an individual, programme and/or system level, stakeholders often anticipate hearing a blaming message that they are part of the problem. To get beyond these feelings, an approach must be used that promotes the ongoing participation of all the stakeholders. The initial objective is to facilitate an alliance that promotes a non-pejorative, non-judgmental approach, so that a joint process of building solutions together can be developed. Rather than focusing on the stakeholders as contributing to the problems and barriers that exist in providing services, it is important to emphasize that all perspectives are important and unique, and that opportunities exist to use the knowledge, experience and creativity of all stakeholders. Such an approach empowers stakeholders in the decision-making process, and allows them to begin seeing themselves as assets and important participants in providing the various elements needed in the service continuum.

Pacing Change

It is important to recognize that, when working with individuals or families, one must be sensitive to the readiness to change at a programme and systems level, and pace challenges accordingly. Programmes and service sectors often have an investment in maintaining the *status quo* when exploring the possibilities about modifying their services to better accommodate the needs of individuals with a dual diagnosis. This should not necessarily be seen as overt 'resistance' to providing service, but may be more of a 'reluctance' arising out of ambiguity about how to provide service, and a fear that committing resources differently may result in being totally consumed by the demands of these individuals. One must recognize this reluctance, its reasons, and be sensitive to the need to address people's concerns by beginning where they are in the process and building on the strengths they bring to the table.

Adopting a non-confrontational approach allows stakeholders to feel less vulnerable, thereby reducing their apparent reluctance, and making them more amenable to hearing the possibility of their participation as 'one' component in the development of an integrated continuum of services and supports. An approach that avoids conflict and confrontation, and provides support through access to additional resources (e.g., access to education and training opportunities), encourages stakeholders, and more often leads to their agreement to provide service and to be a network participant.

Engagement Flexibility

The principle of 'engagement flexibility' is critical to engaging community partners in the development of an integrated continuum of support and services. Similar to the strategies often used in providing community outreach to individuals with a dual diagnosis and their families, service providers may need to be engaged in a manner that reaches out and demonstrates genuineness and sensitivity towards their apprehensions about working with these challenging client situations. Service providers are often more willing to commit resources, or to use them differently if their concerns have been openly addressed, and their perspectives have been validated as being important and unique. To encourage such discussions, stakeholders need to feel safe in being open about their issues, particularly if they are addressing areas which may reflect their lack of knowledge or skill level in working with the dual diagnosis population. There are two strategies that can be particularly effective in achieving engagement flexibility: they are forums and facilitation.

Forums

The use of forums can be helpful in engaging partners. Often the simple process of bringing together representatives of various programmes and systems becomes the first step toward the development of more formal linkages. Effective forums are ones that carefully consider their purpose, membership and process.

Forums can be used flexibly and include: individual/case level discussions (e.g., case conferencing); buddy systems — i.e., partnerships between mental health and developmental service providers across sectors (e.g., joint case management); task groups or service and support development committees (e.g., local cross-sector planning and service implementation groups); and formal inter-ministerial linkages at all levels (e.g., Ministries of Health and Community and Social Services as in the MATCH Project, 1996). This range of forums and the mix of participants provide a variety of information, perspectives, knowledge, and strategies, and often lead to creative opportunities to examine how existing resources might be delivered more effectively. Forums also provide an opportunity for stakeholders to work collaboratively to identify service gaps within the continuum, and to begin joint planning on the type of coordinated service system that they want to develop.

In order to promote the ongoing participation of all stakeholders in the development of a coordinated network of supports, the forums must also reflect the components of an integrated continuum of supports and services. That is, the membership in these forums may include a variety of stakeholders who represent a range of services and sectors (e.g., consumer, developmental services, mental health services, health care providers, and correctional services). Naturally, the stakeholders that might be more willing to attend forums are those with a mandate that includes serving individuals with a dual diagnosis. Although many organizations or services may not see the relevance of their involvement in terms of their primary mandates, once at the table, there is usually a recognition of the value of the forum, and an awareness of just how many of their clients do, in fact, have a dual diagnosis.

Again, one key element to success with such forums is a supportive and safe environment in which stakeholders can have an open and honest discussion. In this way, participants are often better able to identify the types of supports and services their organizations might require to be able to respond flexibly to the needs of individuals with dual diagnosis. Through this sharing of experiences, participants begin to recognize that rather than restricting the consumers' right to service, by working together, they will be better able to meet the needs of consumers and their families. Often, these early joint discussions plant the seed for identifying how existing resources might work better together as a network: this can become the basis for forming an integrated continuum of supports and services.

Facilitation

The role of facilitation is to provide leadership and support between and among cross-sector activities that occur at the individual, programme and system levels. The facilitator's role is to ensure that the engagement of participants is carried out in an objective, flexible manner, and that all perspectives are heard. Also, the presence of a neutral third party can provide mediation and support to the various participants. Depending on the structure and resources of a community, the functions of a facilitator may be performed by one person/agency, or shared among a number of people/agencies. The facilitation role may include:

- (at the individual level) ensuring that services for a consumer are both coordinated and integrated between and among services and sectors to support the development of a comprehensive plan of care — including outreach to all relevant stakeholders in the service planning process and in the development of an individual support network;

- (at the programme level) seeking and developing formal, interagency, collaborative agreements with relevant stakeholders so that resources are adapted, accessible and coordinated between agencies that serve persons with a dual diagnosis (e.g., mental health programmes, developmental service agencies, probation and parole services); and

- (at the system level) identifying and formalizing contractual arrangements with other service delivery sectors that may support the development of an integrated continuum of supports and services (i.e., between children's and/or adult mental health and/or developmental and/or criminal justice and/or addiction sectors) as well as participating in municipal or regional cross-sector planning committees to ensure that the needs of individuals with a dual diagnosis, and service gaps and barriers, are addressed in service planning.

Outreach is also a very important function of the facilitation process. In the discussion above, regarding membership of forums, it was noted that some service providers (particularly those in the generic health and social services sectors) might not initially identify themselves as needing to be part of a process geared to serving individuals with dual diagnosis. Experience has shown that a valuable resource within the continuum may be overlooked or missed if additional outreach attempts are not made to include the more peripheral services or agencies.

It is important that the facilitation process, and/or the facilitator(s) involved in outreach and the development of a network or system design, fully utilize the strategies identified earlier with regard to 'reframing the issue', 'pacing change' and 'engagement flexibility' when building these partnerships. The premise of starting with an agency 'as it is', or being aware that one must be sensitive to pacing engagement efforts to an agency's readiness to change, have been useful concepts when working with stakeholders who may be reluctant to become involved in the planning and service delivery to the dual diagnosis population. Often, a good starting point in these situations is for the agency to be given an opportunity to identify its experiences and challenges in meeting the needs of individuals with a dual diagnosis. This provides a point from which the facilitator and/or other network members can connect and provide support. The fact that the current network partners feel supported by this initiative, and in turn, extend that feeling to the new member, may result in an agency's willingness to participate. The new member is also allowed to first observe and learn what the potential benefits of membership might be

Education and Training

A key aspect to the successful development and implementation of an integrated service continuum and support network is the existence of education and training opportunities for service providers at all levels. This is a common element within each of the components of the continuum of services and supports described earlier. It is also the most frequently identified need by family members, individual service providers, and planning groups, and the one programme activity that, if offered, often convinces stakeholders to commit to membership within a network of services.

Education regarding the nature and impact of dual diagnosis assists all stakeholders to identify strengths, recognize difficulties, and deter potential crisis situations. Training sessions must also develop and enhance direct practice skills and allow service providers to try out directly, (with supervision,) different intervention strategies that have been proven successful. In addition, access to ongoing expertise, consultation and support is necessary if stakeholders are to appreciate being part of the network, and to have the sense that they are part of a larger community working together to improve services for individuals with a dual diagnosis. The combination of education (focussed on the theoretical knowledge base) with training (focussed on the practical application of theory and development of skills) is frequently identified as one of the biggest benefits of being a member of a support network.

Frequently, service providers want one 'magical' agency to exist that can provide all of the education, training and consultation support that is required. In reality, in most geographic areas, this type of service does not exist. Most service organizations have their own limitations in what they can provide. What has been learned from various locales and dual diagnosis initiatives is that many of the providers involved in serving this population bring to the continuum of services and supports a piece of expertise that needs to be shared among the members of the network. (For example, a service that works more with the autistic population may have valuable insight into strategies that might work with an individual who has a dual diagnosis with features that reflect an attention deficit disorder.) The important role of specialized services in dual diagnosis education and training is clearly recognized, but our discussion in this section is intended to emphasize the point that stakeholders must be supported and validated for the expertise they may already possess in working with individuals who have a dual diagnosis.

At a staff level, caregivers may not be aware of, or may have minimized, the strengths they actually possess in working with individuals with a dual diagnosis. Within the context of a network of supports, these strengths can be identified and built upon. For example, members of the Griffin Community Support Network have begun to express greater confidence in their ability to work with individuals with a dual diagnosis. They realize that in most situations there are no magical solutions, but that perseverance and patience are often key to success. They also feel supported and encouraged, since they recognize that they are no longer alone in their attempt to serve this population, and are part of a larger continuum which promotes the concept of mutual aid.

To compliment the informal and community based educational initiatives, formal ongoing education and training activities are an equally important strategy for building community capacity. Examples of this have been discussed earlier in terms of university and college-level training. The results of such system-level commitments can include established standards of care within professional groups, and the development of advanced practice professionals (MATCH Project, 1996). Furthermore, research activity to identify best practices and outcomes is often a natural outcome of formal educational initiatives.

Future Challenges

In summary, this chapter has discussed the evolution to a system focus in service development for individuals with a dual diagnosis. It also presents the current thinking regarding how responsive systems of care for individuals with a dual diagnosis are built. Clearly, the last ten years in Ontario have been particularly productive in relation to service system development. This is so because of the collaboration that has occurred at the individual, programme and system levels. However, as noted earlier, progress in addressing the gaps and barriers has been, and will continue to be, dependent on how the tensions between values and funding are mediated, on political will, and on the capacity for cross-sector integration and flexibility at an individual, programme and system level. The dynamic nature of these issues means that the more we learn and do, the more we learn that there is more to do. Therefore, what follows is a brief overview of new and continuing challenges that face us in achieving a responsive service system for individuals with a dual diagnosis and their caregivers.

An ideal model of a continuum of supports and services for persons with a dual diagnosis is one that does not create artificial barriers and gaps based upon the age of the individual needing support. Typically, in many countries, the service system is strictly divided between services for children and services for adults, with the result that the knowledge and expertise is clearly split. Consequently, significant service gaps are created between the two service systems as the youth reaches transitional age when children's services end and adult services commence. Proposed solutions include:

- creating a seamless system that has no barriers, wherein specialized services for individuals with a dual diagnosis span the entire age range,

or alternatively,

- developing meaningful linkage and coordination mechanisms across the age jurisdictions that facilitate successful transition from one to the other.

In Ontario, this is a particular concern, since services for children are primarily the responsibility of the Ministry of Community and Social Services, or the Ministry of Education and Training, while the Ministry of Health funds mental health services for adults. Coordination and linkages, therefore, are a particular challenge. Where organizations with specialized service responsibility for individuals with a dual diagnosis exist, it may, therefore, be important for their responsibility to span the age groups, and to be expected to support successful transitions and effective inter-organizational linkages.

It is important that sound service evaluation practices be put in place to inform funders, consumers and service providers of what is working. In this way, learning will guide system and programme design. Development of validated outcome measures related to intervention strategies, along with meaningful consumer feedback data, will further enhance the likelihood that future developments are responsive and effective. Also, it is important to ensure that service providers have ongoing access to learning occurring in other jurisdictions and to information about services for other populations that also require integrated approaches and programme adaptation (e.g., psychogeriatric services). This is another means of ensuring that what we do today doesn't become what we need to undo tomorrow.

Recruitment of professionals, both specialists and advanced specialists, will continue to be a tremendous challenge for at least another decade if action is not taken. In order to address this situation, government leadership and initiatives are required immediately to support the development of formal education and training opportunities. Resource gaps in such fields as psychiatry, family practice, psychology, nursing, social work and generic front-line workers need to be addressed. Salary differentials across the sectors also have significant impact. Without committed resources to funding and human resource development, the capacity, expertise and support needed will continue to be inadequate.

Creation of inter-governmental infrastructures that provide opportunities and expectations to plan and organize best practice-policy and service delivery models. For instance, the Ontario Ministry of Health reorganized from a centralized to a regional model, which is consistent with the longstanding regionalization of the Ministry of Community and Social Services. Co-location of regional staff of each Ministry is occurring in some regions which over time, should enhance local planning, service development and cross sector integration.

Furthermore, cross-sector and inter-governmental planning groups at the local and provincial levels must have a mandate that includes reviewing and revising implementation strategies based upon new and emerging community needs and priorities. The Ministry of Community and Social Services is at a key point in the process of implementing its *Making Services Work for People* policy. However, almost consistently across the province, the local discussions have not successfully integrated issues related to serving the dual diagnosis population. At the same time, the Ministry of Health has initiated Mental Health Implementation Task Forces across the province with the mandate of moving forward on the *Making It Happen* policy. Both ministries identify 'coordinated access' in their policies, and the need for cross-sector linkages. This presents an opportunity for dual diagnosis to be placed on the agenda within these separate processes. Additionally, there are natural juncture points for these discussions to "cross the sectors" in relation to mental health mobile crisis services, developmental service case resolution mechanisms, and central information and coordinated access points.

Finally, inter-ministerial provincial commitment is required to ensure development of local continua of service and support with equitable access to specialized services across the province.

Do You Know?

1. The 3 factors that influence dual diagnosis service development
2. The difference between a system and a sector
3. In Ontario, what sectors serve individuals with a dual diagnosis
4. The network of supports and services that can assist an individual with a dual diagnosis
5. Examples within your local community of Prevention and Early Intervention services and supports
6. Two strategies that can be used at the individual level between different community partners that will provide a network of support for an individual who has a dual diagnosis and is on probation for assault

Resources

Creating A Continuum of Supports and Services — A Resource Document, March, 1996: Metro Agencies Treatment Continuum for Mental Health (MATCH) Project

This document provides an overview of the ideal continuum of supports and services for individuals with a dual diagnosis, their families and caregivers. It includes useful tools and additional papers such as a supports and services implementation guide with six stages in the assessment, intervention and treatment planning process, a review of the cross-sector process that provides structure for a shared community change process, a position paper on education highlighting the required attitudes, knowledge and skills, and a framework for an educational continuum.

Available for a small fee from Griffin Centre:
Telephone (416) 222-1153

References

Ayala, G.F. (1995). The open city: A model for genuine integration and inclusion into the community. *International Congress II on the Dually Diagnosed. Proceedings.* NADD, 95-96.

Compton, B.R. & Galoway, B. (1994). *Social work processes.* Pacific Grove, CA: Brooks/Cole Publishing Co.

Dosen, A. (1993). Development of mental health care for persons with handicaps in Europe. *The National Association for the Dually Diagnosed (NADD) Newsletter, 10(6),* 1-4.

Metro Agencies Treatment Continuum for Mental Health (MATCH) Project. (1996). *Creating a continuum of supports and services: A resource document.* Toronto: Author.

McKinnon, K.D. (1999). *Literature review: Findings and recommendations– Dual diagnosis (1986-1999).* A project prepared for Victoria County Association for Community Living.

Menolascino, F.J. (1994). Services for people with dual diagnosis in the USA: Recent advances and practices. In N. Bouras (Ed.), *Mental health in mental retardation* (pp. 343-352). New York, NY: Cambridge University Press.

Puddephat, A. & Sussman, S. (1994). Developing services in Canada: Ontario vignettes. In N. Bouras (Ed.), *Mental health in mental retardation* (p. 353-354). New York, NY: Cambridge University Press.

Trainor, J., Pomaroy, E., & Pape, B. (1993). A new framework for support. [On-line] Available: www.cmha.ca

Chapter 10

The Interdisciplinary Mental Health Team

Jane Summers, Kerry Boyd, Julie Reid, Judith Adamson,
Brenda Habjan, Valerie Gignac, and Charles Meister

Learning Objectives

Readers will be able to:

1. Describe the difference between an interdisciplinary and multidisciplinary team
2. Identify the roles and functions of health professionals on a dual diagnosis team
3. Define the role of the core team
4. Know how to get the most out of a consultation

Introduction

The purpose of this chapter is to describe the roles and functions of a number of health professionals who work with individuals with a dual diagnosis. While members of each discipline make specific contributions, their roles often overlap. We are using our interdisciplinary clinical service as the basis for the information that is presented in this chapter, but want to point out that dual diagnosis teams other than ours may look different (e.g., Ryan, Rodden & Sunada, 1991), depending on a variety of factors such as the philosophy and mandate of the team, its model of service delivery, level of funding, proximity to medical and hospital-based services, and the availability of trained professionals.

We begin this chapter by offering some general comments about issues of importance to the field of dual diagnosis. These comments will be followed by a definition of *interdisciplinary* and *multidisciplinary* health care teams. Although many people use these terms interchangeably, they are in fact different. Afterward, we will describe the roles and functions of the health professionals on our own dual diagnosis team, and use a case example to illustrate our model of service.

General Comments

1. Currently, there is no commonly accepted definition of dual diagnosis. Essential elements of dual diagnosis appear to be a developmental disability and a mental health issue. Our own particular view of mental health issues is fairly broad and encompasses psychiatric, behavioural, emotional and/or communication problems. This perspective is not necessarily shared by everyone; some service providers use a more narrow definition of mental health problems (for example, mental illness or psychiatric disorders).

2. Although there are a few training opportunities in Ontario that prepare professionals to work specifically with clients with a dual diagnosis, the demand for their services far exceeds the supply of trained professionals. Key aspects of the job are often under-recognized or under-funded, such as the importance of ongoing education and research; the

need to allot ample time for assessment and consultation since they often take longer; and the availability of flexible funding arrangements that permit health professionals to be compensated for indirect clinical time. As a result, it is often difficult to recruit and retain trained staff.

3. Particularly for clients with numerous or complex problems (cognitive, medical, psychiatric, neurological, behavioural, communicative), an approach to care is required that draws on information from multiple disciplines and treatment modalities (AACAP, 1999; Fahs, 1988; Silka & Hauser, 1997).

4. Our role as consultants necessitates that we work very closely with a core group of people who know the client best, and who play an ongoing and important role in his/ her life. This *core team* often consists of the client, family members, family physician, case manager and direct care staff, and may include the job coach, teacher, and other personnel. We depend on this core team to provide information during the assessment, and to play a key role in implementing our recommendations.

Definitions

Interdisciplinary Health Care Team

Members of two or more health professional disciplines, using a systematic and integrated approach based on their respective health disciplines' body of knowledge, work together to achieve common clinical goals. Decisions about the assessment, formulation and treatment of cases are made *collaboratively*. This type of approach is well-suited to clients with complex or multiple disabilities (Dowrick, 1996).

Multidisciplinary Health Care Team

Members of two or more health professional disciplines, draw-ing on their own discipline's body of knowledge, work sepa-rately to achieve clinical goals. Decisions about the assess-ment, formulation and treatment of cases are made *independ-ently*. This type of approach is well-suited to clients with few or less complicated disabilities (Dowrick, 1996).

Issues Affecting Interdisciplinary Team Functioning

Effective interdisciplinary team functioning does not occur merely because professionals are placed together who share responsibility for the same population, or who share the same physical workspace. Instead, what is most important is for team members to share a common framework and set of core values. Team members must often shift from a more hierar-chical or "top down" organizational approach to one in which they have equal status, and view each other with mutual re-spect and understanding. A number of obstacles exist that im-pede effective interdisciplinary teamwork; these include pre-conceived notions of differential status among disciplines; the existence of professional rivalries; and differences in philoso-phy or theoretical perspectives (Hollins, 1985; Koskie & Freeze, 2000). The following factors and conditions may pro-mote effective team functioning:

- At the outset, team members should devote sufficient time and attention to developing core group norms that promote and maintain interdependent functioning, including ways to resolve conflict within the team;

- Organizational and administrative supports may need to be engaged to assist with the process of team building, through the provision of mentors or facilitators to lead team building exercises and protected time in which to participate in these activities;
- A working environment that models and rewards interdisciplinary activities needs to be established (Sands, Stafford, & McClelland, 1990; Vinokur-Kaplan, 1995).

Roles and Functions of Mental Health Professionals on the Dual Diagnosis Team

Psychiatric Nursing

What is a Registered Nurse?

A Registered Nurse (RN) has obtained a nursing diploma or baccalaureate degree in nursing from an approved programme, has successfully passed a registration/licensure examination, and holds a certificate of registration with the College of Nurses of Ontario. After completing the basic training requirements, a nurse may choose an area of specialty (for example, psychiatry), and undergo additional training.

What is the role of the registered nurse in working with clients with a dual diagnosis?

1. Triage referrals and prioritize those who will be seen by the psychiatrist.

2. Coordinate the involvement of other mental health professionals on the interdisciplinary team.

3. Interview the client, family and caregivers (staff from the day and residential programme, support worker or case manager, teacher, advocate, as well as anyone who plays a significant role in the client's life).

4. Obtain background information from the family physician and other sources (previous assessments and involvement with other health professionals).

5. Prepare a summary of referral issues and clinical history.

6. Brief the psychiatrist prior to the psychiatric assessment via written summary and verbal report.

7. Coordinate the psychiatrist's schedule.

8. Provide follow-up and monitor the client's response to treatment.

9. Educate the client, family and caregivers about signs and symptoms of psychiatric disturbance, medication effects and side-effects, optimal use of a PRN (as-needed) medication, and a crisis response plan.

What is the role of the registered nurse on the interdisciplinary mental health team?

1. Provide the psychiatrist with background information that allows for the most efficient use of his/her time.

2. Contribute information regarding the cases that are seen by the psychiatrist, and assist other disciplines to identify clinical issues that may warrant a psychiatric assessment.

Psychiatry

What is a psychiatrist?

A psychiatrist is a medical doctor whose specialty is the study and treatment of mental disorders. After receiving an M.D. degree, the physician generally trains for four additional years at a university-based residency programme, and is required to pass written and oral examinations to be certified with the College of Physicians and Surgeons.

What is the role of the psychiatrist in working with clients with a dual diagnosis?

1. To identify psychiatric disorders and address mental health concerns. A further role of the developmental psychiatrist is to understand the communicative function of behaviours if the client cannot verbally report his/her inner experience. This requires a comprehensive assessment, and typically involves a review of the previous reports that have been gathered by the psychiatric nurse, information from other disciplines on the mental health team, and direct information that is obtained from interviewing the client (where this is possible), family members and caregivers. The clinical history can include the following:

    *   Personal information (e.g., age, living/work circumstances, information regarding the developmental disability)
    *   Identified problems:
        *   Baseline information (e.g., functional capabilities, strengths, weaknesses, personality, interests, quality of social interactions) to appreciate whether there has been a change in functioning that may in-

dicate a psychiatric disorder
- History of identified problems:
    - Past Psychiatric History
    - Developmental History
    - Medical History
    - Medication History
    - Social History
    - Educational History

2. Evaluate mental status. This involves direct observation/ interview in appropriate settings, and the clinical impressions that are formed regarding the client's state of consciousness, mood and affect, thinking, speech, motor behaviour, memory, concentration, judgment, and insight.

3. Work with the family physician and other health professionals to evaluate medical conditions that may give rise to or exacerbate mental health problems.

4. Synthesize information from past records, other disciplines and the psychiatric assessment into a biopsychosocial formulation. This may include a psychiatric diagnosis.

5. Formulate comprehensive management recommendations. Management often includes interventions offered by other disciplines (e.g., a behaviour plan, psychotherapy, communication aides) and/or pharmacological treatment.

6. Contact the family physician and/or members of the core team with findings and treatment recommendations.

7. Explain medication benefits/side-effects to the client or his/her substitute decision maker. Obtain informed con-

sent for proposed treatments.

8. Provide education regarding mental health issues to the client, his/her caregivers and other service providers.

What is the role of the psychiatrist on the interdisciplinary mental health team?

1. Contribute information about the client's mental functioning.

2. Consider and synthesize information from other disciplines.

3. Refer the client to other health professionals for further assessment and consultation as needed, and act as a liaison with the mental health team.

What types of questions can be answered by a psychiatric evaluation?

• Does the client have a diagnosable mental disorder?
• If so, what are the most appropriate form(s) of treatment?

Behaviour Therapy

What is a Behaviour Therapist?

A behaviour therapist assists people to change or modify their behaviour through the use of procedures that are based on scientific research. Behavioural therapies can be used to help people learn to behave in ways that are healthier from a physical and a mental health perspective. Common components of a behavioural approach include:

- selecting, defining and recording specific behaviours
- setting targets or goals for change
- breaking complex behaviours down into small steps
- using positive-based approaches to strengthen behaviour
- developing a system to monitor behaviour change

A behaviour therapist has usually obtained an undergraduate degree in psychology or another human service discipline, and has taken courses in the area of behaviour therapy or behaviour modification. Behaviour therapists work in a variety of settings, including hospitals and mental health centres, schools, correctional facilities, developmental service agencies, or private agencies. They are supervised by a registered psychologist in many places. Some Master's level behaviour therapists are registered with the College of Psychologists of Ontario, and have the title of Psychological Associate.

Behaviour therapists use behaviour analytic approaches to study the relationship between behaviour and the environmental context in which it occurs. Applied behaviour analysis, or ABA, is particularly well-suited to working with clients with cognitive and communication deficits who may display severe behaviour problems. Functional analysis is one of the most familiar aspects of applied behaviour analysis, and involves determining the function or purpose that a behaviour serves for a particular individual. Once the reason for the behaviour is understood, along with the conditions that serve to promote and maintain it, an intervention is developed that incorporates strategies for reducing the occurrence of the problem behaviour, and increasing the occurrence of a more "acceptable" behaviour (i.e., one that enhances the client's social and personal well-being).

What is the role of the behaviour therapist in working with clients with a dual diagnosis?

In collaboration with the client and/or caregivers, the behaviour therapist will:

1. Provide an *operational definition* of the target behaviour by describing it in a way that it can be observed and measured. For instance, anxiety may be defined as hand wringing, pacing, and crying.

2. Develop a recording system to track the behaviour, in terms of its *frequency* (how often it occurs), *duration* (how long it occurs for), and *intensity* (its severity), as well as its antecedents (what happens prior to the behaviour occurring), and consequences (what happens after the behaviour occurs). The behaviour therapist uses direct and indirect methods of observation.

Direct measures include:

- Frequency counts
- Antecedent-behaviour-consequence (ABC) data
- Interval recordings
- Scatterplots

Indirect measures include:
- Review of case history
- Interviews of client and caregivers
- Use of questionnaires

3. Set clear objectives or targets for behaviour change that

can be evaluated — for instance, John will use his relaxation strategies when he is becoming anxious in at least 8 of 10 anxiety-provoking situations.

4. Analyze and summarize the data.

5. Develop a multi-dimensional intervention plan to achieve the behavioural objectives that have been identified. The plan should be based on a least intrusive/least restrictive/ non-aversive model, and should address issues such as durability of behaviour change, and generalization of new behaviour to different people, tasks and settings.

What is the role of the behaviour therapist on the interdisciplinary mental health team?

The behaviour therapist on the interdisciplinary team can serve several functions:

1. Translate psychiatric symptoms into observable behaviours that can be measured.

2. Help determine whether a behaviour has a biological or psychosocial basis. For instance, does the client's pacing and agitation occur across settings, tasks and people, or does it occur under specific circumstances (e.g., when a particular person is nearby?)

3. Set up a monitoring system to track and evaluate the effects of treatment (for instance, medication) on the target behaviour.

4. Contribute information regarding the environmental stim-

uli (such as crowds, changes in routines) that are associated with the occurrence of the behaviour, and the consequences that serve to maintain it (e.g., the client is permitted to leave a task whenever he/she strikes out).

5. Work with the speech-language pathologist to help care-
    givers understand the communicative function of a client's
    maladaptive behaviour, and develop more acceptable or
    conventional means for the client's needs to be met.

Psychology

What is a psychologist?

A psychologist is a regulated health professional. Requirements to practice as a psychologist in the Province of Ontario
include a doctoral degree from a programme of study with a
primary focus in psychology, completion of a period of post-
doctoral supervised practice, and passing written and oral examinations, all of which lead to registration with the College
of Psychologists of Ontario. Under the Regulated Health Professions Act, psychologists are permitted to diagnose neuro-
psychological disorders and dysfunctions.

*What is the role of the psychologist in working with clients
with a dual diagnosis?*

1. Diagnose or confirm that the client has a developmental
    disability, and assess the level of disability that is present.

2. Profile the client's strengths and weaknesses to assist with
    diagnostic formulation, habilitative goal setting, and ther-
    apy. Clinical information may be gathered by a variety of

means, including administration of psychological tests, observation, interview, and review of previous records. Assessments may cover the following areas or domains:

- cognitive functioning - intelligence, memory, attention, problem-solving skills
- adaptive skills - e.g., self-care, social and play skills
- expressive and receptive language
- visual-perceptual skills
- academic skills
- vocational skills
- behavioural and emotional functioning
- personality style
- coping responses
- psychopathology
- environmental characteristics and demands

3. Determine the need for further assessments, and refer to the appropriate professional - e.g., assessment by a speech-language pathologist to determine the most appropriate form of augmentative communication for a client with minimal or absent verbal skills.

4. Screen "at-risk" groups for indicators of psychopathology.

5. Provide individual, group or family psychotherapy.

What is the role of the psychologist on the interdisciplinary mental health team?

1. Contribute information on the client's psycho-social functioning in keeping with the biopsychosocial approach.

2. Integrate the findings from the psychological assessment with information that has been gathered by other disciplines.

3. Supervise the behaviour therapist.

What types of questions can be answered by a psychological assessment?

- How well does John perform on this test compared to his non-handicapped peers?
- How well does John perform on this test compared to his peers with developmental disabilities?
- At what age or grade level is John performing?
- Has John's performance on this test changed over time?

Speech-Language Pathology

What is a Speech-Language Pathologist?

A speech-language pathologist (SLP) is a regulated health professional. Requirements to practice as an SLP in Ontario include a Master's degree in speech-language pathology and completion of an initial practice period, both of which lead to registration with the College of Audiologists and Speech-Language Pathologists of Ontario.

What is the role of a speech-language pathologist in working with clients *with a dual diagnosis?*

1. Assess a client's strengths and weaknesses in the areas of communication and swallowing. Assessment includes a combination of the following procedures: review of previ-

ous records; interview with the client, caregivers or others involved in the client's life; observation in a variety of settings; and formal and informal testing. Specific areas of assessment include the following domains:

- Articulation/Phonology
- Language (expressive, receptive and pragmatic)
- Voice
- Fluency
- Augmentative and Alternative Communication (AAC)
- Swallowing (oral and pharyngeal stages)

2. Diagnose or confirm that a client has a disorder in one of the above domains of communication or swallowing.

3. Screen for potential disorders in the area of hearing.

4. Provide management and intervention around a diagnosed communication or swallowing disorder. This may include working with the client, caregivers or others involved in the client's life, and may be in the form of individual or group sessions.

5. Provide clinical and community education around issues related to communication and swallowing disorders.

6. Determine the need for further assessment. For example: psychological, psychiatric, hearing.

What is the role of the speech-language pathologist on the interdisciplinary mental health team?

1. Contribute information on the client's communicative and/or swallowing function.

2. Integrate the findings from the communication assessment with the information that has been gathered by other disciplines on the team for the purpose of developing an approach to optimize the client's mental health through the provision of treatment and support.

3. Supervise the communication disorders assistant on the team.

When to make a referral to a speech-language pathologist:

Whenever a delay or disorder is suspected in any of the following areas:

- Articulation/phonology - e.g., client's speech is hard to understand; mispronounces words
- Expressive language - e.g., client is non-verbal or minimally verbal; uses behaviour as a means to communicate; echolalic (repeats back what he/she has heard); difficulty forming sentences
- Receptive language - e.g., difficulty following directions; difficulty answering questions; doesn't seem to understand what is said to him/her
- Pragmatic language - e.g., lacking in non-verbal skills; difficulty initiating, maintaining or ending a topic of conversation; interrupts others; difficulty with conversational turn-taking
- Voice - e.g., chronic hoarseness; voice too loud or too soft; monotone voice
- Fluency - e.g., sound or word repetitions; sound prolongations; tremors, struggle or tension when speaking; anxiety or frustration around speaking

- Hearing - e.g., doesn't seem to respond to sounds in his/her environment; doesn't respond to his/her name; difficulty following conversation; needs to watch the face of the speaker
- Auditory processing - e.g., significant delay before answering a question; difficulty remembering information; says "huh" or "what" frequently
- Feeding/swallowing - e.g., coughing or choking during or after eating/drinking; excessive drooling; minimal or excessive chewing; difficulty starting a swallow; pocketing of food; gurgly sounding voice after eating or drinking; food or liquid in the nose; history of recurrent chest infections or pneumonia; unexplainable weight loss

Communicative Disorders

What is a Communicative Disorders Assistant?

A communicative disorders assistant (CDA) has received a diploma from an approved programme of study. CDAs may perform tasks as prescribed, directed, and supervised by a speech-language pathologist, working in the areas of augmentative and alternative communication, articulation, phonology, language, fluency, and aural rehabilitation.

What is the role of the Communicative Disorders Assistant in working with clients with a dual diagnosis?

1. Assist the Speech-language pathologist with the intake process.

2. Prepare material for assessment and therapy as directed by the SLP.

3. Assist caregivers to implement individual or group therapy goals for speech, language and swallowing services under the supervision of the SLP.

4. Maintain and demonstrate equipment.

What is the role of the Communicative Disorders Assistant on the interdisciplinary mental health team?

1. Educate the other disciplines about augmentative and alternative communication approaches.

2. Assist the SLP and behaviour therapist to develop approaches to integrate communication and behavioural objectives - e.g., providing a picture communication symbol that a non-verbal client can use to request a break instead of hitting his/ her head to communicate the same message.

3. Provide sign language courses or community education workshops on topics relating to communication disorders in clients with developmental disabilities.

Other Health Professionals Who May Be Asked To Consult With The Dual Diagnosis Team:

- audiologist
- cardiologist
- dietician
- developmental pediatrician
- geneticist
- geriatrician
- gynecologist

- neurologist
- occupational therapist
- ophthalmologist
- orthopedist
- pharmacist
- physiotherapist

Helpful Tips to Consider When Requesting an Evaluation by Health Professionals

1. When making a referral, be clear. Avoid making vague requests such as: "I am looking for a psychiatric evaluation for Sally."

2. Phrase your concerns in the form of a question that can be answered -- for example: "Can you tell me if Sally is depressed?".

3. If you can't come up with a question, state the issue or concern in clear, definable terms -- for instance: "Sally hasn't been sleeping well, is crying a lot, and doesn't want to go out anymore. I'd like to know what is wrong with her, and what I can do to help."

4. In the case of multiple concerns, be sure to provide a clear description for each issue.

How to Prepare for an Evaluation

1. Write down your concerns and questions. Pay attention to when you first noticed the problem, how often it occurs, where it occurs, and with whom. Be prepared to talk about

the client's mood, appetite, sleep, energy, and ability to function in social, leisure and work-related activities.

2. Check with other people to see whether they share your concerns.

3. If the client is unable to provide informed consent, a substitute decision maker (usually a family member) will need to be identified.

4. Make sure the family physician is aware of the referral.

5. Gather background information. If this is not possible, try to find out if the client was seen by any professionals in the past, and when this happened. The following types of reports and records are helpful to obtain:

- medical
- psychiatric
- psychological
- speech and language
- behavioural
- academic
- vocational

5. Make sure the person(s) who knows the client best is present for the assessment.

6. For a psychiatric assessment, record when a medication was started, by whom, the reason why, the client's response to medication (both positive and negative), the date the medication was discontinued, and by whom.

Our Interdisciplinary Mental Health Team: The Area Resource Team

At this point, we would like to describe our interdisciplinary mental health team, and use a fictionalized case example to illustrate how our team functions.

Overview of the Area Resource Team

The Area Resource Team (ART) was created in 1994 to respond to mental health issues in adults with developmental disabilities who live in the region encompassed by Hamilton, Niagara and Brant. The team is funded by the Ontario Ministry of Community and Social Services, and is mandated to provide clinical service, education and training. ART is a community-based consultation service. This means that we try to see clients and their caregivers in their natural environment (such as home, work or school), and to work collaboratively with the service providers in their local area. This model allows us to provide specific expertise when and where it is needed, and to use our resources as efficiently as possible.

We have established satellite offices in each of the three areas we serve, which has helped us develop and maintain working relationships with community service providers, and enhance our profile locally. ART operates out of the Chedoke Child and Family Centre at the Hamilton Health Sciences Corporation. In addition, we have ties to the Faculty of Health Sciences at McMaster University. These factors enable us to bridge the developmental and mental health systems.

Consultation process

As we stated earlier, our conceptualization of mental health issues is fairly broad, and encompasses psychiatric, behavioural, emotional and/or communication problems. Referrals that are reflective of any or all of these issues can be made by anyone who is involved with the client, such as a family member, primary physician, case manager, direct care staff, inpatient or community psychiatrist, mental health worker, teacher, or probation officer, as well as the client him/herself. Referrals are screened to ensure that they meet the eligibility criteria for the service (i.e., the client is an adult, lives within the catchment area, is developmentally disabled, and has a primary physician). If the client is not eligible for the service, the person making the referral will be redirected to the appropriate resource.

Once the referral information is obtained, it is passed along to a member of the team. Discipline-specific referrals are handled by the appropriate health professional, whereas complex or ambiguous referrals are usually addressed by the psychiatric nurse who may request the involvement of other disciplines after clarifying the referral issues.

An intake meeting is held with the client and the members of his or her core team. The purpose of the meeting is to explain the process, obtain consent for consultation and release of information, gather clinical information, clarify expectations for the consultation, establish a tentative time-frame for the team's involvement, and sort out roles and responsibilities for the health professionals and core team members. The consultation proceeds with the interdisciplinary team members conducting

Figure 1- Flowchart of The Area Resource Team Consultation Process

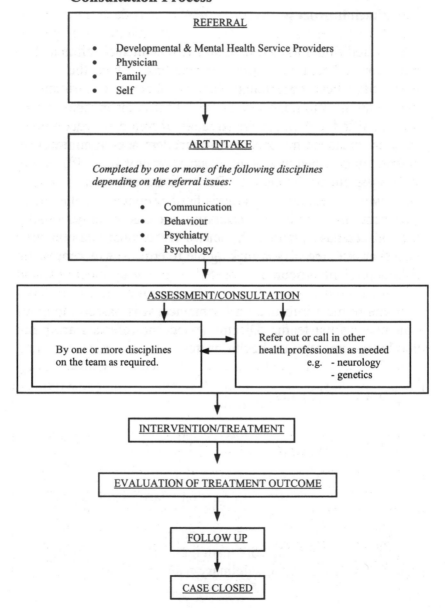

emerging information, and fine-tune the assessment plan.

Team members may make referrals to outside health professionals (e.g., cardiologist, neurologist, audiologist) for specialized or additional assessments to assist with their clinical formulation and treatment recommendations.   Once the assessments have been completed, team members meet to integrate
their findings into a bio-psycho-social formulation, and to outline a unified and comprehensive set of treatment recommendations. This information is presented at a case conference,
and an intervention/treatment plan is developed. Staff training
with regard to implementation of recommendations is provided
as needed. Treatment is initiated and the client's response to
treatment (as well as implementation of recommendations by
the core team) is evaluated by way of systematic and objective
data that are typically gathered by the behaviour therapist on
the team. This process is repeated at follow-up meetings, and
additional consultation may be provided on a short-term basis
regarding specific clinical and systems issues. Once the goals
for the consultation have been reached, the case is closed, but
may be re-opened if the need arises.

The Case of Frank

*Frank is a 40-year-old male who lives with his parents.
His developmental disability is considered mild; however, he has significant difficulties in social situations,
and in retaining employment. He had in the past, participated in anger management groups and individual
behaviour therapy sessions because of long-standing
problems with verbal and physical aggression. The behavioural interventions did not result in significant improvements in his social or occupational functioning.*

Consequently, he was referred to the Area Resource Team by his case manager for an interdisciplinary assessment. Frank's family physician was contacted prior to the initial meeting, and was in support of the referral.

The presenting problems consisted of angry outbursts, anxiety, and lengthy cleaning rituals that interfered with Frank's performance on the job. Frank, along with his parents, case manager and vocational counselor, met with the psychiatric nurse, behaviour therapist and psychologist from the team. During the course of the meeting, it became clear that Frank had extreme difficulty responding to complex interpersonal dialogue. He tended to misread social cues, and was not able to integrate verbal and nonverbal information. Frank concurred with the recommendation to include the speech-language pathologist from the team.

The speech-language pathologist met with Frank and his caregivers to evaluate his communication style, as well as his strengths and weaknesses. The assessment revealed disabilities in the areas of expressive, receptive and pragmatic (i.e. language in social situations) language. These disabilities were a factor in relation to his tendency to misinterpret other people's verbal and non-verbal communications, and his striking difficulties in appreciating their perspectives. Moreover, he appeared to have difficulty maintaining a conversational topic, and giving appropriate non-verbal feedback to his communication partner. Too often, his interactions with others would lead to frustration and visible signs of anxiety or anger.

The behaviour therapist worked with Frank's family and vocational counselor to set up a data collection system to track his outbursts of verbal and physical aggression at home and on the job, providing information about what events and conditions preceded the outbursts (antecedents) as well as what followed them (consequences).

The psychological assessment revealed that Frank had deficits in basic academic skills (reading, spelling and arithmetic) that were more severe than would be predicted on the basis of his intellectual functioning. In terms of adaptive functioning, Frank displayed significant weakness (relative to other skill areas) in the area of social/communicative functioning. His emotional/ behavioural profile revealed that he had difficulty organizing and completing tasks, had poor concentration and a short attention span. A personality inventory indicated that he had a tendency to argue with people, and to verbally challenge authority figures. He liked to do things his own way, and might react negatively to directions, suggestions and constructive criticism.

Frank identified that he had trouble understanding what people were trying to say, especially when he was in a group or when people used complex language. These difficulties were hypothesized to be related to a number of factors, such as attentional problems or difficulties responding to rapidly changing information, and could explain to some extent his tendency to misinterpret social situations, and to respond in an angry or defensive manner.

The team met prior to the psychiatric interview to share

their findings and treatment approaches. The psychiatric assessment supported his mother's theory that Frank had suffered from an undiagnosed obsessive-compulsive disorder since late childhood. In clinical terms, he had recurrent, unwanted, disturbing thoughts (obsessions) that dirt or invisible contaminants needed to be removed from his body or surroundings. He also had an intense need for symmetry and order in his environment. He was unable to suppress or distract himself from these thoughts, and engaged in repetitive behaviours (compulsions) to relieve the anxiety caused by the obsessions. Frank engaged in lengthy washing rituals for much of the day, straightening anything in the home that seemed "out of place", and vacuuming or wiping surfaces in the family home or vehicles whenever another person finished in the area. Although work placements were tailored to capitalize on his apparent interest in cleaning, he could not stop himself from performing cleaning rituals, nor could he tolerate directions or deadlines from supervisors. Apart from the diagnosis of obsessive-compulsive disorder, Frank did not have additional psychiatric, medical or neurological conditions, and was not on any medication. There was no family history of psychiatric or developmental problems.

The interdisciplinary formulation of Frank's longstanding problems with interpersonal conflict and retaining employment, highlighted biological and psychosocial factors that were informed by the speech-language, psychological, behavioural and psychiatric evaluations by the dual diagnosis team. This information was summarized in a written report that was presented at Frank's case conference, and a treatment plan was developed.

Psychiatric treatment for Frank's obsessive-compulsive disorder was initiated through the family physician who prescribed a serotonin reuptake inhibitor, which was started at a low dose and gradually increased. Speech-language therapy targeted verbal and non-verbal communication and perspective-taking. Frank gained an understanding of the role of facial expression and body language in communicative interactions, and was able to apply that knowledge in his relationships. Perspective-taking was more difficult for him to grasp. Therapy sessions focused on the idea that people can "see" situations differently, and that in such situations it was important to attempt to "look" at the other person's point of view. He understood the concept, and could role play perspective-taking in a session; however, he had much more difficulty in real-life situations in which his typical emotional reactions and interactions prevailed.

The behaviour therapist and speech-language pathologist worked together, utilizing a variety of techniques (problem-solving, adaptive self-talk, social stories) to provide Frank with a means to better understand the triggers for his outbursts, and to teach him alternative means to resolve these situations before they escalated into conflict and aggression. Recommendations by the psychologist included allowing plenty of time for Frank to process information, and minimizing visual and auditory stimulation when possible; avoiding vague, imprecise language; and helping him to take personal ownership for his actions while recognizing his need for assis-

tance in the form of explicit teaching, reinforcement and practice in order to learn and apply new skills.

When Frank's response to medication was evaluated, there was an initial marked improvement noted in his overall mood, in that he was less anxious and "edgy". At follow-up three months later, he was better able to engage in a variety of work and leisure activities since his time was not taken up to the same extent with rituals and compulsions. Overall, Frank was pleased with the easing of his anxiety, and the fact that he was able to do new and different things. He also reported getting along better with his parents and his supervisor at work. Frank's family remarked on his improved mood, and mentioned that he was not as defensive and quick to anger.

Summary

In this chapter, we described the roles and functions of health professionals on a dual diagnosis team. We presented a rationale for using an interdisciplinary approach when working with clients with numerous or complex needs. We highlighted the necessity of working closely with a core group of people who are knowledgeable about the client's needs, and will be able to implement our treatment recommendations. We provided suggestions regarding what to consider when requesting an evaluation, and how best to prepare for it. Finally, we described our dual diagnosis service, and used a case example to link our points together.

Do You Know?

1. What is the difference between an interdisciplinary and multidisciplinary team, and which approach is better-suited to clients with multiple or complex needs?
2. What are the roles and functions of health professionals on a dual diagnosis team?
3. What is the role of the core team?
4. How do you get the most out of a consultation?

Resources

College of Audiologists and Speech-Language Pathologists of Ontario
Telephone: 416-327-0876
College of Nurses of Ontario
Telephone: 416-928-0900
Website: http://www.cno.org
College of Physicians and Surgeons of Ontario
Telephone: 1-800-268-7096
Website: http://www.cpso.on.ca
College of Psychologists of Ontario
Telephone: 416-961-8817
Website: http://www.cpo.on.ca
Communicative Disorders Assistant Association of Canada
Telephone: 416-544-3503
Ontario Association for Behaviour Analysis
Telephone: 416-410-6141
Website: http://www.sl.on.ca/ontaba
Ontario Association of Speech-Language Pathologists and Audiologists

Telephone: 416-920-3676
Website: http://www.osla.on.ca
Ontario Medical Association
Telephone:416-599-2580
Website: http://www.oma.org
Ontario Nurses Association
Telephone: 1-800-387-5580
Website: http://www.ona.org
Ontario Psychological Association
Telephone: 416-961-5552
Website: http://www.psych.on.ca

References

AACAP (1999). Practice parameters for the assessment and treatment of children, adolescents and adults with mental retardation and comorbid mental disorders. *Journal of the American Academy of Child and Adolescent Psychiatry, 38 Supplement*, 5S-31S.

Dowrick, P.W. (1996). Principles of interdisciplinary team collaboration. In L.A. Kurtz, P.W. Dowrick, S.E. Levy, & M.L. Batshaw (Eds.), *Handbook of developmental disabilities: Resources for interdisciplinary care*. Gaithersburg, MD: Aspen Publishers.

Fahs, J.J. (1988). Multidisciplinary psychiatric consultation in mental retardation. *NADD Newsletter, 5,* 1-4.

Hollins, S. (1985). The dynamics of teamwork. In M. Craft, J. Bicknell, & S. Hollins (Eds.), *Mental handicap: A multidisciplinary approach* (pp. 281-287). Toronto: W.B. Saunders.

Koskie, J. & Freeze, R. (2000). A critique of multidisciplinary teaming: Problems and possibilities. *Developmental Disabilities Bulletin, 28*, 1-17.

Ryan, R., Rodden, P., & Sunada, K. (1991). A model for interdisciplinary on-site evaluation of people who have "dual diagnosis". *NADD Newsletter, 8,* 2-4.

Sands, R.G., Stafford, J., & McClelland, M. (1990). "I beg to differ": Conflict in the interdisciplinary team. *Social Work in Health Care, 14,* 55-71.

Silka, V.R., & Hauser, M.J. (1997). Psychiatric assessment of the person with mental retardation. *Psychiatric Annals, 27,* 162-169.

Vinokur-Kaplan, D. (1995). Enhancing the effectiveness of interdisciplinary mental health treatment teams. *Administration and Policy in Mental Health, 22,* 521-530.

Acknowledgements

We would like to thank Dr. Elspeth Bradley and Carolyn Houlding for their feedback, as well as Julia Ollinger for her expert computer assistance.

Chapter 11

Developing Social Supports for People who have a Dual Diagnosis

Jo Anne Nugent and Yona Lunsky

Learning Objectives

Readers will be able to:

1. Define social supports
2. Describe why social supports are important in the lives of persons with a dual diagnosis
3. Identify how to effectively develop social supports for persons with a dual diagnosis

Introduction

Think about the last time that you had a problem or weren't feeling well. Chances are that the other people in your life helped you out in many ways, increased your ability to cope, and got you "back on track". Thus, the situation was far less serious for you than it could have been. The same is true for people with a dual diagnosis. Social supports, having others there that care, can prevent problems from occurring, and can also help these individuals to rebound more quickly from the problems that do occur.

In this book, we have adopted the biopsychosocial approach to understanding and working with people. Note that in this approach, the "social" element is given the same importance as the biological and psychological elements. This implies that social issues, including social supports, should be included in any efforts to support people with a dual diagnosis. In fact, they have the same priority as the other two types of factors!

Social support is a topic on which professionals from both developmental services and mental health services agree. Developmental services acknowledge that integration, in particular relationships, leads to both personal happiness and learning of skills. Mental health services recognize that social networks significantly contribute to mental health. Therefore, social supports have the potential to play a vital role in the lives of persons with vulnerabilities, including those with a dual diagnosis (Nugent & Spindel, 2000). Promoting the development and maintenance of social supports should be a *major focus* of our work with these individuals, included in all our planning and service delivery.

What is Social Support?

After more than ten years of research on social support, researchers are still having a difficult time agreeing on exactly what social support means. Ben Gottlieb noted that with each new study, a new definition of social support surfaces (Gottlieb, 1983). Perhaps the easiest way to think about social support is that it is the positive or helpful interpersonal transaction or exchange that occurs between people. Another way to think about social support is that it is the sense of belonging a person has, or the belief that others would be there when needed. This means that social support is both something that occurs "out there", and also is something within the individual- a sense or interpretation.

The research literature on social support and developmental disabilities offers some suggestions regarding what aspects of social support should be considered. First of all, it is important to have a sense of the individual's support structure and what purposes the support serves. It is also important to understand how that individual perceives his or her relationships, especially when these perceptions differ from the perceptions of others. Finally, negative or stressful relationships that the individual encounters are as important to consider as positive ones.

Social Support Structure

When we talk about support structure, we want to know WHO is giving support, and WHO is getting it. Questions one might ask include: How many people are there in the network? How well do they know each other? Sometimes it is helpful when they all know each other well, but at other times, it can be nice to receive support from separate groups of people with different expectations. The positions that these individuals hold in the person's life, and also how well the individual in question provides support to his or her network are also important questions to ask. (Please refer to Guideline 9 on Reciprocal Relationships for more information on this issue.)

Many individuals with developmental disabilities report loneliness and a lack of intimate friendships with others (Chadsey-Rusch, DeStepafo, O'Reilly, & Collet-Klingenberg, 1992). Often, they have no friends who are accessible to them on a regular basis. For example, they may see individuals at work, but not know how to arrange to see them outside of work.

They may also lack romantic support (Koller, Richardson, & Katz, 1988), a fundamental support source for many adults. Some individuals with dual diagnoses find not having a partner to be especially distressing on both a physical/sexual level and an emotional one.

Perceived Social Support

A second area to consider is the perceptions of social support that the individual with the dual diagnosis has, especially when these perceptions do not match the perceptions of others. Some researchers have studied social support from the point of view of caregivers, not realizing that how caregivers see the relationships could be very different from how the person with the disability sees them. Research with persons without disabilities has shown us that what really matters for our mental and physical health is not just what support is out there but what support *we think* is out there (Baldwin, 1992; Lakey, Tardiff, & Drew, 1997). Lunsky and Benson reported, as did Clegg and Standen, that compared to individuals without disabilities, adults with mild developmental disabilities may sometimes overestimate their social support (Lunsky & Benson, in press; Clegg & Standen, 1991). This is relevant to dual diagnosis, in that when they discover that the person whom they like does not care for them in the same way as they thought, a crisis can result. Biased perceptions can lead to other troubles as well. Aggressive individuals with developmental disabilities may perceive anger in interactions with others when the anger is not there, inviting further aggression. It is also possible that interpreting relationships accurately can have harmful consequences. If a poorly supported individual with a developmental disability accurately perceives his/her social situation, it could lead to a subsequent depression. Thus, it is most important to find out from the individual with a dual diagnosis, or one who is at risk for dual diagnosis, how he/she understands his or her relationships. Asking staff or family members alone is not enough.

Negative Support

So far, we have not really considered how difficult relation-ships rather than supportive ones might influence people with development disabilities. We know that they are at greater risk for mental health problems than the general population, and we also know that they often lack social resources and have interpersonal difficulties. It makes sense, therefore, that they are as vulnerable as anyone else when a relationship goes sour. Karen Rook reported that the stressful support provided to widows was more predictive of subsequent depression than was the absence of support to the same individuals (Rook, 1984). Similar findings have recently been reported for people with developmental disabilities (Lunsky, 1999; Lunsky & Havercamp, 1999; Nezu, Nezu, Tothenberg, DelliCarpini, & Groas, 1995).

There is some suggestion that the presence of stressful or negative relationships in the life of a person with a develop-mental disability causes more distress than the absence of good relationships. So, when we talk about social support, we have to think not only about what positive relationships are there for our clients, but also how many difficult interactions they have to endure each day.

Often, individuals with dual diagnoses find themselves faced with negative social interactions that they cannot escape. They may not be able to escape due to limited options in terms of vocational and residential settings. Persons with a dual diagnosis may also lack opportunities because of the difficulties that they have participating in the community. The lack of skills necessary to avoid or escape negative social interactions is a second reason why individuals with dual diagnoses may be more vulnerable; they do not always know how to get out of situations they do not enjoy. One individual confronted with a negative or stressful relationship may choose to appear vegetative or depressed as a form of learned helplessness. Another individual may choose to respond aggressively because s/he does not know how else to escape the negative social situation.

Why Social Supports Are Important

There are three main reasons why social supports are important for persons with a dual diagnosis.

Reason 1: Individuals with a Dual Diagnosis want social supports in their lives

Whether you talk to people with a developmental disability, people with a mental health problem, or people with a dual diagnosis, you will find that majority of them will tell you that their most important goal is to have social supports. Of course, they don't use our jargon. They talk about having friends, being loved, and having people they can count on who will be there over the long run. They may express themselves through their behaviour, rather than words. However, the meaning is the same. This is a very valid quality of life issue, and for this reason alone, we should include social supports in all our work.

Reason 2: Promotion of health

The presence of social supports promotes both physical and mental health. "There is a strong relationship between individual physical-social-psychological health and social supports, and between social isolation and breakdown in these areas of functioning" (Meyer, 1985). Relationships can minimise the impact of problems, acting as the "first line of coping defence" for people labelled as clients (Gottlieb, 1985). Therefore, social supports are a key factor in the *prevention* of mental and physical illnesses.

What is it about social supports that gives them such prevention power? There are both *practical* and *emotional* factors. On the *practical* side, social supports can provide a considerable number of concrete items such as money, housing, jobs, food, child care, clothing, nursing care, fun, guidance, transportation, protection, connections, and opportunities to develop skills. These tangible ingredients are linked to physical and mental health because they help in coping with life and meeting our needs. Never underestimate the impact on mental health of losing your income, housing, or independence.

On the *emotional* side, the presence of social supports can boost self esteem, lower levels of anxiety, minimize stress, offer love, increase the sense of security, build strengths, empower the individual, instill a more positive view of life, and create hope. We can all understand the importance of these emotional factors on mental health. One woman diagnosed as a "chronic schizophrenic" who has lived successfully in the community without relapse for many years, sums it up: "What made the difference? The difference was people. That's what kept me going" (Neugeboren, 1999).

Reason 3: Resilience and recovery

Resilience and recovery are terms used in the mental health field which have considerable significance for dual diagnosis as well. Resilience and recovery describe how, *after* problems occur, people can successfully deal with what has happened to them and still have a good life. Therefore, resilience and recovery refer to what professionals would call the intervention/ treatment phase of supporting people.

First, we will define these two terms, and then discuss their relationship to social supports.

A particularly expressive definition of resilience describes it as "the self righting tendencies" of the person, "both the capacity to be bent without breaking and the capacity, once bent, to spring back" (Valiant, 1993). In other words, problems may arise, but resilience is the ability to survive with minimal damage and then to rebound. This is an inspiring concept that captures the potential of the human spirit.

Recovery is a related term. It is somewhat imprecise, but can be thought of as coming to terms with who you are and living a satisfying life, even within your limitations. Note that recovery *does not mean cure*. Instead, it refers to gaining a sense of control over life and getting on with goals, coping with the reality of who one is: In other words, the person goes on playing the game of life with different rules.

Social supports contribute to both resilience and recovery. A significant amount of research regarding resilience (including one study over a 37 year period!) indicates that the presence of caring people in their lives, helps children to survive considerable hardships, and to end up living ordinary adult lives (Rapp, 1998). Similarly, extensive research confirms that social supports are an important component of recovery. (Sullivan, 1994). Many people say that social supports make them feel less frightened and better able to deal with whatever happens to them.

Therefore, social supports are extremely important. They help prevent problems, lessen the impact of problems, and facilitate recovery. In other words, they are a part of treatment, just like medication or therapy.

<u>Social supports and crisis planning</u>

Unfortunately, people with a dual diagnosis often experience frequent "crises" of various kinds related to their behaviours. We tend to think that only professionals can be useful during a crisis. Yet, social supports can be extremely helpful during a crisis. As a matter of fact, social supports can minimize or even prevent crises.

Every "client" who experiences crises on a relatively frequent basis should have a crisis plan. The crisis plan contains three stages. Social supports should be included at each stage.

Stage One: Prevention: Through careful observation and collection of information, it is possible to determine when crisis is likely to occur for this individual. We should find out what events or situations tend to provoke crisis. Then, every effort should be made to eliminate crisis by dealing with these factors. Crisis could be brought on by changes, ill-health, or lack of emotional support. By brainstorming these issues, it is often possible to develop very effective ways of assisting the individual to cope. Social supports should be included as part of the resources that could be used at this stage.

For example, one young woman with a dual diagnosis frequently had a crisis of a suicidal nature on weekends. Since she was living in an independent situation, she only received eight hours a week of residential staff support, always between Monday and Friday. There were no crises at these times. The woman then became involved with a Friday night camera club and a Saturday square dance club. These two clubs provided her with friendship and activity during her most vulnerable time periods, and the crises virtually disappeared.

Stage Two, Early Intervention: If a particular crisis can not be prevented, it is important to step in early and minimize the negative impact of the crisis. We hope to be able to help the person before his/her behaviour is dangerous, to keep him/her in the community, to maintain his/her dignity, and to build supports for next time. Once again, social supports can be of great assistance.

Another example is a situation in which a young man with a dual diagnosis experienced periods of deep depression that resulted in self-injurious behaviour. Changes in staff were a particular trigger for his depression. Once this was determined, it was decided to form a team of unpaid people who would be in his life on a regular basis. Whenever there was a staff change, this team immediately increased their contact with him to provide him with stability and caring. While he still experienced some problems with depression, his self-injury was less destructive, and the bouts of depression were much briefer in nature.

Stage Three: Recovery after Crisis: Sometimes crisis does occur, and we must act to protect the "client" or others from serious harm. This usually entails considerable involvement with professionals, and intrusive actions such as high doses of medication, restraints, or hospitalization. At this point, though it may seem that social supports have very little role, they can still have a positive effect on recovery. Contact with the people who are social supports can help the person to stabilize and get "back on track" more quickly. Some crisis plans actually utilize with positive results the resources of the social supports during crisis rather than simply hospital staff (Carling, 1998).

Social supports have a flexibility that formalised staffing systems often don't. They can be available at any hour of any day and at any location, without the restrictions of administrative structures such as work shifts. They tend to be more permanent than staffing systems. Plus, people who are in the social support network often have a better sense of the "client's" history, and what works best for him/her.

Social Support Assessment

There are three primary ways to assess social support. We recommend that whenever possible all three methods be considered. The most common form of social support assessment is that of informant ratings. One way to do this is to engage an informant such as a staff or family member in a structured interview (Kraus, Seltzer, & Goodman, 1992). Such a detailed procedure can be very informative, but also very time-consuming. An alternative would be a brief, structured interview such as that developed by Meins (1993). Written rating scales have also been developed that can be completed by informants. One such measure is the Social Circles Questionnaire developed by Lunsky and Benson (1999). This measure takes approximately twenty minutes to complete. It assesses support provided by family, staff, friends, and romantic partner. In addition to looking at the quality of social support, it also allows for ratings of stressful relationships and reciprocity.

As discussed previously, how one perceives his or her relationships is very important information. Therefore, it is best to measure social support whenever possible via self-report. There many ways this can be done depending on the severity of that individual's mental illness or cognitive disability. The simplest way to assess perceived support would be to ask the individual to list or point out who s/he likes. Toni Antonucci developed a Concentric Circles Technique which considers both who is perceived as supportive and the level of closeness perceived (Antonucci, 1986). The Social Support Self-Report is a more elaborate perceived support measure that begins as a structured interview whereby the person identifies important support people in his/her life (Lunsky & Benson, 1997; Reiss & Benson, 1985). Next, the person rates his/her perceptions of support provided by the four categories of individuals listed: family, staff, friends, and partner. A useful perceived strain measure is the 40-item Instrument of Negative Social Interactions developed by Lakey, Tardiff, and Drew (1994).

The final way to assess social support is to observe that individual's interactions. There are several ways this can be done objectively. Newton, Olson and Horner (1995) have emphasized in-depth behaviour observations of social interactions of individuals with severe disabilities. A less rigid approach to this would be naturalistic observation to see who an individual interacts with and how they respond during interactions.

Phone logs and activity schedules can also be helpful sources of information.

Guidelines for the Development and Use of Social Supports

Social supports are of great benefit to persons with a dual diagnosis.   Not only can social supports improve the person's quality of life, they can lessen, or even eliminate, the need for costly and restrictive professional services. As professionals we should be ensuring that social supports are a component of any work we do.

Many of you may feel discouraged about this. You may have tried to develop social supports and found it to be a difficult and ultimately unsuccessful process.   Perhaps you have so many other duties that working on social supports is near the bottom of your "to do" list. In this section, we will offer some suggestions that may assist you.

Guideline 1: Make Social Supports a priority

It is clear that social supports should be a *primary* focus of our work with people who have a dual diagnosis, not just an after-thought or a nice "extra".   Make every effort you can to en-sure that social supports are a priority in your work.   Include them in your own approach.   Educate other people about how important social supports are as a mechanism for prevention, resilience, and recovery (this Chapter and its references can help).   Encourage the organization you work for to recognize social supports as a priority.

Guideline 2: Include Social Supports in all planning

One concrete way of ensuring that social supports are a priority is to include them in *all* your planning processes. At each planning meeting, support the "client" to express his/her goals regarding social supports, and to make certain that his/her wishes are included in any documentation. Insert social supports as a category on any planning forms, and put it at the top of the list. Before making referrals to professional services, explore whether social supports could accomplish the same goal. If referrals are made to professionals, don't forget to include social supports that could increase the effectiveness of professional services. *Every* plan for *every* person should include at least some goals related to social supports.

Guideline 3: Devote resources to developing Social Supports

It is important to "put your money where your mouth is". While including social supports in planning is a significant step, it is just as important to have someone on the team specifically dedicate part of his/her time to develop social supports. This may seem naive to you. How can a staff member focus on social supports while there are so many other critical jobs to be done, and so many problems to deal with? The reality is that developing social supports will only be accomplished if someone is responsible for that job! Keep in mind that, over the long run, social supports can save resources because they foster prevention, resilience, and recovery. This makes it an excellent investment of your time *now* to work on social supports for significant future benefit.

Guideline 4: Build Social Supports based on mutual interests

This a basic rule of thumb for success with social supports. Look for people who share something with the "client" -- topics they are interested in, people they know, places they go, activities they like, their history, or talents. This could encompass family, friends, community members, and staff. Far too often, we try to force the development of social relationships between the "client" and persons with whom s/he has nothing in common. This happens sometimes with volunteers who are recruited to be friends. There is absolutely nothing wrong with volunteers! However, it is far more effective to seek out volunteers from the people who already know the "client" in some capacity, or who have mutual interests that could be expanded upon. This is a more typical and natural process, the way that we all build relationships. It is also much more likely to result in social supports that will last over time, and contribute to the "client's" well being.

To be successful with social supports, it is useful to:
- know the "client" well as a person, his/her interests, skills, lifestyle.
- observe the "client" carefully as s/he goes about the regular routines of life, looking for any potential social supports that could be enhanced.
- become familiar with the community to have a pool of potential social supports in mind.

Guideline 5: Develop a wide range of Social Supports

There are two reasons why it is helpful for the person to have a wide range of social supports. First, it increases the opportunities and benefits that the social supports can provide. Second, it avoids "burn out" of the people who are social supports. This latter point is particularly important. It can be very fatiguing to be one of the few (or the only) supports that someone has. This is especially true if someone has a dual diagnosis, since this may result in that person having many needs, constant crises, and some unpleasant behaviours.

If you think about your own social supports, you will find that you have a range of people in your life. Some people are very close, and you see them frequently. Others have a specific involvement in your life, such as someone on your sports team or your baby sitter. One person may be able to provide you emotional comfort, while someone else is a contact for jobs or a place to live.

Encourage a variety of people to become involved in the social supports of a person with a dual diagnosis with varied ages, personalities, lifestyles, and interests. This will result in different people providing different supports and options for the individual. Also, it will increase the probability that the full range of the "client's" needs are being met – a person can have lots of people giving him/her only one kind of support (practical), and end up feeling relatively empty. The breadth of supports can increase prevention, resilience, and recovery.

Guideline 6: Focus on unpaid persons rather than staff as Social Supports

Staff fulfill many crucial functions in the lives of persons with a dual diagnosis. Frequently, this includes taking on the role of friend. However, we should consider the proportion of paid support providers in the individual's social network. Several research studies have found that individuals with developmental disabilities receive a disproportionate amount of social support from paid support sources (Rosen & Burchard, 1990; Sands & Kozleski, 1994).

It is preferable to focus on developing social supports that consist mainly of unpaid people. This is not meant to be an insult to staff and their dedication to the people they support. However, the rationale for this guideline is quite simple: staff may come and go in "client's" lives. Staff turnover is a fact of life that makes it unwise to create a social support system that is mainly made up of staff. Unpaid people, particularly those who have a lifestyle element in common with the "client", will be there for a lot longer. As well, variety is more likely to be achieved through a network of unpaid people who would usually represent a greater range of ages, experiences, incomes, life experiences, and community connections than staff would. Certainly staff can be part of a social support system, but the effective system includes many unpaid people too.

Guideline 7: Don't Try to Make Social Supports Professional Services

If there are unpaid people who become involved in the life of a person with a dual diagnosis, it is wise to avoid the urge to make them into unpaid staff. We have seen many situations in which well meaning staff incorporated community people into the professional support system. The community people were expected to attend countless planning meetings, develop goals for their friendship with the "client", dedicate a certain number of hours per month to the "client", and even provide programmatic-like descriptions of how they spent their time together! Needless to say, this corrupted the relationship, resulting in frustration for the community people who ultimately opted out.

This process insults the "client", since it implies that only staff would really want to be part of his/her life. It also insults the community person by implying that he/she would only be useful if he/she were organized and supervised like staff.

Staff members are paid professionals who provide specific services. Social supports are people who relate to the individual in an informal, natural, and sincere way. People will offer their time and concern as they can, and in the way that is their own style, and this should be accepted at face value.

Guideline 8: Look beyond middle class values for Social Supports

The group of people whom we call clients are a very wide-ranging group. They come from many different backgrounds, and have many different interests. Typically, service providers represent the middle class in terms of values, education, and income level. We tend to look for social supports that are compatible with our lifestyles. However, it is necessary to consider who the "client" is, and what types of social supports would offer him/her the most. This may mean that staff personnel have to shed their middle class values when developing social supports. The older lady who spends many hours a day in the donut shop, or the man who runs a tattoo parlour may be an excellent and highly compatible friend for a particular "client". We must try to see these folks through the eyes of the "client". Who will offer the practical and emotional resources that will have the most positive impact on this particular "client's" mental health and overall quality of life? Who is a good "fit" or "match" for this person?

Of course, we are not saying that it is acceptable for us to encourage negative or abusive relationships. However, remember that social supports do not have to be people without flaws! Sometimes, staff has impossibly high standards for those who would willingly be involved in a "client's" life. Your friends and family probably aren't perfect. Yet they are a key part of your well being. The same should hold true for "clients" and their social supports. We should be careful that we do not become too demanding of the ordinary, somewhat flawed folks who have potential to make a difference in a "client's" life.

Guideline 9: Create opportunities rather than matches

The best way for a "client" to develop social supports is for that person to be out and about with other people. In that way, s/he will meet others with common interests. This is better than artificially matching people through getting them together in an awkward meeting that has been set up by staff (often called the blind date approach!).

Staff's job is to create opportunities for the "client" to be involved with others. Such opportunities should accurately reflect the "client's" preferences so that there will be real common interests with the others present. This kind of integration provides the potential for social supports to be fostered.

Guideline 10: Encourage reciprocal relationships

Reciprocal relationships are ones in which each person benefits from the situation or gets something out of it. It implies that there is a "give and take" to the relationship. In real life, practically all relationships are built on reciprocity. People would not stay in relationships if there was not some benefit to them. This is not a "bad" thing; it is just human. Of course, the definition of benefit is an individual one, and can include both practical and emotional elements.

Some researchers have argued that social support has its healing effects because of reciprocity (Horowitz, 1996). When reciprocity is lacking, therefore, social support may not really be all that helpful. This can be a problem with paid social support, for example, because by nature it is not reciprocal. That means that if an individual with a dual diagnosis receives most of his or her support from staff, s/he may not be able to return that level of support.

It can be difficult for persons with a dual diagnosis to develop *long-term* social supports since their relationships are quite often not reciprocal. In other words, staff typically examines any potential relationship in terms of how the "client" will benefit. We look for volunteers who will offer the "client" a social life or teach skills. Seldom do we think of helping the "client" to give back in any way. Over time, one way relationships tend to die off, and that is just what happens with many of the social supports that we try to establish for "clients".

As staff members, we can help "clients" to think of ways that they can give back to their social supports and keep our eyes open for opportunities. Reciprocity does not mean that people have to be completely equal in their give and take. However, it does mean being considerate of the other. Therefore, a relatively inexpensive birthday card from a person on a limited fixed income expresses reciprocity just as much as an expensive birthday present from someone with no financial restrictions.

Guideline 11: Teach social skills

It is interesting to consider how important social skills are with respect to human relationships. The ability to behave within the boundaries of society's expectations is far more important to relationships than how smart, talented, or unique a person is. Nothing will ruin a budding friendship more quickly than a person who does not act "right" according to our social rules. This holds true whether we are talking about someone trying to make friends at a community job, to meet a girlfriend or boyfriend at a social event, or to have a close relationship with family members.

Social skills can be thought of as behaviours that pertain to getting along with other people. They include proper greetings, appropriate touching, honouring other people's personal space, eye contact, making conversation, using polite vocabulary, developing more intense relationships at a comfortable pace for the other person, suitable behaviour with the opposite sex, street safe behaviour, table manners, and consideration for others. This is but a partial list.

To increase the "client's" success in developing social supports, it is crucial to assist him/her to develop the best possible social skills. Many excellent materials are available for teaching social skills to persons with different levels of abilities (See the resource list at the end of this chapter). If you have limited time to devote to teaching skills, it will be the most effective if you concentrate on social skills. This will increase the probability that social supports will develop, and these social supports will open the door to many other possibilities in the world.

Guideline 12: Minimize the impact of "negative" behaviours that might impede the development of relationships

This guideline relates to the previous one. Along with improving or enhancing the individual's social skills, we must be very aware of any "negative" behaviours that might make it very difficult to create and maintain social supports. There are two options to working with these types of behaviours.

- Option 1 is to eliminate these behaviours. This is the obvious approach with serious situations such as aggression or self-injury, since these are harmful to the individual and others.

- Option 2 is to seek out situations in which the "negative" behaviours are not as likely to block the development of social supports. There may be people for whom these "negative" behaviours are not important, or places where these "negative" behaviours are acceptable. We are not talking about extreme behaviours, but foibles and idiosyncrasies that are not the norm. One example is that of a 47 year-old man who had an obsession with cars. He talked incessantly about them, in great detail, to the point where many people avoided him. Finding him a job as a helper at a large garage eliminated this issue, since his co-workers were as obsessed as he was! Creativity is the key. One astonishing miracle about human nature is that there are almost always compatible matches for each person, if we think about it.

Summary

This chapter has been developed to provide useful information about social supports for persons with a dual diagnosis on both a theoretical and practical level. We have included a definition of social supports, a review of types of social supports, and a discussion of how important the individual's perception of social supports can be. The *Guidelines for the Development and Use of Social Supports* cited above offer some concrete suggestions to use in real life with persons who have a dual diagnosis. They are based on the experiences of countless people who have demonstrated the validity of social supports as a facet of "treatment".

Do You Know?

1. Why are social supports so important to persons with a dual diagnosis?
2. What are some of the characteristics of effective social supports?
3. What role can staff play in the social supports of persons with a dual diagnosis?
4. What are some ways of measuring a person's social supports?
5. How can social supports be included in someone's crisis plan?

Resources

Amado, A. N. (1993). *Friendships and connections between people with and without developmental disabilities.* Baltimore, MD: Paul Brookes

Carling, P. J. (1995). *Return to community: Building support systems for people with psychiatric disabilities.* New York, NY: The Guilford Press

McKnight, J. L. (1995). *The careless society: Community and its counterfeits.* New York, NY:

Nisbet, J. (1992). *Natural supports in school, at work, and in the community for people with severe disabilities.* Baltimore, MD: Paul Brookes.

Nugent, J. & Spindel, P. (2000). *Creating the context for empowerment: Empowering individuals and creating competent communities.* Toronto, Ontario: Nu-Spin Publishing.

Taylor, S. J., Bogdan, R., & Lutfiyya, Z. M. (1995). *The variety of community experience: Qualitative studies of family and community life.* Baltimore, MD: Paul Brookes

References

Antonucci, T. C. (1986). Hierarchical mapping techniques. *Generations, Summer,* 10-12.

Baldwin, M. W. (1992). Relational schemas and the processing of social information. *Psychological Bulletin, 112,* 461-484.

Carling, P.J. (1998). *Return to community: Building support systems for people with psychiatric difficulties.* New York, NY: The Guildford Press.

Chadsey-Rusch, J., DeStefano, L., O'Reilly, M., & Collet-Klingenberg, L. (1992). Assessing the loneliness of workers with mental retardation. *Mental Retardation, 30,* 85-

92.

Clegg, J. A. & Standen, P. J. (1991). Friendship among adults who have developmental disabilities. *American Journal on Mental Retardation, 95,* 663-671.

Gottlieb. B. (1983). *Social support strategies: Guidelines for mental health practice.* Beverly Hills, CA: Sage.

Gottlieb, B. H. (1985). Assessing and strengthening the impact of social supports on mental health. *Social Work, 30,* 278-292.

Horowitz, A., Reinhard, S. C., & Howell-White, S. (1996). Caregiving as reciprocal exchanges in families with seriously mentally ill members. *Journal of Health and Social Behaviour, 37,* 149-162.

Koller, H., Richardson, S. A., & Katz, M. (1988). Marriage in a young adult mentally retarded population. *Journal of Mental Deficiency Research, 52,* 93-102.

Kraus, M. W., Seltzer, M. M., & Goodman, S. (1992). Social support networks of adults with mental retardation who live at home. *American Journal on Mental Retardation, 96,* 432-441.

Lakey, B., Tardiff, S., & Drew, B. (1994). Negative social interactions: Assessment and relations to social support, cognition, and psychological distress. *Journal of Social and Clinical Psychology, 13,* 42-62.

Lakey, B. & Drew, J. B. (1997). A social-cognitive perspective on social support. In G. R. Pierce, B. Lakey, & I. G. Sarason (Eds.), *Sourcebook of social support and personality* (pp. 112-140). New York, NY: Plenum.

Lunsky, Y. (1999, May). *Social support as a predictor of well-being for adults with mental retardation.* Paper presented at Academy on Mental Retardation Annual Meeting. New Orleans, LA.

Lunsky, Y. & Benson, B. A. (1997). Social support in supported living: A comparison of staff and consumer ratings. *American Journal on Mental Retardation, 102,* 280-284.

Lunsky, Y. & Benson, B. A. (1999). The social circles of adults with mental retardation, as viewed by their caregivers. *Journal of Developmental and Physical Disabilities, 11,* 115-129.

Lunsky, Y. & Benson, B. A. (in press). *Perceived social support and mental retardation: A social-cognitive approach. Cognitive Therapy and Research.*

Lunsky, Y. & Havercamp, S. M. (1999). Distinguishing low levels of social support and social strain: Implications for dual diagnosis. *American Journal on Mental Retardation, 104,* 200-204.

Meins, W. (1993). Prevalence and risk factors for depressive disorders in adults with intellectual disability. *Australia and New Zealand Journal on Developmental Disabilities,* 18, 147-156.

Meyer, C. H. (1985). Social supports and social work: Collaboration or conflict?". *Social Work, 30,* 293-300.

Neugeboren, J. (1999). *Transforming madness: New lives for people living with mental illness.* New York, NY: William Morrow and Company Inc.

Newton, J. S., Olsen, D., & Horner, R. H. (1995). Factors contributing to the stability of social relationships between individuals with mental retardation and other community members. *Mental Retardation, 33,* 383-393.

Nezu, C. M., Nezu, A. M., Rothenberg, J., DelliCarpini, L., & Groag, I. (1995). Depression in adults with mild mental retardation: Are cognitive variables involved? *Cognitive Therapy and Research, 19,* 227-239.

Nugent, J. & Spindel, P. (2000). *"Creating the context for empowerment: Empowering individuals and creating competent communities".* Toronto, Ontario: Nu-Spin Publishing.

Rapp, C. A. (1998). *The strengths model: Case management with people suffering from severe and persistent mental illness.* New York, NY: Oxford University Press.

Reiss, S. & Benson, B. (1985). Psychosocial correlates of depression in mentally retarded adults: I. Minimal social support and stigmatization. *American Journal of Mental Deficiency, 89,* 331-337.

Rook, K. (1984). The negative side of social interaction. *Journal of Personality and Social Psychology, 46,* 1097-1108.

Rosen, J. & Burchard, S. (1990). Community activities and social support networks: A social comparison of adults with and without mental retardation. *Education and Training in Mental Retardation, 25,* 193-204.

Sands, D. J. & Kozleski, E. B. (1994). Quality of life differences between adults with and without disabilities. *Education and Training in Mental Retardation and Developmental Disabilities, 29,* 90-101.

Sullivan, W. P. (1994). A long and winding road. *Innovations and Research, 3(3),* 20.

Vaillant, G. E. (1993). *The wisdom of the ego.* Cambridge, MA: Cambridge University Press.

Chapter 12

Offenders who have a Developmentally Disability

Dorothy M. Griffiths, Peggy Taillon-Wasmund, and
Debra Smith

Learning Objectives

Readers will be able to:

1. Describe why the rates of convicted offenders with developmental disabilities may be misleading.
2. Describe how the developmental disability may present a vulnerability for offending behaviour.
3. Identify how socio-environmental factors can increase a risk for offending behaviour.
4. Identify how the judicial and criminal justice system create risks for persons with developmental disabilities.
5. Describe the components of state of art treatment for offenders who are developmentally disabled.
6. Describe challenges experienced by persons with developmental disabilities who become the common clients of multiple government and agency sectors.

Introduction

In recent years, there has been increased recognition of the challenges that arise when persons with developmental disabilities become involved with the criminal justice system. Persons with developmental disabilities are generally law-abiding members of society. Like society as a whole, some citizens who have a developmental disability will, knowingly or unknowingly, break the law (Conley, Luckasson & Bouthilet, 1992). Individuals, disabled or non-disabled, commit crimes for a range of complex cognitive, social, emotional and economic reasons. There are specific risk factors that correlate highly with the life experiences of persons with developmental disabilities that increase their vulnerability to be perpetrators of certain crimes (Conley et al., 1992; Griffiths, in press). Although Day (2000) has suggested that offending behaviour is uncommon in persons with developmental disabilities, some persons with developmental disabilities will be required to interact with the legal system. In fact, persons with developmental disabilities tend to be overrepresented in their involvement with the legal system. The interaction with the court system may turn out to be a rather uneven and difficult process due to a number of factors. This chapter will review some of the issues related to this population.

Incidence

People with developmental disabilities represent 2-3% of the general population, but they represent 2-10% of the prison population (Baroff, 1996; Denkowski & Denkowski, 1985; Smith, Algozzine, Schmid, & Hennly, 1990), and the statistics are higher for juvenile facilities and jails (Petersilia, 2000). Prevalence rates vary greatly across studies depending on how the data were gathered. Most of the identified prison inmates with a developmental disability are considered mildly disabled (88%), although some (12%) have moderate or lower levels of intellectual disability (Kugel, 1986). Persons with a more severe disability are considered less likely to engage in criminal behaviour, or are diverted from the criminal justice system (Coffey, Procopiow, & Miller, 1989).

The range of criminal behaviour of persons with developmental disabilities is narrower, but similar to that of the non-disabled population (Day, 2000). The majority of offences are crimes of misdemeanour, less serious felonies, or public nuisance. Day (2000) suggests sex offences and arson are over-represented. The majority of the offences committed by persons with developmental disabilities are crimes against persons (e.g., sexual crimes), followed by crimes against property (e.g., arson) (Baroff, 1996; Noble & Conley, 1992).

Vulnerability for Criminal Behaviour among People with the Developmental Disabilities: Fact and Fiction

Dual Diagnosis as a Special Vulnerability

The focus of this chapter is on those individuals who possess a developmental disability, as well as a mental health problem, who are at risk to becoming, or who are currently entangled in the criminal justice system. There is high incidence of emotional and behavioural disorders among those with developmental disabilities (Stark, Menolasciona, Albarelli, & Gray, 1989). Among offenders, this rate is higher. White and Wood (1992) observed that 50% of juvenile offenders, and 56% of adult offenders in a special community probation/parole programme were developmentally disabled. In some programmes, the statistics are even higher (i.e., Day 1988).

People with a mental health problem as well as a developmental disability, present with many complex challenges that may include:

- multiple communication difficulties (e.g., many are unable to verbalise their needs or use picture symbols, sign language or other gestures),
- isolation,
- institutional life experience,
- forced living situations or lack of alternative housing,
- poverty,
- homelessness,
- dependency on others in social problem solving,
- complex medical problems,
- physical disabilities,
- labelling, social stigma and discrimination, and
- limit of choice of living situations.

Three Theories of Increased Vulnerability

As noted above, people with developmental disabilities are overrepresented in the criminal justice system, despite the fact that their crimes are of much less severity. Gardner, Graeber and Machkovitz (1998) reviewed three common theories of explanation for this: the relationship between criminality and disability, social/environmental influence, and the effects of the criminal justice system.

1. Criminality and Disability

At the beginning of the last century, there was common belief that disability was genetically linked to criminal behaviour (Scheerenburger, 1984). Owens (1982) has argued that crimes are committed by persons with disabilities for a number of reasons. They are: unemployed, need money, have emotional problems, follow others, seek approval, act out of impulse, show poor judgement, or have adopted a criminal lifestyle which they may enjoy. These are the same reasons witnessed in the non-disabled population.

While genetic causality for criminal behaviour among persons with developmental disabilities is no longer accepted, there still remains the argument that the nature of the disabling condition may create vulnerabilties that put the person with a disability more at risk for criminal behaviour. The quote cited below is an example:

> Most people with these disabilities have a deep need to be accepted, and sometimes agree to help with criminal activities in order to gain friendship. They may act as lookouts, transport drugs or other contraband, carry a forged check into a bank, or attempt to sell merchandise stolen by others. In an effort not to feel lonely and isolated from their friends, they may willingly go along with any scheme just to be included (Petersilia, 2000, p. 5).

Other authors have suggested the following risk factors associated with persons with disabilities and criminal behaviour:

- poor judgement (Santamour & West, 1977),
- lack of social and cognitive problem solving skills (Brown & Courtless, 1971),
- frustration against society (Santamour, 1989),
- increased risk of psychiatric disorders and associated challenges (Stark, Menolascino, Albarelli, & Gray, 1989), and
- suggestibility and susceptibility to those he/she perceives as having high status (Luckasson, 1988; Santamour, 1989).

Gardner et al. (1998) suggest that these cognitive and personal-social characteristics represent vulnerability features that combine with a variety of other social influences to increase the likelihood for criminal behaviour.

2. Social Environment and Crime

Day (2000) described the typical profile of an offender with a developmental disability as a young male, with mild to borderline intellectual disability, reared in a poor urban environment with a history of psychosocial deprivation, family criminality, behaviour problems/personality disorder, and who has spent considerable time in residential care. This profile was supported in the research by Denkowski and Denkowski (1986). The youths in this study were from poor, broken families, with high rates of mental health and substance abuse, where abuse or neglect was typical. Offenders with developmental disabilities are more likely to stem from low income minority groups (Harris, as cited in Petersilia (2000). In such a profile, the social learning environment is proposed as the basis for the criminal behaviour (Beier, 1964).

3. The Effects of the Criminal Justice System

A major thrust of current thinking places the responsibility for the elevated rates of persons with intellectual disabilities in the criminal justice system squarely on the shoulders of the judicial system. The judicial system faces an inherent challenge when people with developmental disabilities interact with the law. The challenge is to maximise the cognitive and social factors that may help the participants interact with the courts, and at the same time, satisfy the requirements of the legal system (Perlman, Ericson, Esses & Isaacs, 1994). Due to a number of factors (such as the discrepancy between cognitive capability and physical development, and the specialised life experience of persons labelled as developmentally disabled), the interaction with the court system may turn out to be rather challenging (Griffiths & Marini, 2000).

Most offenders with disabilities (75%) are not identified at arrest, and some (10%) are not identified until in prison (McAfee & Gural, 1988). The majority of offenders with developmental disabilities do not present with physical features that would distinguish them as being intellectually challenged to the lay observer. Additionally, people with a developmental disability present themselves in ways that often hide their disability (Edgerton, 1967). Underidentification could be the result of (i) inadequate testing, (ii) inadequate experience of psychologists and psychiatrists with persons with disabilities, (iii) the defendants' attempts to conceal the disability, and (iv) inadequate training of criminal justice personnel (i.e., judges, lawyers, and police) (Bonnie, 1992; McAfee & Gural, 1988; Schilit, 1989; Smith & Broughton, 1994).

Throughout the entire legal process (arrest and prior to trial, during incarceration, and following discharge), persons with developmental disabilities present greater vulnerability within the criminal justice system. See Table 1 for examples of the vulnerabilities associated with each stage of the justice and criminal process for persons with developmental disabilities.

Gardner et al. (1998) suggest that no single theory (Disability and Crime, Socio-Environmental or Criminal Justice Theory) offers a suitable explanation for the apparent disproportionately high percentage of offenders with disabilities in the criminal justice system. Each theory adds an element to our understanding of the challenges for prevention, intervention, treatment and support. However, the judicial and criminal justice system pose unique challenges for persons with developmental disabilities.

Challenges in the Criminal Justice System

Pertersilia (2000) expressed the dilemma facing the criminal justice system:

> On the one hand, we don't wish to excuse the criminal behaviours of offenders who are cognitively impaired. In a world where such persons are finally moving back into local communities and striving to be treated with equality, it would make no sense to demand a double standard in criminal justice matters. In a normalized world, one has to live within society's rules, and accept the consequences of one's actions.
>
> On the other hand, many offenders with cognitive disabilities may not be so much "lawbreakers" as they are low-functioning citizens who lack education on how to function responsibly in a complex society. Some research suggests that they are frequently used by other criminals to assist in law-breaking activities without understanding their involvement in a crime or its consequences (p. 5).

Table 1: Vulnerabilities and the Justice/Criminal System

Stage in Process	Vulnerabilities Experienced by Persons with Developmental Disability in the Justice/Criminal System
From arrest to trial, offenders who are developmentally disabled are more likely to be:	1. Disadvantaged in police interrogations because of impaired understanding of caution and legal rights, and as such, give false confessions (Leo & Ofshe, 1998), or seek approval of authority figures by giving what they believe are correct answers (Ellis & Luckasson, 1985), or confess, provide incriminating evidence, and not plea-bargain (Edwards & Reynolds, 1997; Gudjonsson, 1990); 2. Jailed during pretrial because of failure to meet bail or personal recognizance; people held pre-trial are generally more likely to be convicted (Toberg, 1992); 3. Declared unfit to stand trial (Valenti-Heins & Swartz, 1993 4. Convicted and receive longer terms than similar offenders without disabilities (Laski, 1992).
Once incarcerated, offenders who are developmentally disabled are:	1. Slow to adjust to expectations, and experience more rule infractions (Santamour & West, 1977; Smith et al., 1990); 2. Rarely provided a therapeutic experience or specialised services (Conley, Luckasson, & Bouthilet, 1992; McGee & Menolascino, 1992); 3. Given menial and poorly paid work (Cowardin, 1997),; 4. The target of practical jokes and victimisation (Gold, 1997; Reichard, Spenser, & Spooner, 1982; Sobsey, 1994); 5. Likely to show more maladaptive behaviour (MacEachron, 1979); 6. More likely to be re-classified to higher security levels because of poor institutional behaviour (Hall, 1992); 7. Less likely to experience early release, or parole (Lampert, 1987); 8. Considered poor risk for probation (Denkowski & Denkowski (1986); 9. More likely to serve a longer sentence (Santamour & Watson, 1982).
Upon release, offenders with developmental disabilities:	1. Are rarely placed in specialised caseloads or given additional assistance or rehabilitation; 2. Show higher and quicker rates (60%) of recidivism (Santamour, 1986, 1988; Santamour & West, 1977).

Participation of persons with developmental disabilities in the legal system is not only a fundamental right, but critical to the belief of normalization (Griffiths & Marini, 2000). If persons with developmental disabilities have the same legal rights as non-disabled persons, those who are accused of breaking the law must also be accountable to, and protected by, the same laws that govern us all. With appropriate supports to the courts, persons with developmental disabilities will be able to access their rights, and better assume their responsibilities in the law.

The nature of the disabling condition requires special understanding if fairness and justice are to be upheld for the individual with the disability who comes into contact with the legal system regarding sexual offences. "Access to the justice system is one of the most fundamental rights of all citizens, because without this access, individuals cannot legally defend any of their rights, and are forced to become dependent on others to advocate on their behalf" (Sobsey, 1994, p. 284).

The rights of persons with disabilities to participate in the judicial process are often unfairly restricted by physical and social access to the courts, rules of evidence, and courtroom procedures which fail to make reasonable accommodation to the diverse needs of the individual (Sobsey, 1994). There are several legal decisions that often restrict the access of persons with developmental disabilities in the courts: competence to be a witness, and fitness to stand trial.

Capable of being a witness: Increasingly, persons with developmental disabilities are being given the opportunity to appear as witnesses in court. However, the competence and credibility of such witnesses to give testimony that is valid, consistent, and accurate, is often still raised (Ericson, Isaacs & Perlman, 1999).

Capable of being a witness, in legal terms, means that the individual understands what it means to swear an oath, tell the truth, or communicate what happened. Individuals with developmental disabilities may well understand what is being said in a legal interview, but may need time and support to provide adequate answers (Roeher Institute, 1995). People who are unable to communicate that they understand a promise may be denied the opportunity to give testimony, even if they can communicate what happened to them, and they can show that they have not fabricated a story (Richler, 1995).

Fitness to stand trial: The law assumes that all people accused of a crime are presumed innocent, and entitled to fair and just trial. In order for the accused to receive a fair trial, s/he must be able to understand the charges, and to assist in his or her own defence (such as giving direction to one's legal counsel). This forms the basis for the concept of fitness to stand trial. According to the Criminal Code of Canada (1999), 'unfit to stand trial on account of a mental disorder' means that the person is unable to understand the nature or object of the proceedings, understand the possible consequences of the proceedings, or communicate with counsel.

There are several common misunderstandings about fitness. First, just because a person is capable of being a witness does not mean s/he is fit to stand trial. The legal situation, when a person with developmental disabilities is involved with the courts, can be very complicated. For example a person may be: competent to be a witness, but not have the capacity to stand trial; competent to stand trial, but not be competent to participate in all phases of the trial; or competent to stand trial, but not be competent to plead guilty (Valenti-Hein & Schwartz, 1993).

Second, 'fitness' does not mean the person has the capability of acting in his or her own best interests. A person does not necessarily have to make rational decisions that benefit him or herself.

Third, 'fitness' is not the same as 'not criminally responsible'. Fitness is a test of competence at the time of trial; 'not criminally responsible' involves whether the person was, at the time of the criminal activity, able to appreciate the nature and quality of the act for which s/he has been charged. The burden of proof 'for not criminally responsible' is often quite cumbersome and time consuming, and, as such, many parties do not apply the provision.

Fourth, if someone commits an offence, but does not understand the ramifications of his/her actions, s/he is still culpable. In law, ignorance is no excuse. Therefore, even when a person does not know that his/her action breached a law, s/he is still considered responsible for the act.

Fifth, 'unfitness to stand trial' is not equal to developmental delay. In one study, only one-third of defendants identified as "intellectually disabled" were unfit to stand trial; the likelihood of incompetency to stand trial was more likely when the severity of intellectual disability was increased (Petrella, 1995). Generally, individuals with mild and moderate developmental disability are able to interact with the legal system; individuals with severe and profound intellectual disability are often excluded from participation in the legal process (Doe,

1995).

The results from a standardised and individually-administered IQ test are often used to determine the general level of intellectual functioning of the individual. However, these tests pose a particular danger of misinterpretation by the criminal justice system (Fedoroff, Griffiths, Marini, & Richards, 2000). It is vital that the expert witness, who is providing the psychological evaluation, understands that an evaluation of an individual's cognitive ability is more than just an IQ score. It is not just a number, but a continuum of skills that represent both quantitative but qualitative differences in abilities and a different developmental pattern, in both timing and degree (McGee & Menolascino, 1992).

With few exceptions, there are no formal and validated procedures to evaluate fitness to stand trial for persons with developmental disabilities (Everington & Dunn, 1995). Therefore, many defendants are tried without adequate fitness assessment (Bonnie, 1992; Conley, Luckason & Bouthilet, 1992). Assessment of these factors has been standardised in the Competence Assessment for Standing Trial for Defendants with Mental Retardation (CAST-MR) (Everington & Luckasson, 1992; Everington & Dunn, 1995). While standardised assessments like the CAST-MR are helpful, they cannot replace clinical assessment (Fedoroff et al., 2000).

There are several differences noted between persons with developmental disabilities who are fit to stand trial and those deemed unfit. Research has noted differences in their understanding of their legal situation and the potential consequences (Petrella, 1995). Persons with developmental disabilities who are found unfit generally have difficulty providing a coherent narrative about the event. Their understanding of, and ability to participate in the evaluation process, is an important factor in determining fitness (Petrella, 1995). Smith and Hudson (1995) found the understanding of courtroom procedures to be highly correlated with findings of fitness in persons with developmental disabilities. They are understanding of:

- court strategy,
- the concept of pleading,
- the concept of giving testimony, and
- the concept of a jury.

Communication plays a large role in attempting to determine someone's fitness. Persons with developmental disabilities: (i) may reverse terms such as "guilty" and "not guilty" (Smith, 1992), (ii) rarely say they do not understand unless they are asked, (iii) have difficulty following run-on sentences or multiple questions, and (iv) may use pronouns incorrectly or out of context (Ericson et al., 1994). In addition to verbal challenges, many people who have a developmental disability have co-morbid physical disabilities, such as impaired hearing, sight or mobility (Ericson et al., 1994). Many people with a developmental disability communicate through pictures, symbols or physical gestures. If assistive communication systems are not used when needed, errors may be made in assessing cognitive skills, including fitness (Ericson, et al., 1994). In some cases, where the person with a developmental disability uses an alternative communication method, the interviewer may need the assistance of someone who can interpret the information. Although it is helpful if the interpreter is familiar with the individual, great care must be taken to ensure that it is the accused and not the interpreter who is assessed (Fedoroff et al., 2000).

The recommendation of 'fitness to stand trial' is made to the court by a physician. However, it is up to the court to make the final judgement. If a person is deemed unfit to stand trial, the legal proceeding must be "set aside". Often the person is sent to a secure psychiatric facility until s/he is fit to stand trial, at which time the court can proceed. This law was basically designed for those who were unfit due to a mental health problem, and whose lack of fitness may be transitory. In some cases, the court will make a "treat to fit" disposition to order necessary treatment to make the person fit for trial (i.e., psychiatric, training in court procedures). However, for many persons with developmental disabilities, fitness may never be achieved. Consequently, the person with developmental disabilities may remain in a psychiatric facility indefinitely being unable to establish fitness and exercise his or her right to a trial (See Fedoroff et al., 2000).

Challenges to Treatment

Traditional approaches to criminal justice intervention for people with a developmental disability and a mental health problem are often ineffective. It is socially accepted that if one commits a crime, swift punishment that is rehabilitative and restorative in nature should follow, in order for the offender to become a contributing member of society. Often, people with a developmental disability and a mental health problem who have committed a crime, especially a non-serious offence, are not acting out of disregard of social laws and norms. Rather, their offence is symptomatic of larger social problems, such as poverty, homelessness, or another life crisis. Placing such people in the criminal justice system is simply **victimising the victim** that only serves to create a cycle of recidivism and eventual habitual conflicts.

Charging a homeless person with a criminal offence and moving him/her through the justice system will not address the issues that contributed to his/her homelessness in the first place. Developmental disability, mental health problems, communication difficulties, complex medical needs, and lack of viable supports are linked to homelessness. By peeling away the layers and examining the broader issues, and looking at the person's life, one can begin to address why s/he is in crisis. Simply put, non-serious offences committed by a vast majority of this population are symptomatic of broader personal, systemic, and social issues, not criminal ones.

Day (2000) suggests that offending in the population of persons with developmental disabilities "occurs in the context of undersocialization, poor internal controls, and faulty social learning compounded by educational underachievement, lack of social and occupational skills, and poor self-concept" (p. 361).

The criminal justice system is designed to provide secure containment of prisoners, and to maintain order with a hope that the punitive procedures will produce an inhibiting effect on criminal behaviour. However, as Gardner et al. (1998) suggest, the premise is based on the belief that the offender has an alternative prosocial behaviour that he or she can select to use after release. This assumption may be faulty when referring to persons with developmental disabilities. A skill development approach to habilitation is required if there is to be effective change in the behaviour post incarceration (Gardner et al., 1998).

Treatment is therefore targeted toward reducing some of the vulnerabilities that have put this individual at risk of offending. In order to develop an individualised treatment plan, a comprehensive evaluation is necessary. This includes a detailed history (individual and family, the offence and how the person perceives it), medical and mental status examinations, and other related areas, such as personality tests, adaptive functioning, and EEG studies. This forms the basis for treatment planning (Day, 2000). This history and evaluation is totally different from the purpose of the evaluation conducted prior to the trial. Part of the assessment might be evaluation of dangerousness or likelihood of recidivism. There are several clinical tools for evaluating risk assessment (See Resources below). Treatment then flows from the identification of individual vulnerabilities and needs.

Treatment of the dually diagnosed offender poses additional concerns. First, there is the treatment of symptoms of the mental disorder (i.e., medications to treat underlying psychiatric conditions). However, there is no evidence that medication alone represents effective treatment, since it neglects all of the social and environmental factors. The offending behaviours of those with a developmental disability may reflect the influence of a broad range of biomedical, psychological and social-environmental factors. Therefore, treatment must correspond to address the array of factors that directly or indirectly contribute to the offending behaviour (Gardner et al., 1998). In order to address the broader biopsychosocial needs of persons with developmental disabilities (See Chapter 3).

Gardner et al.. (1998) have suggested that treatment programmes should address the major factors contributing to a person's criminal behaviour, which may include:

- limited understanding of the nature and consequences of the behaviour;

- impulse control under conditions of increased emotional arousal;
- limited internalised inhibitions under conditions of temptation;
- low self-esteem;
- deficits in internalised social (moral) standards of conduct;
- limited skills in postponing immediate gratification;
- limited conflict resolution skills;
- limited skills in viewing oneself as accountable or responsible for one's actions; and
- other personal factors that may relate to an undersocialised personality, such as isolation and loneliness, or limited social, sexual, vocational or community skills which serve as vulnerabilities for re-offence.

The treatment plan should reflect habilitative rather than rehabilitative intervention. The rehabilitative model rests on the premise that the offender at some time possessed the skills necessary to live a non-offending lifestyle. Whereas, the habilitative model, which is more apt for persons with developmental and mental disabilities (dual diagnosis), is based on the understanding that the person never possessed the skills. Gardner and associates (1998) suggest that the rehabilitative model is faulty when applied to offenders with developmental disabilities because it assumes that they were at some time able to demonstrate some level of personal or social independence.

Day (2000) identified nine key components of a treatment package that offenders may need. They include: (i) providing a legal framework, (ii) life skills training (personal and interpersonal, social, occupational, education, recreational and sociosexual), (iii) counselling and supportive psychotherapy, (iv) treatment/ amelioration of medical distress and mental illness,

(v) socialization programmes, (vi) psychological treatment (self management and coping strategies, or specific pro- grammes for sex offenders or arsonists), vii) drug therapy, (viii) family and caregiver support, and (ix) rehabilitation, af- tercare and relapse prevention. For a complete description of these programmes see Day (2000). Each treatment package would, however, be carefully designed based on the individual needs of the offender.

Additionally, criminal behaviour occurs in a socio- environmental context (Gardner et al., 1998). If the individual returns to the subculture that encouraged a criminal lifestyle, there is little likelihood of positive and sustaining change. Thus, treatment must address issues related to the challenges presented by the environment. Treatment is best done in a community that offers more opportunity for socialization and training (Day, 2000) and generalization (Gardner et al., 1998). Individuals may remain with their families or community-care programme, and use the range of community supports. In some cases, treatment must coincide with alternative placement to reduce the likelihood that the person is exposed to these influ- ences (Gardner et al., 1998). Most critical, according to Day (2000), is access to a full weekly occupational training pro- gramme to build skills and give people something to do. White and Wood (1988) and Wood and White (1992) provide a de- scription of community programmes. Day (2000) suggests that hospitalised treatment may be required for some if the offence history is serious or persistent, the person poses a danger to the public, or if there is a need for supervision, assessment and treatment that cannot be provided in the community.

Specialized Programmes for the Offender with a Developmental Disability

No single programme can meet the requirements of all offenders with a developmental disability. There is a need for a continuum of treatment options ranging from community treatment and probation programmes, through specialised programmes in forensic mental health facilities, to those involving maximum security in correctional services (Gardner et al., 1998).

Gardner et al. (1998) identify seven model programmes:

1. Interventions for persons determined incompetent to proceed (Norley, 1995),
2. Community parole/probation model (Wood & White, 1992),
3. Community adolescent repeated offender programme (Denkowski & Denkowski, 1985, 1986),
4. Intensive treatment model (Finn, 1995),
5. Developmental residence for adult repeat offenders (Day 1983, 1988),
6. Prison (Hall, 1992; Pugh, 1986), and
7. Specialized treatment for those with a dual diagnosis.

Bridging the Gaps Between Sectors and Services

Professionals from mental hospitals claim that the developmentally disabled offender is not mentally ill. Developmental services often do not have services adapted for the offender. Correctional services would like to remove such persons from their setting, since they are both inadequate and inappropriate for persons who have a developmental disability (Brown &

Courtless, 1967).

In the mental health system, although the presumed mental illness that contributed to the criminal act may be treated, other critical issues (i.e., social skills or vocational needs) go untreated, leaving the person vulnerable to repeated criminal behaviour (McGee & Menolascino, 1992). In developmental services, the typical habilitation services are not sufficiently specialised and diverse to address the needs of the offender (Laski, 1992). In the correctional facilities, persons with developmental disabilities: are victimised by more able inmates, disrupt the programme routine of the facility, and present security risks and training needs that most facilities are unable to meet (Gardner et al., 1998). Brown and Courtless (1967, 1971) suggest that the correctional facilities are ill-equipped in both staff and physical facilities to meet the training and care needs of individuals with more significant challenges. Persons with developmental disabilities require treatment and care in the health and welfare systems, rather than punishment in the criminal justice system (Day 2000).

The concept of a kaleidoscope provides an analogy that identifies what happens to the person with developmental disabilities, and mental health challenges, who faces a criminal charge. S/he is the **common client** of a labyrinth of developmental, mental health, and health services, and the criminal justice system, including the courts, parole and the police. Although the person never changes while moving through this labyrinth s/he will experience an ever changing pattern of interactions, similar to that of a kaleidoscope that changes as it moves. The pieces are the same as when it started out, but as it moves, the kaleidoscope looks different, especially as different people look at it from their various perspectives.

A person who is charged with a criminal offence must wade through the maze of the many systems that are attached to the charge. If an individual is placed on probation following his/her many court appearances, s/he is forced to deal with the bureaucracy of another vast system that is extremely inundated with high volumes of cases to manage. The common client has moved through a number of different systems, and most likely has had several evaluations and labels attached to him/her.

Usually, files are not transferred between systems, and the language varies when a new system picks up the case. All systems label the person something different. Developmental services may identify the person as having Down Syndrome. Mental health may recognize that this person is struggling with a developmental disability as well as a personality disorder, and is dually diagnosed. Justice may label the person an offender. Corrections may label the person according to the offence, and the level of risk associated with it. If the person has an addiction, this will become part of the label. Again, the person has not changed; yet, s/he has been labelled in several different ways, and viewed differently depending on how the kaleidoscope has moved.

In recent years, government sectors and the agencies that report to them, have recognized the need for collaboration and coordination. Reform has to start with a multi-governmental, multi-agency and multi-disciplinary approach that truly focuses on the best interest of the person.

Five key systems must combine resources and establish best practices to respond to those people with a developmental disability and a mental health problem. These are as follows: mental health, developmental services, police, courts, and corrections. Intervention could occur at various points in the system:

Figure 1– Target Areas for Intervention

(i) Prevention

(iv)
Post sentencing
Custody
Community supervision
Ease management
Risk assessment
Release planning
Conditional or
unconditional release

(ii)
Incidence response
Investigation
Intervention
Laying charges/Diversion
Information

(iii)
Pre-trial release
Pre-trial remand
Psychiatric assessment
Fitness determination
Trial
Pre-sentencing report
Sentencing

Petersilia (2000) made the following suggestions for accomodating persons with developmental disabilities in the criminal justice system:

1. Increased justice-related education for clients and their family/care providers;
2. Establishment of a legal advocate to assist arrestees;
3. Routine education of justice system personnel on developmental disabilities;
4. Implementation of a system to identify offenders with developmental disabilities at jail intake;
5. Education of public defenders on how to represent people with disabilities;
6. Establishment of appropriate sentencing options for people with developmental disabilities, including diversion where appropriate; and
7. Management of the transition from prison to community.

Summary

People with developmental disabilities have a statistically increased risk of being accused of a crime. However, when they become entangled in the justice system, they have a real risk of being deemed unfit to stand trial, or being escorted through the system without their special needs being recognised or accommodated. Appropriate habilitative treatment is rarely provided.

There is no simplistic solution to the reduction of criminal offence among those labelled as developmentally disabled, nor to creating appropriate support and treatment for those who have become involved in the criminal justice system. However, the recent recognition of the inadequacy of the system to support the offender who is developmentally disabled is a first step.

Do You Know?

1. What is the difference between **fitness to stand trial** and **not criminally responsible**?
2. What does the term **common client** mean, and what challenges does being a common client present to the person with developmental disabilities who has been accused of a crime?
3. Why have typical correctional approaches failed with persons with developmental disabilities? What type of treatment could be used to prevent offences or reduce repeated offences in persons with developmental disabilities?

Resources

Day, K. (2000). Treatment and care of mentally retarded offenders. In A. Dosen & K. Day (Eds.), **Treating mental illness and behaviour disorders in children and adults with mental retardation** (pp. 359-390). Washington DC: American Psychiatric Press.

Everington, C.T. & Luckasson, R. (1992). **Competency assessment for standing trial (CAST-MR)**. Orlando Park, Ill.: International Diagnostic Systems Inc.

Mikkelsen E.J. & Stelk, W.J. (1999). **Criminal offenders with mental retardation: Risk assessment and the continuum of community-based treatment programs.** Kingston, NY: NADD Press.

Quinsey, V.L., Harris, G.L., Rice, M.E., & Cormier C. A. (1998). **Violent offenders: Appraising and managing risk.** Washington DC: American Psychological Association.

References

Baroff, T.S. (1996). The mentally retarded offender. In J. W. Jacobson & J.A. Mulick (Eds.), **Manual of diagnosis and professional practice in mental retardation** (pp. 311-321). Washington, DC: American Psychological Association.

Beier, D. C. (1964). Behavioural disturbance in the mentally retarded. In H. Stevens & R. Heber (Eds,). **Mental retardation: A review of research** (pp. 453-488). Chicago: University of Chicago Press.

Bonnie, R.J. (1992). The competency of defendants with mental retardation to assist in their own defense. In R. W. Conley, R. Luckasson, & G.N. Bouthilet (Eds.), **The criminal justice system and mental retardation** (pp. 97-120). Baltimore: Brookes.

Brown, B. & Courtless, T. (1967). **The mentally retarded offender.** Washington, DC: The President's Commission on Law Enforcement and Administration of Justice.

Brown, B. & Courtless T. (1971). **The mentally retarded offender.** Washington, DC: Center on Studies of Crime and Delinquency, National Institute of Mental Retardation.

Coffey, O.D., Procopiow, N. & Miller, N. (1989). **Programming for mentally retarded and learning disabled inmates: A guide for correctional administrators.** Washington DC: National Institute of Corrections.

Conley, R.W., Luckasson, R., & Bouthilet, G.N. (Eds.) (1992). **The criminal justice system and mental retardation.** Baltimore: Brookes.

Cowardin, N. (1997). Advocating for learning disability accommodation in prisons. **Wisconsin Defender, 5,** 1-14.

Day, K. (1983). A hospital-based psychiatric unit for mentally handicapped adults. **Mental Handicaps, 11,** 140-147.

Day, K. (1988). A hospital-based treatment programme for male mentally handicapped offenders. **British Journal of Psychiatry, 153,** 635-644.

Day, K. (2000). Treatment and care of mentally retarded offenders. In A. Dosen & K. Day (Eds.), **Treating mental illness and behaviour disorders in children and adults with mental retardation** (pp. 359-390). Washington DC: American Psychiatric Press.

Denkowski, G.C. & Denkowski, K.M. (1985). The mentally retarded offender in the state prison system: Identification, prevalence, adjustment and rehabilitation. **Criminal Justice and Behavior 12,** 55-70.

Denkowski, G.C. & Denkowski, K.M. (1986). Group home designs for initiating community based treatment with mentally retarded adolescent offenders. **Journal of Behavior Therapy and Experimental Psychiatry, 14,** 141-145.

Doe, T. (1995). Access to justice and children with disabilities. In Roeher Institute (Ed.), **As if children matter: Perspectives on children, rights and disability** (pp.49-56). Toronto: Roeher Institute.

Edgerton, R. (1967). **The cloak of competence.** Los Angeles: University of California Press.

Edwards, W. & Reynolds, L. (1997). **Defending and advocating on behalf of individual with "mild" mental retardation in the criminal justice system,** IMPACT 10(2). University of Minnesota College of Education and Human Development, Minneapolis.

Ellis, J.W. & Luckasson, R.A. (1985). Mentally retarded criminal defendants. **George Washington Law Review,** *53,* 414-493.

Ericson, K., Isaccs, B., & Perlman, N. (1999). Enhancing communication: The special case of interviewing victim-witnesses of sexual abuse. In I. Brown & M. Percy (Eds.), **Developmental disabilities in Ontario** (pp. 453-462). Toronto: Front Porch Publishing.

Ericson, K., Perlman, N., & Isaacs, B. (1994). Witness competency, communication issues and people with developmental disabilities. **Developmental Disabilities Bulletin,** *22,* 101-109.

Fedoroff, P., Griffiths, D., Marini, Z. & Richards, D. (2000). One of our clients has been arrested for sexual assault. Now what? The interplay between developmental and legal delay. **Bridging the Gap Conference Proceedings** (7th Annual NADD Conference). Kingston, NY: NADD

Finn, J. (1995). Center for intensive treatment. Unpublished manuscript [Available from John W. Finn, Bureau of Forensic Services, Office of Mental Retardation and Developmental Disabilities, 44 Holland Avenue, Albany, NY 12229-0001]

Gardner, W.I., Graeber, J.L. & Machkovitz S.J. (1998). Treatment of offenders with mental retardation. In Robert M. Wettstein (Ed.), **Treatment of offenders with mental disorders** (pp. 329-364). New York: Guilford Press.

Gold, S. (1997). **Amicus Curiae Brief,** Pennsylvania Department of Corrections vs Yeskey, US Supreme Court, No 97-634, October.

Griffiths (in press). Sexual aggression. In W. I. Gardner (Ed.), **Aggression and persons with developmental disabilities**. Kingston, NY: NADD Press.

Griffiths, D, Gardner, W.I. & Nugent, J. (1998). **Community behavior supports.** Kingston, NY: NADD Press.

Grifiths, D. & Marini, Z. (2000). Interacting with the legal system regarding a sexual offence: Social and cognitive considerations for persons with developmental disabilities. **Journal on Developmental Disabilities,** *7*, 76-121.

Gudjonsson, G.H. (1990). The relationship of intellectual skills to suggestibility, compliance and acquiescence. **Personality and Individual Differences, 11,** 227-231.

Hall, J.N. (1992). Correctional services for inmates with mental retardation: Challenge or catastrophe? In R.W. Conley, R. Luckasson. & G.N. Bouthilet (Eds.), **The criminal justice system and mental retardation** (pp. 167-190.) Baltimore: Brookes.

Kugel, R.B. (1986*).* **Changing patterns in residential services for the mentally retarded.** Washington, DC: President's Committee on Mental Retardation.

Lampert, R.O. (1987). The mentally retarded offender in prison. **Justice Professional,** *2,* 60-69.

Laski, F.J. (1992). Sentencing the offender with mental retardation: Honoring the imperative for immediate punishments and probation. In R.W. Conley, R. Luckasson, & G. N. Bouthilet (Eds.), **The criminal justice system and mental**

retardation (pp. 137-152). Baltimore: Brookes.

Leo, R. & Ofshe, R. (1998). The consequences of false confessions: Deprivations of liberty and miscarriages of justice in the age of psychological interrogation. **The Journal of Criminal Law and Criminology,** *88,* 1-68.

Luckasson, R. (1988). The dually diagnosed client in the criminal justice system. In J.A. Stark, F.J. Menalascino, M. H. Albarelli, &V.C. Gray (Eds.*),* **Mental retardation and mental health** (pp. 354-360). New York: Springer-Verlag.

MacEachron, A.E. (1979). Mentally retarded offenders: Prevalence and characteristics. **American Journal of Mental Deficiency,** *84,* 165-176.

McAfee, J.K. & Gural, M. (1988). Individuals with mental retardation and the criminal justice system. In R. W. Conley, R. Luckasson, & G.N. Boutilet (Eds.), **The criminal justice system and mental retardation** (pp.55-77). Baltimore: Brookes.

McGee, J. & Menolascino, F.J. (1992). The evaluation of defendants with mental retardation in the criminal justice system. In R. W. Conley, R. Luckasson, & G.N. Bouthilet (Eds.), **The criminal justice system and mental retardation** (pp. 55-77). Baltimore: Brookes.

Noble, J.H. & Conley, R.W. (1992). Toward an epidemiology of relevant attributes. In R.W. Conley, R. Luckasson, & G. N. Bouthilet (Eds.), **The criminal justice system and mental retardation** (pp. 17-53). Baltimore: Brookes.

Norley, D. (1995). Program descriptions: The mentally retarded defendant program. Unpublished manuscript. [Available from author, 529 North Sans Souci Avenue, Deland, FL 32720].

Owens C. (1982). **The black mentally retarded offender: Concerns and challenges.** In A. R. Harvey & T. L. Carr (Eds.), The black mentally retarded offender (pp. 27-38). New

York: United Church of Christ.

Perlman, N.B., Ericson, K.I., Esses, V.M. & Isaacs, B.J. (1994). The developmentally handicapped witness: Competency as a function of question format. **Law and Human Behaviour, 18**, 171-188.

Petersilia, J. (2000*).* **Doing justice? Criminal offenders with developmental disabilities.** University of California, Berkeley: California Policy Research Centre.

Petrella, R.C. (1995). Defendants with a developmental disability in the forensic services systems. In R.W. Conley, R. Luckasson, & G.N. Bouthilet (Eds.*),* **The criminal justice system and mental retardation: Defendants and victims** (pp. 79-96). Baltimore: Paul H. Brookes.

Pugh, M. (1986).The mentally retarded offenders program of the Texas Department of Corrections. **Prison Journal,** *66,* 39-51.

Reichard, C.L., Spenser, J., & Spooner, F. (1982). The mentally retarded defendant-offender. In M. Santamour (Ed.), **The retarded offender** (pp. 121-139). New York: Praeger.

Richler, D. (1995). The United Nations Convention on the Rights of the Child: A tool for advocacy. In Roeher Insitute (Ed*).,* **As if children matter: Perspectives on children, rights and disability.** Toronto, Canada: Roeher Institute.

Roeher Institute (1995). **Harm's way: The many faces of violence and abuse against persons with disabilities.** Toronto: Author.

Santamour, M. (1986). The offender with mental retardation. **The Prison Journal,** *66,* 3-18.

Santamour, M. (1988). **The mentally retarded offender and corrections.** Laurel, MD: American Correctional Association.

Santamour, M. (1989). **The mentally retarded offender and corrections: An updated prescriptive package.** Washington, DC: St. Mary's Press.

Santamour, M. & Watson, P. (Eds.) (1982). **The retarded offender.** New York: Praeger.

Santamour, M. & West , B. (1977*).* **The mentally retarded offender and corrections.** Washington, DC: Law Enforcement Assistance Administration, Department of Corrections.

Scheerenburger, R.C. (1984). **The history of mental retardation.** Baltimore, MD.: Brookes.

Schilit, J. (1989). The mentally retarded offender and criminal justice personnel. **Exceptional Children,** *56,* 16-22.

Smith, S.A. (1992). Confusing the terms "guilty" and "not guilty": Implications for alleged offenders with mental retardation. **Psychological Reports,** *73,* 675-678.

Smith, D., Algozzine, B., Schmid, R. & Hennly, T. (1990). Prison adjustment of youthful inmates with mental retardation. **Mental Retardation,** *28,* 177-181.

Smith, S.A. & Broughton, S.F. (1994). Competency to stand trial and criminal responsibility: An analysis in South Carolina. **Mental Retardation,** *32,* 281-287.

Smith, S.A., & Hudson, R.L. (1995). A quick screening test of competency to stand trial for defendants with mental retardation. **Psychological Reports,** *76,* 91-97.

Sobsey, D. (1994). **Violence and abuse in the lives of people with disabilities: The end of silence acceptance.** Baltimore, MD: Brookes.

Stark, J.A., Menolascino, F.J., Albarelli, M.H. & Gray, V.C. (Eds.), (1989). **Mental retardation and mental health: Classification, diagnosis, treatment, services.** New York: Springer-Verlag.

Toberg, M.A. (1992*).* **Pretrial release: A national evaluation of practice and outcomes.** McLean, Va: Lazar Instiute.

Valenti-Hein, D.C. & Schwartz L.D. (1993). Witness competency in people with mental retardation: Implications for prosecution of sexual abuse. **Sexuality and Disability, 11,** 287-294.

White B.L. & Wood, H. (1992). The Lancaster county mentally retarded offenders programme. In J.A. Stark, F.J. Menalascino, M.H. Albarelli, & V.C. Gray (Eds.), **Mental retardation and mental health: Classification, diagnosis, treatment, services**. New York: Springer-Verlag.

Chapter 13

Sexuality and Mental Health Issues

Dorothy M. Griffiths, Debbie Richards, Paul Fedoroff, and
Shelley L. Watson

Learning Objectives

Readers will be able to:

1. Compare the sexual wellness of persons with
   developmental disabilities to the sexual health of non-
   disabled persons.
2. Define sexual abuse of persons with developmental
   disabilities and apply the double-edged definition to
   the history and life experiences of persons labelled as
   disabled.
3. Identify the key mental health challenges that relate to
   the sexuality of persons with developmental disabilities and how the disability may create increased risks.
4. Identify appropriate treatment options for persons with
   developmental disabilities who present with sexual
   challenges.

Introduction

The sexuality of persons with developmental disabilities raises
serious mental health issues. It is actually not the sexuality of
persons with disabilities, but how society has misunderstood

and responded to their sexuality, that pose challenges for their mental health. Myths regarding the sexuality of persons with developmental disabilities have contributed to more than a century of abuse and repression for persons who have been labelled (Griffiths, 1999), and have created an increased risk that persons with developmental disabilities will develop sexuality related problems. In this chapter, the following topics related to persons labelled as developmentally disabled will be explored:

1. Sexuality as a normal part of mental well-being,
2. Sexuality as a mental health risk
3. Sexual abuse: Unwanted forced sexual contact
4. Sexual abuse: Restricted sexuality
5. Mental health risk factors associated with sexually inappropriate behaviour

1. Sexuality as a part of mental well-being

Healthy sexuality is essential to mental wellness. The necessary requirements for the development of healthy sexuality have been identified by the World Health Organization (1975). They are as follows: (i) the establishment of the capacity to enjoy and control sexual and reproductive behaviour in accordance with social and personal ethics; (ii) freedom from fear, shame, guilt, false beliefs, and other psychological factors that inhibit sexual response and the establishment of sexual relationships; and (iii) freedom from organic disorders, diseases, and deficiencies that interfere with sexual and reproductive functions.

In reality, the World Health Organization criteria for sexual health is not being met for most persons who are developmentally disabled. Facts are as follow:

1. Persons with developmental disabilities are less likely to have control over their sexuality and reproduction.
2. They often experience restriction, punishment and recrimination regarding their sexuality, and are further denied privacy, opportunity, knowledge and choice regarding their sexual expression. They are more often the victims of sexual assault and abuse.
3. They are more likely to experience physical and medical challenges that interfere with their sexual experience and reproduction. As shown in Table 1: Syndromes and Effects on Sexuality, many conditions common among persons with developmental disabilities may have sexual implications.

Thus on all three levels, the sexual well-being of persons with developmental disabilities is jeopardized.

2. Sexuality as a mental health risk

One of the silent mental health challenges for persons with developmental disabilities is sexual abuse. For the purpose of this chapter, the following definition will be adopted.

> Sexual abuse is defined as including unwanted or forced sexual contact, unwanted touching or displays of sexual parts, threats of harm or coercion in connection with sexual activity; denial of sexuality, denial of sexual education and information, forced abortion or sterilisation (The Roeher Institute, 1994, p. vi).

Table 1: Syndromes* and their effects on sexuality

Syndrome*	Gender Affected	Effect(s) on Sexuality
Asperger's Syndrome	7:1 male to female ratio	Inappropriate sexual behaviour due to social skill deficits
Down Syndrome	Males and females	Males are generally sterile; Fertility rate in females is low
Fetal Alcohol Syndrome	Males and females	Inappropriate sexual behaviour related to impulsivity
Klinefelter Syndrome	Specific to males	Hypogonadism Gynecomastia Delayed development of secondary sexual characteristics Lack of sperm; usually sterile Elevated gonadotropic hormones Decreased libido
Noonan Syndrome	Males and females	Cryptorchidism Gonadal defects vary from severe deficiency to apparently normal sexual development
Prader-Willi Syndrome	Males and females	Hypogonadism; Small penis Underdevelopment of genitals and breasts Cryptorchidism
Rubinstein-Taybi Syndrome	Males and females	Cryptorchidism
Smith-Magenis Syndrome	Males and females	Polyembolokoilamania
Tourette's Syndrome	3-4 times more common in males	Inappropriate sexual activity due to impulsivity associated with comorbid ADHD Inappropriate touching due to complex motor tics
Turner's Syndrome	Specific to females	Infertility; Ovarian dysgenesis May lack secondary sexual characteristics
William's Syndrome	Males and females	Menstrual problems Inappropriate sexual behaviour due to increased sociability

*The syndromes on this table have been selected by the authors as samples only. Other syndromes may also have sexually related issues.

3. Sexual Abuse: Unwanted or forced sexual contact

The sexual abuse of persons with developmental disabilities will be explored relative to the incidence, causes, impact of abuse on mental health, and its consequences. The relationship between abuse as a serious mental health risk will be identified.

Incidence:

In the early 1990s, researchers increased the awareness among the developmental disability field as to the widespread sexual abuse and exploitation of persons with developmental disabilities. One study reported that 75-85% of women with developmental disabilities, living in community residential programmes, had experienced sexual assault (Davis, 1989). The majority of offences occurred in private homes (57.3%), or settings where services were being received, such as group homes (8.5%), institutions (7.7%), hospitals (1.7%), rehabilitation services (4.3%) (Mansell, Sobsey, & Calder, 1992).

The research by Mansell and her associates indicates that persons with developmental disabilities were abused at the hands of family members, neighbours, or babysitters, just as were non-handicapped persons. However, they were also at increased risk of abuse from other persons with disabilities, especially when clustered with potential offenders in residential programmes, and from persons in a care-giving role or those who gain access to the person through the disability services. The offenders were typically male, and were known to the victim (Sobsey, 1994; Mansell et al., 1992).

In a study involving 119 victims of sexual abuse, Mansell et al.

(1992) reported that abuse was generally repetitive (10.3%), or had occurred on many occasions (53.8%). Only 19.2% of the victims reported that the abuse had been singular, or had occurred 2-10 times (16.7%).

Cause:

The person's disability is not the direct cause of the increased vulnerability for abuse. The social conditions and systems, in which persons with developmental disabilities must interact as a result of their disability, create the increased risk (Griffiths et al., 1996, Roeher Institute, 1988, Sobsey, 1994). Several risk factors have been associated with the social conditions in which most persons with developmental disabilities find themselves. They include the following:

- social isolation and economic disadvantage;
- reliance on caregivers, who may lack training and support;
- lack of opportunity to gain socio-sexual knowledge, or to access social interactions;
- lack of empowerment and concurrent emphasis on compliance;
- limited communication or credibility;
- socialized tolerance for a breach of socio-sexual boundaries; and
- lack of credibility given to abuse reports.

Recent research and theory has suggested that the socially circumscribed world, within which persons with developmental disabilities usually live, and the nature of the roles and relationships in such settings, may result in confusion or distortion of interactions that can reduce the natural boundaries for abuse. When the healthy boundaries between support-providers and support-recipients become blurred or breached, there is a potential for sexual abuse to be tolerated, or even worse, misinterpreted as appropriate social approach behaviour (Owen, Griffiths, Sales, Feldman & Richards, 2000). In some cases, persons with a developmental disability may be unaware of the expected limits of support-providers' behaviour beyond care-giving duties, and may not know or feel they have the right to defend themselves. Without clear policies and procedures with regard to appropriate boundaries, caregivers can rationalise inappropriate behaviour, and support-recipients will remain unclear as to appropriate and inappropriate caregiver behaviour (Owen, et al., 2000).

Impact of Abuse on Mental Health:

Myths exist that people with developmental disabilities, especially those who are more disabled, are insensitive to pain and are asexual (Sobsey & Mansell, 1990), and will not be affected by sexual abuse. However, Mansell et al. (1992) reported that most persons with developmental disabilities demonstrate negative effects following abuse. The experience of the negative effects following sexual abuse is idiosyncratic, and often related to pre-abuse history, the understanding of the abusive event, the nature of the abuse, the relationship with the abuser, and post abusive experience. Some individuals may experience the event as abusive and even traumatic; other individuals may experience the event with less negative overtones, or misinterpret it as love because of a lifetime of learned tolerance to an institutionalized abuse or misunderstood intentions (Owen et al, 2000). In either case, the person with a disability is likely to demonstrate behavioural symptoms. These symptoms are often not understood, nor treated effectively as abuse reactions. Rather, symptoms can be poorly managed through behavioural control and sedation and the reason for the symptoms may never be appropriately assessed or treated.

Consequences:

Crimes, including sexual crimes, against persons with developmental disabilities are rarely reported (Wilson & Brewer, 1992). Following abuse, persons are often removed from their home or programmes (Mansell et al., 1992).

In summary, the pervasive occurrence of sexual abuse, the nature of the abusive relationships, the lack of intervention following abuse, and the lack of natural consequences for abusers of persons with developmental disabilities, and the potential aftermath of disruption in their lives creates a severe mental health risk for persons with developmental disabilities.

4. Sexual Abuse: Restricted Sexuality

As stated earlier, abuse of the sexuality of persons with disabilities can involve restriction of sexuality through practice, policy, medication and denial of knowledge.

History:

At different times in history, persons with developmental disabilities were treated as "the sexually innocent", who needed social protection. At other times in history, such as the beginning of the twentieth century, the Eugenics Movement branded persons with developmental disabilities as "sexually dangerous or promiscuous", and in need of sanctioning. Persons with developmental disabilities were congregated with other populations typified by crime, sexual promiscuity, mental illness and poverty. The professional community, armed with scientific data from hereditary studies, pursued most aggressively such restrictive measures as controlled marriage, sterilization, and segregation through institutionalization" (Scheerenburger, 1983). In the later part of the 20th century, forced sterilization eventually gave way to voluntary sterilization, and sex education was introduced. However, the facts about the sexuality of persons with disabilities have been slow to emerge from the myths (Griffiths 1992, 1999).

Despite the advent of massive deinstitutionalization and the expansion of community living for persons with developmental disabilities, most agencies that support persons with developmental disabilities do not teach about or permit sexual activity, appropriate or inappropriate. Today, many agencies still hold written or unwritten policies that fail to recognize the sexuality of the persons they serve. Age-appropriate, consensual and private sexual activity is often restricted or punished.

Hingsburger (1992) observed that the sexual experiences of individuals with developmental disabilities may have been so suppressed, controlled or punished that some individuals experience a negative reaction tendency to anything sexual. This is called erotophobia. Symptoms of this erotophobic behaviour include fear of one's own genitals, a negative reaction to any discussion, pictures or act involving sexual things, denial and anger over one's own developing sexuality, self-punishment following sexual behaviour, and a conspiracy of denial (Hingsburger, 1992).

Medication Use and Misuse:

Persons with developmental disabilities often receive a variety of medications for conditions associated with their disability, for psychiatric treatment or behavioural control, and to control sexual behaviour.

Many of the medications prescribed to persons with developmental disabilities have sexual side effects. Additionally, the sexual side effects are more common as the dose and number of drugs increase, as often happens with persons with developmental disabilities. Too often, however, persons with developmental disabilities are not informed of the potential side effects that a medication can have on their sexual urges, fantasies or expression. Anti-convulsant medications, neuroleptics and antihypertensive medications are all associated with sexual dysfunction (Crenshaw and Goldberg, 1996). "Unwanted sexual activity", as defined by health-care providers was often "treated" with sedating neuroleptic medications (Mason & Granacher, 1980). In addition to causing tiredness and alterations in sexual desire, neuroleptics often cause erectile dysfunction, inhibited orgasm, and retrograde ejaculation in men (Lingjaerde, Ahlfors, Bech, Dencker, & Elgen, 1987). In women, neuroleptic medications have been associated with decreased vaginal lubrication, inhibited orgasm, and dysmennorhea (alteration in menstrual periods). Gallactorrhea (breast milk let-down) has been reported in both men and women (Lingjaerde et al., 1987). {See Table 2 for a partial list of such sexual active drugs. The medications in Table 2 have been selected based on the frequency with which they are prescribed for people who have a developmental disability.}

Most experts now agree that neuroleptic medications should never be prescribed for the purpose of controlling sexual behaviour (Fedoroff, 1995). This is because better pharmacological interventions are now available, and because of the potentially lethal side effects of neuroleptic malignant syndrome (Levenson, 1985), and the disfiguring and incurable neuroleptic induced syndrome of tardive dyskinesia (American Psychiatric Association, 1992).

Table 2: Sexual Side Effects in Commonly Prescribed Medications

Name	Primary Indication	Side Effect(s)
Cardiovascular		
Chlorothiazide	Blood pressure control	Sexual difficulties
Digoxin	Heart disease	Decreased sex drive; erectile dysfunction
Enalapril	Blood pressure control	Erectile dysfunction (rare)
Nadolol	Heart disease; blood pressure control	Decreased sex drive; erectile dysfunction
Propranolol	Heart disease; blood pressure control	Loss of sex drive (M & F); Erectile dysfunction
Central Nervous System		
Alprazolam	Anxiety	Decreased sex drive; trouble with ejaculation (M) & orgasm (F)
Amitriptyline	Depression	Decreased sex drive; erectile dysfunction; no ejaculation
Buproprion	Depression	Erectile dysfunction
Carbamazepine	Seizure disorder/ mood stabilizer	Erectile dysfunction
Chlorpromazine	Psychotic disorder	Decreased sex drive; erectile dysfunction; priapism; no ejaculation
Citalopram	Depression	Decreased sex drive; delayed ejaculation (M); problems with orgasm (F)
Diazepam	Sleeping difficulties/ anxiety disorder	Decreased sex drive; delayed ejaculation; delayed or no orgasm (F)
Doxepin	Depression	Lower sex drive; problems with orgasm (F) or ejaculation (M); erectile dysfunction (rare)

(table continues)

Name	Primary Indication(s)	Side Effect (s)
Fluoxetine	Depression	Decreased sex drive; delayed ejaculation
Fluvoxamine	Depression	Decreased sex drive; problems with orgasm (F); delayed ejaculation (M)
Haloperidol	Psychotic disorder	Erectile dysfunction; change in libido; painful ejaculation; priapism
Imipramine	Depression	Decreased sex drive; erectile dysfunction; Painful delayed ejaculation; delayed orgasm (F)
Levodopa	Parkinson's Disease	Increased sex drive
Lorazepam	Sleeping difficulties/ anxiety disorder	Decreased sex drive; delayed ejaculation; delayed or no orgasm (F)
Lithium	Bipolar disorder/ mood stabilizer	Erectile dysfunction
Mesoridazine	Psychotic disorders	Erectile dysfunction; ejaculation problems; priapism
Methadone	Pain control	Decreased sex drive; erectile dysfunction; no orgasm; delayed ejaculation
Nefazadone	Depression	Decreased sex drive; erectile dysfunction; delayed ejaculation; trouble with orgasm (F)
Nortripyline	Depression	Erectile dysfunction; decreased sex drive
Oxazepam	Sleep disorders/ anxiety	Decreased sex drive; delayed ejaculation; delayed or no orgasm (F)
Paroxetine	Depression	Decreased sex drive; erectile dysfunction; delayed ejaculation; trouble with orgasm (F)
Phenobarbital	Seizure disorder	Erectile dysfunction
Phenytoin	Seizure disorder	Decreased sex drive; erectile dysfunction; priapism
Primidone	Seizure disorder	Change in sex drive; Erectile dysfunction (uncommon)

(table continues)

Name	Primary Indication(s)	Side Effect (s)
Sertraline	Depression/ anxiety	Decreased sex drive; erectile dysfunction; delayed ejaculation; trouble with orgasm (F)
Tenazepam	Sleeping difficulties/ Anxiety disorder	Decreased sex drive; delayed ejaculation; delayed or no orgasm (F)
Thioridazine	Psychotic disorder	Change in sex drive; erectile dysfunction; delayed, painful, retrograde, or no ejaculation
Trazodone	Depression	Priapism; change in sex drive; retrograde ejaculation
Trifluoperazine	Psychotic disorder	Erectile dysfunction; painful or no ejaculation; spontaneous ejaculation; increase in sex drive for women
Chemo-therapeutic		
Methotrexate	Cancer treatment	Loss of sex drive; erectile dysfunction
Gastrointestinal		
Cimetidine	Ulcer therapy	Decreased sex drive (M & F); erectile dysfunction
Misoprostol	Ulcer therapy	Erectile dysfunction; decreased sex drive (both infrequent)
Ranitidine	Ulcer therapy	Decreased sex drive; erectile dysfunction (occasional)
Genitourinary		
Medroxyprogesterone	Contraception	Change in sex drive; trouble with orgasm
Oxybutyrin	Urinary incontinence	Erectile dysfunction
Musculoskeletal		
Naproxen	Arthritis	Erectile dysfunction; no ejaculation

Denial of Knowledge:

By the late 1970s, most facilities reported having sex education to some degree, but sexual behaviours, other than masturbation, continued to be sanctioned (Coleman & Murphy,
1980). Pioneer sexuality educators, such as Kempton (1975)
and Gordon (1971) began to move away from the moralistic
approach to sex education, toward providing information, not
just about sexual biology, but about relationships, marriage,
dating and child-rearing. Even today, although the field generally recognizes the importance of sociosexual education for
persons with developmental disabilities, most agencies do not
provide ongoing access to sociosexual training for the persons
they support. Generally, persons are provided sociosexual
training only after they have engaged in a sexually inappropriate behaviour, or have become overtly sexual (Griffiths, 1999).

The restricted treatment of sexuality of persons with developmental disabilities throughout history, the use and misuse of
medication, and the denial of sexual knowledge pose a threat
to mental health of persons with developmental disabilities.
These, in addition to the high rates of direct sexual abuse
through forced or unwanted sexual contact, renders sexual
abuse as one of the greatest mental health risks to persons
who are labelled as developmentally disabled.

5. Mental health risk factors associated with sexually in-
    appropriate behaviour

In the previous two sections, we have shown that persons with
developmental disabilities are (i) less likely to have sexual experiences that enhance their mental health, and (ii) more likely
to experience abusive sexual events which may contribute to

mental health challenges. These risk factors and others contribute to an increased vulnerability for persons with developmental disabilities to develop more sexually inappropriate behaviour.

Statistics on Sexually Inappropriate Behaviour:

Gilby, Wolf and Goldberg (1989) reported that persons with developmental disabilities often engage in more inappropriate behaviours such as public masturbation, exhibitionism and voyeurism, but less serious sexual violations, than do nondisabled persons. Edgerton (1973) suggested that persons with developmental disabilities do not tend to demonstrate any more sexually inappropriate behaviour than do non-disabled persons *if* they are provided a normative learning experience. However, the sexual learning experience of many persons with developmental disabilities is anything but normative.

Offence Statistics:

Studies on population statistics have shown that individuals with developmental disabilities are over-represented in the population of convicted sexual offenders (Shapiro, 1986; Steiner, 1984, Langevin, 1992). However, these statistics have been debated. Some argue that they are overestimated because the data is based on the number of people convicted, and people with developmental disabilities are more likely to get caught, to confess and unable to mount a suitable defence (Santamour & West, 1978; Murphy et al., 1983).

Although the rate of serious sexual assaults may be overestimated among this population, it is likely that the rate of "sexually inappropriate behaviour" may not be. It is likely that persons who commit such violations are often diverted into residential programmes rather than correctional facilities, or the charges are dropped (Day, 1994).

Nature of Sexually Offensive and Inappropriate Behaviour:

Sexual behaviour, defined as offensive or inappropriate, can take many forms. According to the DSM-IV (APA, 1994), there are a number of diagnostic codes under the rubric of *paraphilia*, meaning love of the unusual. *Paraphilia* is described as: "recurrent sexually arousing fantasies, sexual urges or behaviours generally involving (1) non human objects, (2) the suffering or humiliation of oneself or one's partner, or (3) children or other non-consenting persons, that occur over a period of at least six months" (p. 522).

Day (1994) suggested that *paraphilia* does occur, but rarely among persons with developmental disabilities. It is, however, often misdiagnosed. Among this population, there is a higher experience of abuse (Griffiths, Quinsey & Hingsburger, 1989; Gilby et al., 1989), poor self-esteem (Lackey & Knopp, 1989), lack of sociosexual knowledge and experience (Hingsburger, 1987), and poor social problem-solving skills (Hingsburger, 1987). The Diagnostic and Statistic Manual of Mental Disorders (4th ed.) (DSM-IV) states that in persons with developmental disabilities there may be a "decrease in judgement, social skills, or impulse control that, in rare cases, leads to unusual sexual behavior" distinguishable from *paraphilia* (APA,1994, p. 525).

The latter behaviours can be differentiated from *paraphilia* since these acts do not represent a person's preferred and recurring sexual behaviour (APA, 1994). This non-paraphilic sexual behaviour usually occurs at a later stage in development, and is often sporadic. The DSM-IV description, while accurate in some cases, does not provide diagnostic criteria for differentiating between *paraphilia* and what some authors have called "counterfeit deviance".

The term "counterfeit deviance" was used in an article by Hingsburger, Griffiths, and Quinsey in 1991. They provided case examples to demonstrate that often, the sexual misbehaviour of persons with developmental disabilities is the product of experiential, environmental, or medical factors, rather than a *paraphilia*. Such misbehaviour can result from a lack of privacy (structural), modeling, inappropriate partner selection or courtship, lack of sexual knowledge or moral training, or a maladaptive learning history, or medical or medication effects (Hingsburger et al., 1991).

Day (1994) identified two types of sexual offenders among those with developmental disabilities. They were (a) those who committed sex offences only, and (b) those who committed a range of offences, including those of a sexual nature. He observed that the latter group demonstrated a higher incidence of sociopathic personality disorder, brain damage, family dysfunction, and other inappropriate behaviour. This group was less sexually naïve, and more specific and persistent in sexual offending. In contrast, those who committed only sexual offences were generally mildly disabled and without associated psychopathology, brain damage or generalized problem behaviours. This latter group committed less serious offences and was less specific in choice of offence behaviour or victim. Offenders in this group were typically shy, lacking sexual knowledge or experience, and often were from sexually repressive environments (Day, 1997). In contrast to non-disabled offenders who target mostly females, offenders with developmental disabilities offend equally against males and females (Gilby et al., 1989; Griffiths, et al., 1989). In addition, offenders with developmental disabilities appear to have far fewer victims.

The presence of various biomedical, psychological and socio-environmental variables that are more likely to be present in the lives of persons with developmental disabilities, can create increased risk for the development of sexually offending or inappropriate behaviours (Griffiths, 2002). These variables are discussed in depth in Griffiths (2002); however, they are discussed briefly below.

Biomedical Factors:

Neurological challenges and mental illness are more often witnessed in the population of persons who commit sexually offensive or inappropriate behaviours; these conditions are more likely to coexist in persons with developmental disabilities (Nezu, Nezu, & Gill-Weiss, 1992). Persons with developmental disabilities experience the same range of mental health challenges as persons without disabilities. As such, they are vulnerable to the same range of mental health challenges that may present as non-specific sexual symptoms (i.e., mania or obsessive compulsive disorder).

Psychological Factors:

Psychological factors such as lack of attachment bonds, lack of prosocial inhibition, childhood sexual trauma, and deficits in skills and empathy, are risk factors for development and occurrence of sexual challenges in the nondisabled population. Persons with developmental disabilities have been found to be as likely or more likely to experience these psychological vulnerabilities (Griffiths, 2002).

Although the experience of abuse does not predict that an individual will commit a similar sexual crime, among persons with developmental disabilities who have engaged in sexually offensive behaviour, there is a high percentage of persons who have experienced childhood abuse (Griffiths, as cited in The Roeher Institute, 1988; Hingsburger, 1987). If early sexual abuse may condition some individuals to respond sexually to the presence of certain individuals, or when confronted with specific situations reminiscent of early experiences of abuse, then the increased sexual abuse may represent a risk for future sexual problems. Moreover, because persons with developmental disabilities are denied education, counselling or opportunity to develop healthy sexual experiences to counter-condition the early abuse, they may be more likely to be influenced by that experience of abuse. For example, one man who had been abused repeatedly as a young boy within his family, then went on to abuse young boys when he became older because was unaware that his behaviour was unacceptable. For the young man, age-inappropriate sexual contact was the only standard of conduct he had been taught. This man had neither cognitively nor experientially encountered any instruction or moral view contrary to his experience.

Socio-Environmental Factors:

Day (1997) suggested that the high rates of sexually inappropriate behaviour attributed to persons with developmental disabilities reflect the generally repressive and restrictive attitudes toward the sexuality of persons with disabilities. Individuals with developmental disabilities may experience a differential conditioning to sexuality. Persons with developmental disabilities have often been punished for normal sexual behaviour. The environments in which many persons with developmental

disabilities live may reverse the natural contingencies of reinforcement and punishment for sexual behaviour. Appropriate
and consenting sexual behaviours are often punished at the
same or greater rates than an inappropriate and perhaps non-
consenting sexual encounter.

Additionally, for many persons with developmental disabilities, sexually inappropriate behaviour has failed to bring about
natural aversive consequences. Persons with developmental
disabilities may lack knowledge of the law, or the relevance of
the law to their sexual misbehaviour. If persons with developmental disabilities are charged with sexually inappropriate behaviour, the charges are often dismissed and the person is
placed in settings other than correctional facilities. Thus, the
natural consequences are often not taught nor experienced.

Risk Assessment:

An important challenge for mental health professionals,
charged with the assessment and treatment of people with developmental delay, is the accurate assessment of risk of violent
or sexual offences. Typical interviewing and testing procedures require adaptation and caution when used with this
population (i.e., phallometric testing) (Murphy, Coleman, &
Haynes, 1983).

One of the most well established actuarial assessment instruments for the prediction of sex offences is the Sex Offender
Risk Appraisal Guide (SORAG) (Quinsey, Harris, Rice, &
Cormier, 1998). Recent research by Fedoroff, Smolewska,
Selhi, Ng, and Bradford (2001) demonstrated that persons with
developmental disabilities are more likely to score significantly higher overall when compared to other offenders with

an equal number of victims. On two subscales, they rated significantly higher on two scores when compared to a matched sample of nondisabled offenders. The subscales were related to marriage and living with natural parents up to age 16. Fedoroff et al. (2001) suggest it is likely that the factors that may contribute to a man being unable to establish a romantic relationship, or to hold a job, have a different developmental path for a man who has developmental delay than in a man without cognitive handicaps. As we have stated before, the opportunity for appropriate sociosexual interaction have been denied in the population of persons with disabilities. Thus, the increased risk may be the result of the life experience afforded persons with disabilities in our society, such as limited options for meaningful work, lack of opportunity to develop relationships and marry, isolation from family and community.

Treatment Programmes:

In the early part of the century, sexual behaviour (appropriate or inappropriate) resulted in castration or incarceration in segregated facilities (Pringle, 1997). In the 1970's, behavioural control techniques were adopted to stop sexual behaviour such as masturbation. Approaches included the use of time-out, omission training, or punishments like response cost, overcorrection, or squirts of contingent lemon juice in the mouth following this behaviour (Griffiths, Quinsey & Hingsburger, 1989). Informally, persons with developmental disabilities were ridiculed, sanctioned or denied privileges.

In the early 1980's, few programmes offered treatment for persons with developmental disabilities who demonstrated sexually offensive behaviour (Coleman and Murphy, 1980). In the past two decades, however, an increasingly rich body of clinical literature on intervention programmes for sex offenders with developmental disabilities has emerged (Murphy et al., 1983; Griffiths, Hingsburger & Christian, 1985, Griffiths et al., 1989; Haaven, Little, & Petre-Miller, 1990; Lund, 1992; Ward et al., 1992). More recently, the treatment focus has shifted toward promotion of the development of adaptive sexual behaviours (Griffiths, et al., 1989; Haaven, et al., 1990; Lindsay, et al., 1998; Nezu, Nezu & Dudeck, 1998; Ward et al, 1992).

Based on a growing body of clinical experience, specialized treatment providers have reported that sex offenders with developmental disabilities, particularly those individuals who were mild and moderately disabled, have been surprisingly responsive to treatment (Lackey & Knopp, 1989). However, to date there is minimal empirical demonstration of the treatment effectiveness with this population (Griffiths, Watson, Lewis, & Stoner, in press).

The recidivism rates for persons with developmental disabilities who commit sexual offences present contradictory data for persons in community and institutional settings. Demetral (1989, as cited in Nolley, Muccigrosso & Zigman, 1996) reported a recidivism rate of less than 2% within a community programme; Haaven et al. (1990) indicated a rate of recidivism of 23% for their population of institutionalized offenders. Nolley et al. (1996) suggested that treatment outcome in the community is enhanced by the use of qualified facilitators, increased social opportunities for persons with developmental disabilities, the enlistment of natural support systems, and teaching about culturally acceptable ways of sexual expression.

Treatment strategies should involve:

1. *Teaching and reinforcing alternative replacement behaviours that will serve the same or similar function as the sexually aggressive behaviour by:*
   - **Providing an appropriate means for the individual to achieve the desired interaction and sensory state, which the person is now receiving through an inappropriate means, both acted out and in fantasy;**
   - **Overcoming barriers to the development of appropriate socio-sexual outlets currently unavailable because of such vulnerabilities as a lack of social skills; and/or**
   - **Providing an alternative and appropriate means for the individual to reduce, remove or alter the aversive internal state the person is currently escaping through the sexually aggressive behaviour or fantasies.**

2. *Altering the maintaining consequences that have been sustaining the behaviour:*
   - **For many persons with developmental disabilities, this often means teaching the legal consequences of sexual aggression, and that as a citizen, they will be held responsible for such behaviour, and**
   - **Teaching individuals to use the naturally punitive consequences (legal, social and moral) of the behaviour, to inhibit sexual aggressive behaviour and/or fantasies through cognitive self-management methods such as covert sensitization or masturbatory reconditioning (Griffiths et al., 1989).**

3. *Judicious use of medication or hormonal therapy:*
   - **Medication and hormonal therapy may be an important *addition* to treatment plans for individuals whose sex-**

ual interests pose a risk to themselves or others. Table 3 describes a lists of common medications used to treat sexual deviations. Apparent from the table, the potential side-effects of the medications can be significant.

Table 3– Class of Medications for Sexually Inappropriate Behaviour

Class of Medication	How they work	Effects and side-effects
Antiandrogens	Decrease testosterone	Decrease sex drive Decrease fertility Glucose intolerance Increase risk of thromboembolic disorders Alter liver function
Luteinizing Hormone Releasing Hormone (LH RH) Analogues	Supress gonadotropin production	Decrease sex drive Decrease fertility Osteoporosis Glucose intolerance Increase risk of thromboembolic disorders Alter liver function
Selective Serotonergic Reuptake Inhibitors (SSRI's)	Increase post-synpatic serotonin availability	Antidepressant Decrease impulsivity Alter sex interest Alter sleep and appetite

- When considering medication or hormonal therapy for the treatment of sexual problems in people with developmental delay, the practice guidelines should be followed:

Box 1: Practice Guidelines for Medications or Hormonal Therapy for Sexual Offending Behaviour

(i) Medication or hormonal therapy should only be prescribed to patients who understand the risk and benefits of treatment with these medications, and who are able to give voluntary consent.

(ii) Medication or hormonal therapy should be used as part of a comprehensive treatment plan which includes healthy sex education and psychotherapy.

(iii) Medication or hormonal therapy should only be prescribed in cases in which their efficacy can be monitored (e.g., there is no point in prescribing medication or hormonal therapy to a person with sexual interests in children if that person has no contact with children, and is not otherwise distressed by their interests in children (paedophilia).

(iv) Medication or hormonal therapy should only be prescribed by physicians who are able to assess their efficacy and diagnose medical contraindications to their use.

(v) Other treatment options should always be considered.

Summary

There is a complex interplay of biomedical, social and psychological factors, related to the experience of being a sexual person with a developmental disability in our society.

A) Although sexuality is considered an important factor in

mental health and wellness (World Health Organization, 1975), the sexuality of persons with developmental disabilities is often negatively affected because of the following:

a) denial of opportunity to enjoy and control sexual and reproductive behaviour in accordance with social and personal ethics;

b) the experience of fear, shame, guilt, false beliefs, and other psychological factors that inhibit sexual response and the establishment of sexual relationships; and

c) the co-existence of organic disorders, diseases, and deficiencies that interfere with sexual and reproductive functions.

B) Persons with developmental disabilities are more likely to be sexually abused, and to have their sexual expression repressed and punished. They are also less likely to receive treatment for their sexual abuse experiences. These abusive and repressive experiences represent serious behavioural and mental health risks for persons with developmental disabilities.

C) The statistics show that individuals with developmental disabilities are more likely to engage in sexually inappropriate behaviour as a result of conditioning, and are more likely to be involved in less serious sexual crimes, because they will likely get caught, confess, and not negotiate a plea bargain, or gain appropriate defence. Moreover, they are less likely to receive appropriate treatment for their challenging sexual behaviour.

The sexuality of persons with developmental disabilities poses significant mental health risks, not because of the disability, but because of the societal response to the sexuality of those who are labelled in our society. The World Health Organization has proclaimed that we are all sexual beings, and that includes those with a disability. Failure to recognize this reality poses a great threat to the mental health integrity of individual with disabilities.

Do You Know?

1. What are some of the key mental health risks that face people with developmental disabilities regarding their sexuality?
2. Why are people with developmental disabilities over-represented in correctional facilities regarding sexual crimes?
3. What factors could contribute to the development of sexual problems in persons with developmental disabilities?
4. Can individuals with developmental disabilities benefit from sex offender treatment programmes? What should be the focus of treatment?

Resources

Sexuality and Persons with Developmental Disabilities

Fegan, L., Rauch, A., & McCarthy, W. (1993). *Sexuality and people with intellectual disability* (2nd ed.). Baltimore, MD: Paul H. Brookes.

Monet-Haller, R.K. (1992). *Understanding and expressing sexuality: Responsible choices for individuals with developmental disabilities.* Baltimore, MD: Paul H. Brookes.

Rowe, W., & Savage, S. (1987). *Sexuality and the developmentally handicapped.* Queenston, Ont.: Queenston, Ontario. (out of print)

Socio-sexual Education

Cowardin, N. & Stanfield J. (1986). Life facts I: *Sexuality and life facts II: Sexual abuse.* Santa Monica, CA: Stanfield Publishing

Kempton, W. (1988). *Life Horizons I and II.* Santa Barbara, CA.: Stanfield Publishing.

Kempton, W. (1993). *Sexuality and persons with disabilities that hinder learning: A comprehensive guide for teachers and professionals.* Santa Barbara, CA.: James Stanfield Publishing.

Watson, S., Griffiths, D., Richards, D., & Dykstra, L. (2002). Sex education for persons with developmental disabilities. In D. Griffiths, D. Richards, P. Fedoroff, & S. Watson (Eds). *Ethical dilemmas: Sexuality and developmental disability (pp. 175-225).* Kingston, NY: NADD

Sociosexual Assessment

Wish, J.R., McCombs, K.F., & Edmonson, B. (1979). *The socio-sexual knowledge and attitude test.* Wooddale, IL: Stoelting.

Relationship Training

Champagne, M.P. & Walker-Hirsch, L. (1993*). Circles: Intimacy and relationships.* Santa Barbara, CA: James Stanfield Publishing.

Sexual Abuse

G. Allan Roeher Institute (1988). *Vulnerable.* Toronto, Ont.: Author.

Sobsey, D. (1994). *Violence and abuse in the lives of people with disabilities.* Baltimore, MD: Paul H. Brookes.

Sexual Policies

Griffiths, D., Owen, F., Lindenbaum, L. & Arbus, K. (2002). Sexual policies in agencies supporting persons who have developmental disabilities, Part II: Practical Issues and Procedures. In D.Griffiths, P. Fedoroff, D., Richards, & S. Watson (Eds.), *Ethical dilemmas: Sexuality and developmental disability* (pp. 77-132). Kingston, NY: NADD.

Owen, F., Griffiths, D. & Arbus, K. (2002). Sexual policies in agencies supporting persons who have developmental disabilities, Part I: Ethical and Organizational Issues. In D. Griffiths, P. Fedoroff, D. Richards, & S. Watson (Eds.), *Ethical dilemmas: Sexuality and developmental disability* (pp. 53-76). Kingston, NY: NADD.

Sexually Inappropriate Behaviour

Griffiths, D. (2002). Sexual aggression and persons with developmental disabilities. In W.I. Gardner (Ed.), *Aggression in persons with developmental disabilities: Biomedical and psychosocial considerations in diagnosis and treatment* (pp. 326-397). New York: National Association for Dual Diagnosis.

Griffiths, D., Quinsey, V.L., & Hingsburger, D. (1989). *Changing inappropriate sexual behavior.* Baltimore, MD.: Paul H. Brookes. (out of print)

Haaven, J., Little, R., Petre-Miller, D. (1990). *Treating intellectually disabled sex offenders.* Orwell, VT: Safer Society.

Hingsburger, D., Griffiths, D., & Quinsey, V. (1991). Detecting counterfeit deviance. *The Habilitative Mental Healthcare Newsletter, 10,* 51-54.

Ward, K.M., Heffern, S.J., Wilcox, D., McElwee, D., Dowrick, P., Brown. T.D., Jones, M.J., & Johnson, C.L., (1992). *Managing inappropriate sexual behavior: Support-*

ing individuals with developmental disabilities in the community. **Anchorage, Alaska: Alaska Specialized Education and Training Services.**

Reading for Parents
Schwier, K. M. & Hingsgburger, D. (2000). *Sexuality: Your sons and daughters with intellectual disabilities.* **Baltimore, MD: Brookes Publishing.**
Hingsburger, D. (1993*). I openers. Parents ask questions about sexuality and children with developmental disabilities.* **Vancouver, BC: Family Supports Institute Press.**

Social Skills
Griffiths, D. (1990). Teaching social competency: Part 1 Practical guidelines. *Habilitative Mental Health Care Newsletter, 9(1),* **1-5.**
Griffiths, D. (1990). Teaching social competency: Part 2 The Social Life Game. *Habilitative Mental Health Care Newsletter, 9(2),* **9-13.**
Valenti- Hein, D. (1990) The dating skills program for adults with mental retardation. *The Habilitative Mental Health-Care Newsletter, 9(6),* **47-50.**
York Behaviour Management Services (1979). *Social Life Game.* **Richmond Hill, ON: author.**

Sociosexual Resources:
Canadian Guidelines for Sexual Health Education www.hc-sc-gc.ca/main/lcdc/web/publicat/sheguide
Disabled Woman's Network Canada
    www.indie.ca/dawn/index1.htm
National Clearninghouse on Family Violence
    www.hc-sc.gc.ca/nccn
SIECCAN (Sex Information and Education Council of Canada) www.sieccan.org

SIECUS (Sex Information and Education Council of the US) www.siecus.org
Safer Society www.safersociety.org
Sexual Health Network: Sexuality and Disability or Illness Information Help Therapy www.sexualhealth.com

References

American Psychiatric Association (1994). *Diagnostic and statistical manual of mental disorders (4th ed.)*. Washington, DC: American Psychiatric Association.

American Psychiatric Association (1992). *Tardive dyskinesia: A task force report*. Washington, DC: author.

Coleman, E.M., & Murphy, W.D. (1980). A survey of sexual attitudes and sex education programs among facilities for the mentally retarded. *Applied Research in Mental Retardation, 1,* 269-276.

Crenshaw, T. L., & Goldberg, J. P. (1996). *Sexual pharmacology*. New York, NY: W. W. Norton & Company.

Davis, M. (1989). Gender and sexual development of women with mental retardation. *The Disabilities Studies Quarterly, 9,* 19-20.

Day, K. (1994). Male mentally handicapped sex offenders. *British Journal of Psychiatry, 165,* 630-639.

Day, K. (1997). Clinical features and offence behaviour of mentally retarded sex offenders: A review of research. In R.J. Fletcher & D. Griffiths (Eds.), *Congress proceedings-International congress II on the dually diagnosed* (pp. 95-99). New York: NADD.

Edgerton, R. (1973). Socio-cultural research considerations. In F.F. de la Cruz & G.G. La Veck (Eds.), *Human sexuality and the mentally retarded* (pp. 240-249). New York: Brunner/Maze.

Fedoroff, J. P. (1995). Antiandrogens vs. serotonergic medications in the treatment of sex offenders: A preliminary compliance study. *The Canadian Journal of Human Sexuality, 4(2),* 111-122.

Fedoroff, J.P., Smolewska, K., Selhi, Z., Ng., E., & Bradford, J. (2001). Assessment of violence and sexual offense risk using the 'VRAG' and 'SORAG' in a sample of men with developmental delay and paraphilic disorders: A case controlled study. *International Academy of Sex Research, 27th Annual Meeting Abstracts,* p. 17.

Gilby, R., Wolf, L. & Golberg, B. (1989). Mentally retarded adolescent sex offenders: A survey and pilot study. *Canadian Journal of Psychiatry, 34,* 542-548.

Gordon, S. (1971). Missing in special education: Sex. *Journal of Special Education,* 5, pp. 351-354.

Griffiths, D. (2002). Sexual aggression and persons with developmental disabilities. In W.I. Gardner (Ed.), *Aggression in persons with developmental disabilities: Biomedical and psychosocial considerations in diagnosis and treatment* (pp. 326-397). New York: National Association for Dual Diagnosis.

Griffiths, D. (1999). Sexuality and people with developmental disabilities: Mythconceptions and facts. In I. Brown & M. Percy (Eds.), *Developmental disabilities in Ontario.* (pp. 443-452). Toronto: Front Porch Publishers.

Griffiths, D. (1992). *Mythconceptions about sexuality and persons with developmental disabilities.* {Video}. Kingston, New York: National Association for Dual Diagnosis.

Griffiths, D., Baxter, J., Haslam, T., Richards, D., Stranges, S., Vyrostko, B (1996). Building healthy boundaries: Considerations for reducing sexual abuse. *National Association for Dual Diagnosis Annual Conference Proceedings* (pp. 114-118). Kingston, NY: NADD.

Griffiths, D., Hingsburger, D., & Christian, R. (1985). Treating developmentally handicapped sexual offenders; The York Behaviour Management Treatment Program. *Psychiatric Aspects of Mental Retardation Reviews, 4,* **45-52.**

Griffiths, D., Quinsey, V.L., & Hingsburger, D. (1989). *Changing inappropriate sexual behaviour.* **Baltimore, MD: Paul H Brookes.**

Griffiths, D., Watson, S., Lewis, T., & Stoner, K. (in press). **Sexuality research of persons with intellectual disabilities. In E. Emerson, C. Hatton, T. Parmenter,, & T. Thompson (Eds.),** *Handbook of research and evaluation in intellectual disabilities.* **London: Wiley.**

Haaven, J. Little, R., & Petre-Miller, D. (1990). *Treating intellectually disabled sex offenders: A model residential program.* **Orwell, VT: Safer Society Press.**

Hare, R. D. (1991). *The revised psychopathy checklist.* **Toronto: Multi-Health Systems.**

Hingsburger, D. (1987). **Sex counselling with the developmentally handicapped: The assessment and management of seven critical problems.** *Psychiatric Aspects of Mental Retardation Reviews, 6,* **41-46.**

Hingsburger, D. (1992). **Erotophobic behavior in people with developmental disabilities.** *The Habilitative Mental Healthcare Newsletter, 11,* **31-34.**

Hingsburger, D., Griffiths, D., & Quinsey, V. (1991). **Detecting counterfeit deviance.** *The Habilitative Mental Healthcare Newsletter, 10,* **51-54.**

Kempton, W. (1975). *Sex education for persons with disabilities that hinder learning.* **Massachusetts: Duxbury Press.**

Lackey, L.B., & Knopp, F.H. (1989). **A summary of selected notes from the working sessions of the First National Training Conference on Assessment and Treatment of Intellectually Disabled Juvenile and Adult Sexual Offenders. In F. Knopp (Ed.),** *Selected readings: Sexual offenders* *identified as intellectually disabled.* Orwell, VT: Safer Society Press.

Langevin, R. (1992). A comparison of neuroendocrine abnormalities and genetic factors in homosexuality and in pedophila. *Annals of Sex Research, 6,* 67-76.

Levenson, J. L. (1985). Neuroleptic malignant syndrome. *American Journal of Psychiatry, 142,* 1137-1145.

Lindsay, W.R., Olley, S., Jack, C., Morrison, F., & Smith, A.H.W. (1998). The treatment of two stalkers with intellectual disabilities using a cognitive approach. *Journal of Applied Research in Intellectual Disabilities, 11,* 333-344.

Lingjaerde, O., Ahlfors, U. G., Bech, P., Dencker, S. J., & Elgen, K. (1987). The UKU side-effect rating scale for psychotropic drugs and cross-sectional study of side-effects in neuroleptic-treated patients. *Acta Psychiatrica Scandanavica, 76*((Suppl. 334)), 1-99.

Lund, C.A. (1992). Long-term treatment of sexual behavior in adolescent and adult developmentally disabled persons. *Annals of Sex Research, 5,* 5-21.

Mansell,S., Sobsey,D., & Calder, P. (1992). Sexual abuse treatment for persons with developmental disabilities. *Professional Psychology: Research and Practice, 23,* 404-409.

Mason, A. S., & Granacher, R. P. (1980). Further clinical applications of antipsychotic drug therapy, *Clinical handbook of antipsychotic drug therapy* (pp. 164-166). New York, NY: Brunner/Mazel.

Murphy, W.D., Coleman, E.M., & Haynes, M. (1983) Treatment and evaluation issues with the mentally retarded sex offender. In J. Greer & I. Stuart (Eds.), *The sexual aggressor: Current perspectives on treatment* (pp. 22-41). New York, NY: Van Nostrand Reinhold.

Nezu, C.M., Nezu, A.M., & Dudeck, J. (1998). A cognitive behavioural model of assessment and treatment for intellectually disabled sexual offenders. *Cognitive and Behavioural Practice, 5,* **25-64**.

Nezu, C.M., Nezu, A.M. & Gill- Weiss, M. (1992). *Psychopathology in persons with mental retardation: Clinical guidelines for assessment and treatment.* Champaign, Ill: Research Press.

Nolley, D., Muccigrosso, L., & Zigman, E. (1996). Treatment successes with mentally retarded sex offenders. *Sex Offenders Treatment,* **125-141**.

Owen, F., Griffiths, D., Feldman, M., Sales, C.A., & Richards, D. (2000). Perceptions of acceptable boundaries by persons with developmental disabilities and their care providers. *Journal on Developmental Disabilities, 7(1),* **34-49**.

Pringle, H. (1997). Alberta barren. *Saturday Night, June,* **30-74**.

Quinsey, V. L., Harris, G. T., Rice, M. E., & Cormier, C. A. (1998). *Violent offenders: Appraising and managing risk.* Washington DC: American Psychological Association.

Santamour, W., & West, B. (1978). *The mentally retarded offender and corrections.* Washington, DC: U.S. Department of Justice.

Scheerenberger, R.C. (1983). *A history of mental retardation.* Baltimore, MD: Paul. H. Brookes.

Shapiro, S. (1986). Delinquent and disturbed behavior within the field of mental deficiency. In A.V.S. deReuck & R. Sobsey, D. (1994). *Violence and abuse in the lives of people with disabilities.* Baltimore, MD: Paul H. Brookes.

Sobsey, D. & Mansell, S (1990). The prevention of sexual abuse of persons with developmental disabilities. *Developmental Disabilities Bulletin, 18,* **51-65**.

Steiner, J. (1984). Group counselling with retarded offenders. *Social Work, 29,* **181-182**.

The Roeher Institute. (1988). *Vulnerable: Sexual abuse and people with an intellectual handicap.* **Toronto: G. Allan Roeher Institute.**

The Roeher Institute (1994). *Violence and people with disabilities: A review of the literature.* **Ottawa, ON: National Clearinghouse on Family Violence.**

Ward, K.M., Heffern, S.J., Wilcox, D.A., McElwee, B.S., Dowrick, P., Brown, M.J., Jones, M.J. & Johnson, C.L. (1992). *Managing inappropriate sexual behaviour: Supporting individuals in the community.* **Anchorage, Alaska: Alaska Specialized Training Services.**

Wilson, C. & Brewer, N. (1992). **The incidence of criminal victimization of individuals with an intellectual disability.** *Australian Psychologist, 2,* **1114-117.**

World Health Organization (1975). *Educational and treatment in human sexuality: The training of health professionals.* **Technical Report Series Nr. 572. Geneva Switzerland: Author.**

Chapter 14

Substance-related Disorders in Persons with Developmental Disabilities

Chrissoula Stavrakaki

Learning objectives

Readers will be able to:

1. Describe substance abuse disorders.
2. Identify how frequently they are diagnosed in this group of people.
3. Describe how substance abuse affects persons with a developmental disability.
4. Describe how effectively we can treat and manage these disorders in persons with developmental disabilities.

Introduction

Think how often you have encountered people in your life who either use substances of abuse as social entertainment or as a stress reliever, or simply because they have become addicted to these substances. Consider your feelings and knowledge on this issue. Mind and perception-altering substances are very dangerous to individuals and also to the public in general due to the inevitable accidents, misbehaviour and/or social inappropriateness which result from their use. We also share the view that early recognition, appropriate treatment, and development of social networks are of extreme importance in facing and coping with these disorders. The same is true for persons with developmental disabilities who abuse substances. These persons need all the help and support they can get to assess and treat them when faced with these disorders, as well as attempting to prevent further abuse. These measures not only help to modify the frequency of occurrence of these disorders in people with a developmental disability, but they also assist in minimizing the sequelae such as criminal records, incarceration and other negative restrictions.

In this book, the biopsychosocial model has been used in assessment, treatment and prevention of mental health disorders. As a result, we need to understand how these disorders come to exist, what factors affect their occurrence, and how individual treatment and social networks are of extreme importance in modifying their outcome.

What are substance-related disorders?

According to the Diagnostic and Statistical Manual, (APA, 1994), substance-related disorders include "disorders related to the taking of a drug of abuse (including alcohol), to the side effects of medication, and to a toxin exposure". In this chapter, we will only deal with disorders related to drug abuse. The issues of side effects of medication and/or toxin exposure are being dealt with elsewhere in this manual.

The essential feature of substance dependence is a cluster of cognitive, behavioural and physiological symptoms indicating continuous use of the substance despite significant substance-related problems. This pattern of abuse exhibits itself as a repeated self-administration that usually results in tolerance, withdrawal, and compulsive drug-taking behaviour. In order to understand the various aspects associated with substance-related disorders, we have to define Substance Dependence according to the DSM-IV (APA, 1994).

Substance Dependence is defined as a cluster of three or more symptoms as follows, as defined by APA (1994):

- Tolerance (Criterion 1): *This is the need for greatly increased amounts of the substance to achieve intoxication to avoid a very much-diminished effect with the continued use of the same amount of the substance* (p. 181).
- Withdrawal (Criterion 2a): *This is a maladaptive behavioural change with physiological and cognitive concomitants that occur when blood or tissue concentrations of the substance decline in an individual who has maintained prolonged use of the substance.*

In order to relieve or avoid the effects of withdrawal, the person is likely to take the substance (Criterion 2b), typically using the substance throughout the day.

- A pattern of compulsive substance use (Criterion 3) has to be present. *This means that individuals take the substance in larger amounts or over a longer period than was originally intended despite their recognition that this behaviour is alien to themselves and beyond their control.*

What are the common substance-related disorders?

The most common substance-related disorders are:
- Alcohol-related disorders

- Amphetamine related disorders
- Caffeine-related disorders
- Cannabis-related disorders
- Cocaine-related disorders
- Hallucinogen-related disorders
- Inhalant-related disorders
- Nicotine-related disorders
- Opioid-related disorders
- Phencyclidine-related disorders
- Sedative-Hypnotic or anxiolytic-related disorders

How frequent are these disorders in the person with developmental disability?

The identification, assessment and treatment of substance-related disorders in this population, has received little attention in the past. The relative rarity of review articles and/or research studies on this topic is strong evidence of the lack of understanding and acknowledgement of the frequency of these disorders in the dually diagnosed group.

With deinstitutionalization, and the move of these persons to community settings, the opportunity and availability of substances of abuse to this group have arisen greatly (Longo, 1997). As a result, the prevalence of these disorders has increased in recent years (Westermeyer, Phaoblong, & Neither, 1988; Westermeyer, Crosby, & Nugent, 1998; Longo, 1997).

In the National Household Survey on Drug Abuse (1994) conducted by the Substance Abuse and Mental Health Administration, 10.8 percent of respondents admitted to the use of illicit drugs in the past twelve months. In their well-publicized study, Drs. Westermeyer, Crosby, and Nugent (1998) surveyed

642 persons receiving substance abuse treatment at two university-affiliated clinics. They identified two subgroups with substance-related disorders, the MR + SD group (Mental Retardation and Substance Disorder) and the SD only group (SD, Substance Disorder).

They found that the MR + SD group comprised 6.2 percent of their total population. This finding is very troubling, if we consider that persons with Developmental Disability comprise about 1-3% of the general population. This could indicate that the person with a developmental disability experiences addiction- related crises and mental health problems at almost twice the rate of the general population.

Other data seem to emerge indicating the seriousness and high frequency of developmental disability in substance-related disorders. The Wright State University School of Medicine in Dayton, Ohio, operates the Substance Abuse Resources and Disability Issues (SARDI) Program and the Rehabilitation Research and Training Centre (RRTC). In 1996, the RRTC published results indicating that developmental disability was the primary disability in 4.3% of the respondents; learning disability was the primary disability in 14.3% of the total respondents' group. In the same survey, 12.8% of the respondents were self-identified as having mental retardation/ developmental disability, and abused illicit drugs in the past twelve months.

Despite the limited data available in this area, it appears that a person with a developmental disability has the same or higher prevalence of substance related disorders (Annand & Rus, 1998). S/he also appears to develop crises and is in need of specialized services almost twice as much as the general population. Additionally, s/he experiences a lower overall rate of recovery. The pattern of inheritance is similar to that of the general population. More specifically, the fathers of the developmentally disabled + SD group were found to have had increased rate of alcoholism (Westermeyer et al, 1998). This may indicate that initially, the cause of the developmental disability was the abnormalities in the sperm, and/or that environmental influence is of great importance in the genesis of these disorders (Edgerton, 1986; Westermeyer et al., 1998).

What are the characteristics of substance-related disorders in the person with developmental disability?

As already discussed, persons with developmental disabilities develop substance-related disorders in a similar fashion to the general population. However, there are specific characteristics that these individuals present as compared to the general population. They are as follows:

- Substance-related disorders, as other mental health problems, are linked to the degree of cognitive impairment/potential. The higher the IQ, the higher the prevalence of these disorders (Edgerton, 1986; Campbell & Malone, 1991).

- The commonly held belief that people with DD + SD would be more vulnerable to the intoxicating effect of the substance of abuse has been, in part, borne out.

- People with developmental disabilities tend to drink alcohol or use illicit drugs in lower amounts as compared to the general population. As a result, they are more difficult to identify. Often, caregivers consider this to be part of the individual's "life pattern".

- The inherent limitation that persons with developmental disabilities face in their lives, and the resulting anxiety and depressive disorders (Stavrakaki, 1998; Stavrakaki & Mintsioulis, 1995; 1997) tend to render these individuals vulnerable to increased use and abuse of mind altering substances in order to relieve stress, or as a self-medication (Longo, 1996; Ruf, 1999).

- Mental Disorders that are common in this population such as Bipolar Mood Disorder, and Schizophrenia, tend to increase the prevalence of substance-related disorders in this group (Westermeyer et al., 1988; 1996; Longo, 1997).

Social Factors

Social factors that seem to influence the occurrence of substance-related disorders in people with developmental disability are:

- Level of education:
  It was found that their level of education was lower by 2-3 academic years compared to the general population.

- Marital Status/Residence:
  It was found that persons who were developmentally disabled and experienced substance-dependence tended to be single and live alone.

Other differences found between the two groups were:

- Age of onset:
  It was found that the age of onset of the abuse was later than that of the general population.

- The severity of the substance disorder was less in the group of persons with mental retardation.

- The crises related issues were found to be higher in this group.

- The individuals with developmental disabilities that have become chemically dependent are more difficult to treat effectively with short-term interventions.

- Lack of specialized services and social networks specifically related to chemical dependence and developmental disabilities account for the rather resistive process and poorer outcomes.

- The level of cognitive limitation is also linked with the poorer prognosis (the lower the IQ, the more resistive the process and the poorer the outcome) (Longo, 1997; Westermeyer et al., 1998; Ruf, 1999).

What types of addictions do we encounter in persons with developmental disabilities?

In reviewing the recent literature, it seems that all types of substance-related disorders can be found in this group. Certain types of substance abuse, however, are more frequent than others. This could be due to the fact that there is greater availability and opportunity for this group to use substances of abuse, such as, caffeine, nicotine and alcohol. It is also true that higher functioning persons with developmental disabilities are more afflicted by these disorders. Indeed, very few examples of moderately afflicted people, and almost none with severe and profound degrees of involvement have been quoted in the literature as suffering from substance-related disorders. This is in part due to the fact that the identification of these disorders in these persons is very challenging, and in part due to the lack of availability and/or opportunity for these persons to access such substances.

Caffeine and nicotine-related disorders are, by far, the most frequently found in this group. As in other disabled populations, caffeine and nicotine are substances that are consumed in greater quantities, as they are easily accessible and relatively inexpensive.

The Case of Christopher

Christopher, a 24 year old male, lived with family until two years ago when he had a "nervous breakdown" and was hospitalized. He was diagnosed with schizophrenia (Axis I), Dependent Personality Disorder (Axis II) and Developmentally Disability to mild or moderate degree (Axis II).

Following his hospitalization, Christopher was moved to a community setting, since his parents were not able to deal with problems and daily issues of his illness. Social supports through a community agency were offered to Chris, who, by reports through a community agency were offered to Chris, who by then was able to manage reasonably well on his own.

A parental interview revealed that the most disturbing of Chris's behaviours had been:

- *restlessness*
- *agitation*
- *aggressivity*
- *insomnia*
- *explosiveness*

When further questioned on Christopher's daily routine, his parents expressed their frustration that he woke up very early (4 a.m.), and began to smoke cigarettes and drink coffee. Chris would then continue to chain smoke and drink coffee "all day long". By 4 to 6 p.m. Chris' "temper" would be impossible to control, and any attempt to pacify him would fail.

The only way that he would be "liveable" would be to allow him to continue his "terrible habits". Consequently, his parents were forced into a very difficult position. They had to lock their bedroom door for fear of being attacked, and would "feed his habits" (caffeine and nicotine addiction) to have relative peace. They had not realized, nor were they ever told, that these two substances as common as they may be in everyday lives, were very addictive, and that Chris suffered from the classic symptoms of both addictions. He had developed a dependence on caffeine. This was exemplified by symptoms of withdrawal and the need to take more of the substance to avoid these symptoms.

*He also began to take incredible amounts of abuse sub-
stances to achieve the same results (tolerance). He exhibited compulsive substance taking. His addiction occupied
all of his day and greatly interfered with his attendance at
any day program.*

*Through daily rehabilitation for two years in a day hospi-
tal setting, Chris was able to modify his addictions to
more appropriate levels (i.e., smoking only ten cigarettes
daily, and drinking decaffeinated coffee only, up to two
cups a day). In order to maintain the good results, Chris
requires a case manager who sees him every third week,
or more frequently if necessary. A friend volunteer is
helping Chris with his budgeting and shopping, and a
housekeeper attends to his housekeeping needs.*

Chris' story illustrates how 'deceptive' the addictions can be,
and how easily they can be missed by family, caseworkers,
managers, and counsellors. It also exemplifies the social issues faced by individuals like Chris, and the increased need for
treatment and social support to prevent the mental health occurrences and "revolving door" scenario.

Caffeine can be consumed from a number of different sources,
including coffee, tea, caffeinated soda, over the-counter analgesics and cold remedies, stimulants and weight-loss aids. The
average intake of caffeine in the United States is approximately 200 mg/day. Individuals who drink large amounts of
coffee display some aspects of dependence on caffeine and exhibit tolerance and perhaps withdrawal. (See Table 1 for the
full diagnostic criterion for caffeine intoxication.)

Table 1- Caffeine Intoxication
(adapted from APA, 1994, p. 213)

A diagnosis is reached if there is excess consumption of caffeine, usually more than 2-3 cups of coffee, which results in at least five symptoms, which may include the following:

> *restlessness, nervousness, excitement, insomnia,*
> *flushed face, diarises, gastrointestinal disturbance,*
> *muscle twitching, rambling flow of thought and speech*
> *tachycardia or cardiac arrhythmia, periods of*
> *inexhaustibility, and/or psychomotor agitation.*

The impact of the symptoms must be clinically significant to the extent that it affects social, occupational or other impairment on the person's functioning.

The DSM-IV (APA, 1994) distinguishes between caffeine intoxication and the following:

A. Caffeine-induced anxiety disorder, which is anxiety symptoms due to the direct physiological effects of caffeine.
B. Caffeine-induced sleep disorder, where severe disturbance in sleep is produced by the effects of caffeine.

All caffeine-related disorders have been found amongst the developmentally disabled group. They have to be considered when agitation, aggression, sleeplessness and nervousness are the symptoms and behaviours in this population. These disorders have to be identified and treated before any other diagnosis or mental health problems are presumed. Caffeine-related disorders are preventable to some extent;

therefore, the ways and means to do so have to be considered very seriously. Other non-addictive substances can be used to modulate this issue.

Nicotine-Related Disorders

Nicotine dependence and withdrawal can develop with use of all forms of tobacco. The relative ability of these products to produce dependence and/or to induce withdrawal, is associated with the rapid absorption characteristic of the route of administration (oral over transdermal), and the nicotine content of the product. Nicotine dependence is very common in individuals who have a developmental disability. As in the general population, a larger number of addicted individuals attempt to stop smoking. However, a very small number (up to 5%) are successful in doing so. Chain-smoking is very characteristic of nicotine dependence, and is highly prevalent amongst higher functioning developmentally disabled adults. The harmful effects of nicotine are well known. Persons with developmental disabilities not only suffer the ill effects of smoking, but also financial consequences in an already limited budget. Prevention of nicotine dependence in this group, as in others, is by far the better approach in the long run.

The Case of Paul

Paul, is a 27-year-old male who lives in a high support community group home. Paul lived with foster parents until the age of 18 years, when he had a "breakdown" and had to be hospitalized. During this hospitalization, Paul was diagnosed as suffering from:

- *anxiety/depressive disorders (Axis I)*
- *Dependent Personality Disorder (Axis II)*
- *mild degree of Developmental Disability (Axis II)*

He was treated with antidepressant medication and counselling and was released after two months. Since his parents had many difficulties coping with Paul's "extreme behaviours", Paul was placed in an apartment, living alone with staff's support (daily visiting, assistance with budgeting, shopping, and homemaking). During the following six months, it was observed by several staff members that, at times, "Paul seemed rather high, excitable, almost euphoric". They also noticed that on one occasion, empty beer bottles were stacked at the side of the kitchen counter. Staff also noticed that Paul, at other times, would be "depressed, dejected, withdrawn and highly anxious". It was during those times that Paul's behaviour would be at its worst. Behaviours such as:

- *aggression*
- *agitation*
- *restlessness*
- *insomnia*
- *fatigue*
- *tremors of upper extremities*
- *decreased appetite*

Upon further questioning of Paul's staff support members, it was noted that:

- *Paul always had a drinking habit.*
- *This habit would wax and wane based on "Paul's*

moods" (worse when down and depressed, less when high and excitable).

- *These moods were present since Paul was 14 years old, and his drinking habit started close to that time.*

His parents were asked at the hospital about Paul's drinking habit. They felt that "this was Paul", and did not report it. Parents also felt that his excessive moods were part of "Paul's personality". Never did it occur to them to link this with the history of Paul's uncle who had similar patterns of behaviour (highs and lows). The uncle was an alcoholic. Following the discovery and recognition of Paul's primary mental disorder as Bipolar Mood Disorder, treatment became more appropriate, and rehabilitation of the alcohol abuse was started with reasonable results. However, Paul had to be moved to a more protective and consistent environment of a high support community.

Paul's story illustrates that the use and abuse of substances such as alcohol is a means of self-medication in the presence of mental illness. This remained undiagnosed for a lengthy period of time. It also identifies the issues of lack of understanding, and early recognition of addictions by parents, professionals, and caregivers.

In most cultures, alcohol is the most frequent substance of abuse, and the cause of considerable morbidity and mortality. Alcohol-related disorders are frequent in persons with developmental disabilities (APA, 1994; Ferrara, 1992).

Based on DSM-IV criteria, these disorders include:

- Alcohol dependence/abuse
- Alcohol-induced disorders, such as, intoxication, withdrawal, delirium dementia, psychotic, mood and anxiety disorders.

Higher functioning people with developmental disabilities tend to suffer most from these disorders. An accurate estimation of the prevalence of alcohol-related disorders in this group is difficult to establish. Under-reporting of substance abuse, as well as life patterns of being single and living alone, make it impossible to have exact rates of prevalence in this population.

The ill effects of substance abuse are not only chemically related but also socially-related. Westermeyer et al. (1996) reported several cases of substance abuse in people with developmental disabilities who invariably had been victimised during or following an episode of intoxication. For men, this involved being robbed and/or beaten. For women, this involved being raped and/or beaten (or both). Perpetrators of this violence had been people whom they met in the alcohol or drug use context, although the assaults typically occurred elsewhere.

Other Substance-Related Disorders

Persons with developmental disabilities are frequently "treated" with multiple prescription drugs and other related substances. As a result, they can become addicted to over-the-counter or prescribed medication as the following case illustrates multiple substance abuse.

The Case of Irene

Irene is a 40 year old woman, who at present resides in a boarding home. Irene had spent her initial twenty years with her family. Unfortunately, Irene's mother died when Irene was 20 years old. Her father and her other siblings felt that they could not care for Irene the same way, and "placed her" at a nearby institution.

During her stay, Irene was diagnosed as suffering from:

- *grief reaction*
- *anxiety and depression disorders (Axis I)*
- *mild degree of developmental disability (Axis II)*

Various medication regimes were given, and Irene ended up with multiple medication use. In later interviews, Irene would recall her need to be safe and protected, the "panic and shakiness" that she experienced "deep to her soul", and how these problems "would go away" when she received medication, sometimes as simple as Tylenol.

At 30 years, Irene was discharged from the institution, and moved to a community boarding home. She felt "very insecure initially", but "liked the change". A month following her move to her new home, Irene started getting "bad attacks" when she felt "insecure and unprotected". She made it a habit to go to the staff and asked for "peace medication". When staff refused to comply with her request, Irene fulfilled her need at the local pharmacy. She took Tylenol daily. Eventually, Irene's inability to afford this medication forced her to resort to shoplifting. She was caught and reported to police. Her apprehension led

> *to her rehabilitation in a specialized unit. Irene re-*
> *sponded well to counselling and individual psychother-*
> *apy, somewhat alleviating the feelings of guilt that Irene*
> *had carried for so many years over the loss of her mother*

Irene's history highlights the major difficulties that people with developmental disabilities face in their lives, and the amount of support that they require in order to avoid such occurrences. It also addresses the multifaceted nature of the substance-related disorders as they apply to this group.

Why early identification and appropriate levels of treatment are so important for this group

As the previous cases exemplify, addictions and substance-related disorders tend to be "low key", and as such, do not attract notice. They are also often considered as part of the "person's life and habits", so that the magnitude of the detrimental effects of these so called "habits" is denied. Parents and caregivers are often reluctant to report their son/daughter/ client because of feelings of guilt and betrayal. Lack of systematic observation of daily habits and routines can also become difficult since many individuals live alone, and are quite "secretive" about their lives. Privacy and confidentiality are very important social values that we all enjoy. However, when issues of physical or mental health arise, our rights to privacy and confidentiality have to be seriously questioned, and appropriate measures to restore the person's health should prevail. In the face of a mental health problem, early identification, correct diagnosis and appropriate treatment are of paramount importance since these disorders can lead to problems that are almost impossible to solve.

In the case of Chris, his dependence on caffeine and tobacco were masked by his major mental illness. However, in part, his symptoms were the result of these abuses, and led to social disarray in his life.

In the case of Paul, his dependence was the result of his primary mental illness. However, the dependence itself caused major ill effects, and complicated his treatment further by prolonging his hospitalization. They also necessitated major social intervention, resulting in a more restricted and less independent social life than he could have enjoyed should these complications not have existed.

In the case of Irene, the chemical dependence served as a stress reliever initially, but subsequently became a damaging interference in her life as the dependence increased.

In all three examples, the substance-related disorders were either familial in nature (running in the family), or caused by other mental health problems and/or life circumstances. Early recognition and appropriate handling of the underlying pathology of these problems would have minimized the complications of these addictions.

What is known to help these individuals in their plight?

Many Detoxification/Rehabilitation Centres are generic in their application of the various treatment modalities for substance-related disorders. The long waiting lists and lack of specificity in addressing the DD + SD group makes it virtually impossible to accommodate and modify the disorders sufficiently, and address the specific needs of our clients. Additionally, many treatment modalities offered, cannot benefit this group of people since the cognitive limitation does not allow their participation on an"equal level" during such processes as group sessions, group counselling, or individual therapies not adapted to these clients. The resulting feelings of insecurity, frustration, inadequacy and low self-esteem may become a detriment to these clients.

The lack of specialized expertise amongst the various professional teams, including psychiatry, makes it very difficult for these clients. In order for the full benefit of these centres to be felt, these clients need one-to-one support, specific explanations /instructions, and acknowledgement of the realities of their lives (limited community participation, limited finances, limited extended family supports, and fewer networks).

Let us take a look now into the various ways that substance-related disorders can be addressed. It is advisable to emphasize, once again, that prevention (primary and secondary) is the best way of avoiding these problems. Improved public education and awareness of the many ill effects of substance abuse cannot only prevent a person from becoming addicted, but also can reduce the incidence of the developmental disabilities/learning disabilities in total.

Treatment Modalities

As in any other mental disorder, substance related disorders could be treated by following the biopsychosocial model.

Biological Remedies/Medication

Medication continues to be a helpful adjunct treatment available to professionals in the treatment of mental illness. In persons with developmental disability who experience substance abuse, few such remedies can provide improved rate of success in combination with other approaches. The primary medications, which are specific to these individuals, are as follows:

Specific interventions include the following:

- *Serotonin Stabilizers*: Serotonin is responsible for and can affect areas such as: mood, impulse control, emotionality and negative self-feelings. As such, medications that enhance the serotonin transmission (e.g., fluoxetine, sertraline, citalopram, to name a few) may moderately decrease the alcohol consumption.

- *Anti-anxiety Agents*: Anti-anxiety medication has been found very helpful in the treatments of substance abuse especially when linked with underlying anxiety disorder. However, some of the anti-anxiety medications can cause dependence. As a result, they are used usually in acute crisis situations, and are avoided by many professionals. Buspirone (Buspar) is a non-benzodiazepine anti-anxiety agent that may also stabilize serotonin, and may alleviate alcohol or other substance abuse.

- *Naltrexone*: Naltrexone is one of the most promising medications in alcohol abuse and alcohol craving. Studies of adults in veteran's hospitals have shown that naltrexone reduced relapse rate of heavy alcohol consumption over a twelve-week period by about 50%. It also appeared to decrease alcohol craving greater than placebo did. More studies specific to our clients are necessary in order to establish the efficacy of Naltrexone in this population.

- *Antabuse:* Antabuse has been in use for many years and has been found somewhat helpful in the treatment of alcohol abuse. Antabuse works by blocking acetaldehyde dehydrogenase, the liver enzyme responsible for the removal of acetaldehyde, the major breakdown product of alcohol. When a person has taken Antabuse and consumes alcohol, he/she experiences very unpleasant side effects. However, these ill effects can be at times, very dangerous. Therefore, for the developmentally disabled population, it is preferable to use Naltrexone.

- For caffeine and nicotine addiction, measures such as healthier diet, stress relieving exercises, and other programmes that improve self-esteem and decrease anxiety levels, are very beneficial in the treatment of these disorders. New ways of addressing nicotine addictions can include the patch, Zobin (an anti-compulsive agent), lower nicotine-content cigarettes, and gum.

- In other major addictions, more specific interventions with medication, therapies, hospitalization, day programme, and detoxification/rehabilitation programmes may be needed to modify and ameliorate the addictions.

There is not enough data to date to evaluate treatment outcome specific to this population. More research is needed to provide useful information, and to serve as a springboard for further developments. Treatment centres such as the Waryas House in

Poughkeepsie, New York were established to serve this population better and improve outcome.

Psychological Therapies

These are of primary importance in the therapeutic process of these disorders. All types of psychotherapies can be very useful in addressing these disorders in persons with developmental disabilities. Modification of applied psychotherapies to fit the level of cognitive ability is very important, as is the recognition that every therapeutic step has to be broken down into smaller, easier to understand steps. Cognitive therapy, brief focussed therapy, and art/play therapies have been used very successfully in various addiction centres to address underlying issues such as depression, anxiety, and low self esteem. Group and family therapies are very important as adjunct therapies. They improve existing relationships, and increase the individual's and/or family's understanding of the illness itself, as well as other factors that contribute to the continuation of these disorders.

Social therapies – Environmental/Milieu Therapies

Social interventions are of equal importance and have to be offered simultaneously if it is at all possible with the other approaches. These remedies address the life of the individual in its totality. Housing, finances, day occupation, social networks, recreational activities and physical exercises are of paramount importance in establishing a healthier way of living. They complement the other therapies, and provide higher success rate in improving symptom presentation as well as in preventing further relapses, and the "revolving door" scenario.

Dr. Matthew Ferrara has developed an addiction treatment model for persons with DD/SD. His advice is that counsellors should expect the treatment to take longer (perhaps up to three to four times longer), to repeat all interventions many times, to use written assignments judiciously, and keep them simple.

The barriers for successful intervention identified by the various experts are:

- high staff turnover
- longer-term support needed
- familial patterns and collusion within the family system
- feelings of negative self-esteem and frustrations that may continue the negative spiral of the addiction
- loneliness, social isolation, and single status may aid in keeping these individuals "trapped in their addictions"
- cognitive limitations that can hinder best outcome
- family and counsellors who may be "overly sympathetic" and may not confront the family member/client on his/her addiction.
- existing services for Substance Disorders that are disorganized and geared towards "rapid recoveries" that are not conducive to the persons who have a developmental disability and who abuse substances

Finally, technological and medicinal advances, increased financial support, and specific programmes for these clients would certainly improve outcome, offer better quality of life, and increase our understanding of these disorders.

As Tomasulo stated in 1998, for persons with developmental disabilities and addiction, the usual channels for treating substance abuse are neither prepared nor inclined to provide effective services. He further states that the combination of cognitive limitations, developmental delay, and psychiatric intervention create a need for a different approach to the treatment of alcohol abuse.

Summary

This chapter has attempted to provide you with helpful information on the substance-related disorders as they apply to the person with a developmental disability. Ways of recognizing these disorders in this group, as well as early identification, assessment, and existing treatment approaches have been presented with real life vignettes to enable you to understand the course and processes of the disorders themselves, and the individual's plight. Ways of preventing many of these disorders/ addictions have been highlighted to assist in the primary prevention process so much needed in this population.

Do You Know?

1. What are substance-related disorders?
2. Which of these disorders mostly affect persons with developmental disabilities?
3. What are the specific characteristics of the substance disorders in this population?
4. What is known to help these individuals in their plight?
5. Are some of these disorders preventable?
6. What supports do we need to develop to assist this group?

Resources

Longo, L. (1997). Alcohol abuse in persons with developmental disabilities. *The Habilitative Mental Health Care Newsletter; 16(4)*, 61-64.
Substance Abuse Resources and Disability Issues (SARDI) Newsletter Online (1997) *Substance Abuse 8(1)*.

References

American Psychiatric Association (1994). *Diagnostic and statistical manual of mental disorders*. (4th ed.). Washington, DC: Author.
Annand, G.N. & Rug, G. (1998). Over-coming barriers to effective treatment for persons with mental retardation and substance abuse problems. *National Association for the Dually Diagnosed Bulletin, 1(2)*, 14-17.
Campbell, M., Malone, R. (1991). Mental retardation and psychiatric disorders. *Hospital Community Psychiatry*, 42, 374-389.
Edgerton, RB. (1986). Alcohol and drug use by mentally retarded adults. *American Journal of Mental Deficiency, 90*, 602-609.
Ferrara, M. (1992). *Substance abuse treatment for persons with mental retardation*. Texas Commission on Alcohol and Drug Abuse.
Longo, L. (1997). Alcohol abuse in persons with developmental disabilities. *The Habilitative Mental Health Care Newsletter, 16(4)*, 61-64.
National Household Survey (1994). *Drug abuse, substance abuse and mental health services administration*.
Ruf, G. (1999). Addiction treatment for people with Mental Retardation and hearing disabilities: Why we need Special-

ized Services. *The National Association of Developmental Disabilities Bulletin, 2(3).,* 95-101.

School of Medicine, Wright State University (1996). *Substance abuse among consumers of vocational rehabilitation services: Executive summary of an epidemiological study rehabilitation research and training centre on drugs and disability.*

Stavrakaki, C. (1999). Depression, anxiety and adjustment disorders in people with developmental disabilities. In N. Bouras (Ed.), *Psychiatric and behavioral disorders in developmental disabilities and mental retardation* (pp. 175-187). Boston, MA: Cambridge University Press.

Stavrakaki, C. & Mintsioulis, G. (1995). Pharmacological treatment of obsessive-compulsive disorders in Downs syndrome individuals: Comparison with obsessive-compulsive disorders of non-Downs mentally retarded persons. *In Proceedings of the International Congress II on the Dually Diagnosed.* (pp. 52-56). Boston, MA.

Stavrakaki, C. & Mintsioulis, G. (1997). Anxiety disorders in persons with mental retardation: Diagnostic, clinical, and treatment issues. *Psychiatric Annals, 27,*182-189.

Substance Abuse Resources and Disability Issues (SARDI) Newsletter Online (1997) *Substance Abuse, 8(1)*, Fall.

Tomasulo, D. J. (1998). Drug abuse treatment for people with mental retardation. Who will do it? *Mental Health Aspects of Developmental Disabilities, 1(1),* 20-22.

Westermeyer, Y., Crosby, R., Nugent, S. (1998). The Minnesota Substance Abuse Problems Scale: Psychometric analysis and valication in a clinical population. *American Journal on Addictions, 7(1)*, 24-34.

Westermeyer J., Phaoblong, T., Neither, J. (1988). Substance use and abuse among mentally retarded persons: A comparison of patients and a survey population. *American Journal of Drug and Alcohol Abuse 14,*109-123.

Chapter 15

Dual Diagnosis In Children

William Mahoney

Learning Objectives

Readers will be able to:

1. Identify specific factors contributing to emotional and behavioural problems in children and youth with developmental disabilities.
2. Describe manifestations of emotional disorders at different ages and stages of development.
3. Discuss different treatment approaches towards emotional and behavioural disorders in children and youth with developmental disabilities.

Introduction

Matthew is a 6-year-old boy with Down Syndrome. Both the school and the family are concerned because he is very active, impulsive, and resistant to appropriate behavioural management strategies despite being supported by an educational assistant in school. The family has followed through on recommendations of the behaviour management team. They ask if there are any other interventions that might help since the behaviour is interfering significantly with his social interactions. They wonder if it is possible for a student with Down Syndrome to have an attention problem.

There are a number of emotional and behavioural problems in children that have different frequencies, courses and manifestations when compared to an adult population. As well, service delivery systems for children may have separate linkages and different resources. Issues and demands related to education and to family evolution are dynamic, changing factors that require consideration and collaboration both for assessment and intervention when dealing with children with a potential dual diagnosis.

About 15 percent of children and youth without developmental disabilities have significant emotional and behavioural problems (Cadman, Boyle, Szatmari, & Offord, 1987). When this concerning number was discovered in Ontario, in the early 80's, only 15% of children with significant problems had received services to address them. Although the frequency of problems, in general, is fairly consistent throughout the childhood years, the types of problems do change as children evolve into adolescents. In younger children, disruptive behaviours are more prevalent and affect males more frequently. In adolescence, emotional disorders such as anxiety and depression become more common, affecting females more often than males. The same study showed that children with chronic conditions and some form of disability have three times the frequency of a behavioural or emotional problem compared to their non-disabled peers. In another survey, 41% of children age 4-18 years with a developmental disability also had a severe emotional or behavioural problem (Einfeld & Tonge, 1996). It is quite clear that professionals dealing with children and adolescents with developmental disabilities will inevitably come in contact with a number of children with significant behavioural and emotional challenges.

What is 'normal' behaviour?

It is expected that many, if not most, young children will present some behaviour challenges to their parents and caregivers. Attention-seeking behaviour, non-compliance, tantrums and aggression are relatively frequent occurrences. Such skills and strategies such as positive approaches to changing behaviours, setting limits, and giving consistent messages, are helpful in caring for all children. Community initiatives to develop parenting skills and the training of care providers of all children are significant investments that allow straightforward problems to be addressed, and permit specialized services to address complex situations in a timely way.

Dealing with the concept of dual diagnosis in children must therefore range from usual and common issues to problems that are extremely complex. The range of services to support emotional and behavioural problems in children with problems of development will need this same type of overlay to respond to individual needs.

Family issues and needs

Parents experience a wide range of emotions when they receive information about their child's condition. A supportive, family centred approach can greatly assist parents as they come to as much acceptance as possible of the implications of the problems in both the short and long term (King, Rosenbaum, & King, 1996). In infancy and early childhood, strategies that focus on attachment, and that give parents as much information as possible, in a manner that they are able to assimilate, are investments in the prevention of problems later on.

As children get older, parents often feel very self-conscious that their child's behaviour is a reflection of their parenting skills. Experiencing a care system that allows them to express their concerns and frustrations without a sense that they are major contributing factors, will allow them to develop confidence in their own problem solving skills to deal with difficult behaviours, as well as to build positive relationships with support services.

Assessment/diagnostic issues

When a condition or problem is serious enough to cause significant impairment, there is often a search for a diagnosis of a "disorder". Current approaches to classifying childhood behaviour and emotional problems use particular terminology based on some of the manuals and tools that are currently in use. The term "Disorder" is used when a child's symptoms meet the criteria for a diagnosis of an entity that is listed in the Diagnostic and Statistical Manual of the American Psychiatric Association Fourth Edition (DSM-IV) (American Psychiatric Association, 1994). The criteria regarding the various disorders have come from that manual. To be diagnosed, an assessment by a qualified professional must occur. In Ontario, this would be a licensed medical doctor or psychologist. When terms like Attention Deficit Hyperactivity Disorder (ADHD), or Obsessive Compulsive Disorder (OCD) are used, the implication is that a process of diagnosis has occurred. The statistics quoted above regarding the prevalence of significant emotional and behavioural problems reflect children and adolescents who actually have one of these disorders.

The boundaries between "problems" and "disorders" are fuzzy. Questions such as "When does active behaviour become hyperactive behaviour? or "Are habits a compulsion?" are difficult to answer clearly or quickly for children without developmental disabilities. This reality suggests that the implementation of strategies known to help or change behaviours when they are issues, keeping track of their outcomes and looking for assistance and further assessment when the problems are getting worse, or continuing to significantly interfere with function, are very appropriate courses of action.

Approach to classification

Sally is a 6-year-old girl who is non-verbal. In the morning when getting dressed for school, she is very angry, yells a lot and hits her mother. This pattern of behaviour has been present for about a month.

Another way of looking at emotional and behavioural problems in children is to classify them as either internalizing or externalizing. Internalizing problems are symptoms felt within oneself such as anxiety, sadness or depression. Externalizing problems are acting out behaviours such as aggression, arguing or defiance. The interventions for internalizing problems are different than for externalizing problems. Counselling and individual therapy might help a child who is sad where behaviour modification could reduce aggression.

Since the development of the classification of behavioural/ emotional problems, we have come to realize that many children experience both types of problems simultaneously. The term used to describe this phenomenon is co-morbidity. As well, one issue can lead to another. For example, Sally has aggressive tantrums in the morning. She may be extremely anxious about the school bus ride or an issue in her educational programme. The anxiety, an internalizing problem, is leading to the aggressive behaviour, an externalizing problem. The most appropriate intervention would be to reduce the anxiety, and potentially modify some parts of the academic programme. In addition, the teaching of alternative ways to Sally to express frustration could be important to prevent a recurrence when encountering a new frustration. This situation illustrates the complexities of supporting children with a dual diagnosis, and emphasizes the need for a careful assessment of multiple factors when deciding on an intervention programme.

There is a strong relationship between behaviour and expectations of people in the child's environment. It is important to have a sense of a child's developmental level in order to make judgments about whether one is dealing with expected behaviour for a child around that functional level, or whether the behaviour is clearly atypical. Even when the behaviour is consistent with the child's developmental level, it may be interfering with his or her success in a particular environment; and therefore, may be felt to need some modification.

An understanding of the child's specific developmental strengths and weaknesses is also relevant. Children with developmental disabilities very frequently have difficulties with the use of language. Adults use language to give instructions, and to make requests, and they often have an expectation that a child will follow through with communications directed at them. This is often the source of frustration and concern. Children who have trouble communicating verbally may express their frustration through behaviour such as irritability, aggression, tantrums or withdrawal from the situation. If the environment continues to be overly demanding, or a high level of frustration continues for a period of time, maladaptive behaviour patterns can become established and be difficult to change, even when the communication abilities improve.

The possibility of a significant additional attention problem is often considered by caregivers. Children with weaknesses in specific areas such as fine motor skills will show limited attention to fine motor activities, reflecting a natural tendency to avoid activities that are difficult. Although, in this situation, the concern is raised about attention abilities, the key strategy would be to modify either the task or the caregiver's approach in order to have the child participate for a gradually longer period of time.

The achievement of developmental milestones leads both to a sense of accomplishment as well as new challenges. For example, parents of children around the age of one year focus on the development of skills such as walking. There is a sense of pride when this is accomplished, but the child now is able to run and climb and escape from the parents' attention much more quickly. This will require new strategies to protect the child from dangers to which he or she now has access. Since a child may not have a good concept of danger, child proofing would be the recommended intervention.

Biological issues

Biological issues associated with developmental disabilities may be identified at birth, in early infancy, or during an evaluation for causes of delays in development. There are a number of conditions where certain behaviours and personality styles are quite common. It is now felt that certain genetic disorders such as fragile x or Williams Syndrome lead to patterns of behaviour that are neurologically based and associated with the specific genetic diagnosis, a so-called behavioural phenotype. Some examples of syndromes or conditions are listed in Table 1 along with their common behavioural issues, and some implications for the development of remedial strategies.

It is also known that injury to certain parts of the nervous system can be associated with specific behavioural manifestations. For example, damage to the right side of the brain may lead to specific problems analyzing and responding to body language. Injury to the front part of the brain may be associated with very impulsive behaviour.

This background information is important when a professional or caregiver is considering what issues may be leading to specific behavioural concerns, and is selecting strategies that may be helpful in changing the behaviour.

Specific Psychiatric Disorders

The criteria used to make a diagnosis of a specific disorder are the same in children and adults for the internalizing and emotional disorders such as anxiety and depression. Children with developmental disabilities may express their emotions through their overt behaviour. However, the issues may be more difficult to sort out since an individual may not have established a consistent pattern of behaviour where change in behaviour can lead someone to suspect a specific, significant emotional problem. It can be important, therefore, to suspect an additional or

Table 1- Examples of Syndromes and Behavioural Issues

Problem	Common Behavioural Characteristics	Developmental Issues	Intervention Implications
Down Syndrome	Externalizing behaviour including ADHD (25%) Autism more frequent (7%) Task avoidance	Specific difficulty with pronunciation	Need for behaviour support to parents early when requested May need assessment for psychiatric disorder
Fragile X Syndrome	Up to 80% ADHD Over stimulation may lead to aggression Gaze aversion and repetitive behaviours Shy and anxious in social situations Hand biting Females - anxiety and social avoidance	Delays in language and motor skills. Pronunciation and conversational problems	Intervention must consider anxiety Treatment for ADHD
Prader - Willi Syndrome	Strengths in visual organization and perception 50% behavioural outbursts Anxiety Skin picking	Motor and coordination problems Articulation problems Weakness in auditory processing	Strategies to reduce anxiety and prevent behaviour
Klinefelter Syndrome	Social withdrawal pre adolescence Impulse control and over assertive in adolescence	Speech and language delay Auditory processing problems, reading, spelling problems	Direct intervention for learning issues Hormonal treatment may be needed in adolescence
Williams Syndrome	Attention problems, anxiety, eating and sleeping problems, very perceptive of feelings of others.	Motor abilities much weaker than language	Intervention considers anxiety
Tuberous Sclerosis	Hyperactivity Autism in up to 50%. Sleep disturbance	Difficult to control seizures	Medication for seizures can affect behaviour
Angelman Syndrome	Poor attention Episodes of laughing	Limited expressive language	Behaviour strategies to improve attention Augmentative communication techniques

new problem when usual interventions and appropriate developmental programming have not been successful.

The following section will discuss problems where the diagnosis is usually made in childhood.

Pervasive Developmental Disorders

The Pervasive Developmental Disorders (PDD) are characterized by significant problems in three major areas:
1. verbal and non-verbal communication
2. reciprocal social interaction
3. restricted interests, preoccupations, fascinations and repetitive behaviours.

Onset is typically before the age of 2-2 ½, but rarely may develop in a child over this age who has shown normal development to that point. PDD includes Autistic Disorders, Rett's Disorder, Childhood Disintegration Disorder, and Asperger's Disorder. Each of the disorders presents differently.

The diagnosis of autism implies that the individual has significant problems in all three of the major areas; atypical autism is used when one of the major areas of difficulty is not present or if the course is unusual. Rett's Syndrome only occurs in girls, and is associated with poor head growth, seizures and deterioration in motor abilities. Asperger's Disorder occurs in children who have fairly normal language developmental milestones and intelligence. When it is felt that the child has PDD, but it is not possible to identify the subtype, the term PDD not otherwise specified or PDD NOS is used.

The functional areas that are evaluated to make a diagnosis are listed in Table 2:

Table 2– Autistic Disorder Criteria
For compete diagnostic categories for Autistic Disorders of the DSM IV (APA, 1994, pp.70-71).

> **_Impairments in Social Interaction_** *There is impairment such that there is not the development of typical social and emotional interaction and engagement with peers. The person tends to present non-verbally in a distinct manner with regard to facial expression, body movements and gestures and eye contact.*
>
> **_Impairments in Verbal And Non-Verbal Communication_** *Conversation is delayed or missing or typified by language that is stereotyped, repetitive or idiosyncratic. There is little developmentally typical play behaviour.*
>
> **_Problems with Restrictive, Repetitive and Stereotyped Behaviour, Interests and Activities_** *This is typified by preoccupation, and inflexibility, to change.*

About 80% of children with autism also have a significant delay in their cognitive abilities; some have quite a severe delay. It is unclear what proportion of children with the other subtypes also have a significant delay since the definition of these subtypes is relatively recent. It is important to emphasize that the delay and PDD are two issues that require an intervention plan. This chapter will not deal specifically with the treatment of PDD. Different strategies and more intensive interventions will be needed if PDD and a significant delay in development co-exist. The age of diagnosis of PDD has decreased as research has suggested that the presence of autism at age 2 will continue through early childhood. Children who meet some but not all of the criteria at an early age may have a different, more positive course (Lord, 1995).

Attention Deficit Hyperactivity Disorder

There is good evidence that at least 4% of the childhood population has ADHD (Landgren, Pettersson, Kjellman, & Gillberg, 1996; Wolraich, Hannah, Baumgaertel, & Feurer, 1998; Wolraich, Hannah, Pinnock, Baumgaertel, & Brown, 1996). The frequency is more common in children with developmental disabilities, particularly with some specific entities such as fragile x syndrome. It is difficult to make a definitive diagnosis in young children of preschool age, since active behaviour, frustration in communication, and difficulties following rules are all very common, and often exist in the same child simultaneously. The structure and routine of many preschools and the training and skills of preschool teachers provides a supportive environment for many children who have attention weaknesses. The issue often becomes more focused as the child enters the school system.

ADHD is thought to be caused by differences in the brain functions responsible for paying attention, inhibiting impulses and inhibiting motor activity. Current evidence suggests that these traits may be inherited. Children who have had a brain injury, either before or after birth, that damages the front part of the brain, also often have ADHD.

There are thought to be three subtypes of ADHD: (1) ADHD primarily inattentive type, (2) ADHD primarily hyperactive-impulsive type, and (3) ADHD combined. The diagnosis is best made by ensuring that other contributions to behaviour have been identified, using behavioural rating scales that measure these behavioural traits, ensuring the child meets criteria for the diagnosis, and implementing behavioural interventions that change difficult behaviour.

The domains that are evaluated to make a diagnosis are listed in Table 3. It is important that the child exhibits the symptoms extensively or very often. Too many children will be identified if the symptoms only are present some of the time.

Table 3- Attention Deficit Hyperactivity Disorder Criteria (For complete criterion refer to the DSMIV (APA, 1994, pp. 83-85).

Attention Deficit Hyperactivity Disorder includes 2 major subtypes: primarily Inattentive and primarily Hyperactive Impulsive

Onset must before the age of 7 years and be evidenced in more than one environment. The disorder must be sufficient to significantly impair the individual socially, academically or occupationally..

Inattention *This includes frequent presentation of a range of symptoms including distractibility, difficulty organizing or remembering daily activities, loss of objects, inability to sustain attention, listening or tasks to completion.*

Hyperactivity *This includes fidgeting, over-activity and restlessness, impulsivity in turn-taking, interruption or intrusion, and difficulty in quiet activity.*

Children with ADHD will have another psychiatric disorder associated at least 30 % of the time. (August, Realmuto, Mac Donald, Nugent, & Crosby, 1996).

Other Disorders

Oppositional Defiant Disorder (ODD)

A summary of behaviours exhibited by children with ODD are listed in Table 4. This term is used to identify children who are frequently angry, argumentative, and frustrating for caregivers. It is felt that environmental issues more frequently contribute to oppositional behaviour than to ADHD behaviour. Many of these behaviours are thought to be part of ADHD, but it is important to view them separately since the approach to dealing with them is different.

Table 4- Oppositional Defiant Disorder Criteria

For complete criterion on Oppositional Defiant Disorder refer to the DSM-IV (APA, 1994, pp. 93-94).

Oppositional Defiant Disorder *This is typified by frequent outbursts including anger, temper, arguments, noncompliance, defiance and resentment.*

A cluster of behaviours must be frequently observed over a period of 6 months; the behaviours must be of such severity to cause significant impairment.

The behaviours must not be otherwise related to mood disorder or conduct disorder.

Obsessive behaviour

Children with developmental disabilities of all types frequently have pre-occupations, fascinations and repetitive behaviours. Whether the child has PDD or not, professionals are often asked about or become concerned about these behaviours, particularly when they have lasted a long time, or may be interfering with other expected activities. Some adults may use the child's repetitive behaviours as a barometer of the child's condition, seeing their reduction as a sign of improvement. There is controversy about the mechanisms for these behaviours, and whether direct intervention is needed to change them.

Obsessive Compulsive Disorder (OCD) may have its onset in childhood. The symptoms include obsessive thoughts that intrude and cause significant anxiety and stress, attempts to suppress the thoughts, and the person recognizing that the thoughts are the product of his or her own mind. The compulsions are behaviours that the person feels driven to perform, and they are aimed at preventing or reducing stress. The symptoms cause significant difficulties. Since children with developmental disabilities may not have the verbal skills to describe their thoughts, it is extremely difficult to clearly define the mechanisms behind their behaviours. Definition may be important, however, to decide the most appropriate interventions (AACAP, 1998).

Intervention and Treatment

When there are concerns about a behaviour or emotional disorder, the first question is to define the importance of intervening. For example, although a child may tend to be anxious, (and when very anxious may display a tantrum), if the caregivers have skills to recognize the signs of anxiety and reduce the stress, no direct intervention may be necessary. This also illustrates an important principle of intervention: prevention. It can be very appropriate to agree that a certain behaviour does not need direct intervention at a given point in time, but a strategy applied to a group or a family can actually prevent, decrease or eliminate negative behaviours that may have an emotional basis. An example of a group strategy is peer mediated schoolyard conflict resolution, which can reduce aggression in the schoolyard, and decrease modeling of this behaviour for all children, including the anxious child with a developmental disability.

An overall approach to intervention is to consider a layered system. The layers include: (1) universal, population based intervention, (2) targeted interventions to certain groups, and (3) individual interventions, which can be group or individually delivered.

A universal intervention is delivered to a population or programme such as a day-care where all children regardless of the presence of a problem are involved. An example is class-wide social skills, where outcomes such as increased cooperation occur among all children. An example of a targeted intervention is a group education programme for parents who would use the information to help with behaviour. This could be directed at all families or families of children with a developmental disability. An example of the individual approach is a behavioural assessment and programme for a child with aggressive behaviour who is quite anxious.

Most regions of the province have programmes for assessment of children with developmental delays, and behaviour intervention programmes for children, adolescents, and adults with developmental disabilities. There are physicians in many centres who are aware of specific psychiatric and emotional disorders and medical options for treatment. The development of a treatment plan is best done through a coordinated approach from these services.

There are many situations where medical therapies are suggested. There are instances where there is research supporting the effectiveness of medication such as in ADHD. There are other situations where appropriate behaviour programmes and support have not been successful, and the symptoms are interfering with the child's success. Finally, there will be rare situations where there is a crisis and nobody is coping. Care must be taken since there is always the potential for side effects from medication, and there is limited information about the use of a number of medications in children. It is also important to be cautious of the long-term use because children's nervous systems are constantly changing as they mature. Due to these concerns, there is an increasing tendency to try "natural" or alternative substances. Since these therapies also are thought to affect the nervous system, the same cautions are appropriate.

When a specific entity has been diagnosed, there are ranges of treatment options that may be suggested or indicated. This next section will discuss some of the options related to specific disorders.

Attention Deficit Hyperactivity Disorder (ADHD)

The 3 main components of intervention for ADHD are: (1) parent education, (2) behaviour modification and (3) medication. Each one of these components has been demonstrated to be helpful. The nature of ADHD is that it may well be present over a long period of time. This implies that long term planning and support to the family may well be required. Also important, interventions must be applied when the behaviour is occurring. If the child is having significant problems on the school bus, a behavioural intervention must focus on motivating and rewarding appropriate behaviour on the school bus.

Parent education has been proven to be most effective when done in a group format (Cunningham, Bremner, & Boyle, 1995). Behavioural interventions must promote motivation for appropriate behaviours and monitoring the reinforcement value of the rewards, since this fades much more quickly for children with ADHD compared to those without ADHD.

The medical options for treatment of ADHD include the stimulants, methylphenidate (Ritalin), and dextro-amphetamine (Dexedrine), as the first choice medications. Other medications are considered when these are not effective, but it is important to obtain thorough diagnostic information in order to ensure that ADHD is the condition leading to the behaviours. Each dose of methylphenidate or dextro-amphetamine lasts about 4 hours unless a long acting form is used. The dosage is decided by age, weight and titration of the medication based on improvement in the core symptoms of ADHD. Medication can be given one, two or three times per day. The common side effects include headaches, abdominal pain, loss of appetite and difficulties falling asleep. Side effects occur in approximately 50% of children who take stimulant medication. There is a suggestion that the appetite and sleeping problems are slightly more common with dextro-amphetamine.

Sometimes, stimulants are not effective, or other behaviours such as aggression and conduct problems are resistant to usual intervention. One medication that has been used in children in this situation is clonidine. This appears to reduce agitation, and can help children fall asleep who have significant sleeping problems. There is less research on its use and safety than with the stimulant medications.

Anxiety

It is quite difficult to make a definitive diagnosis of an anxiety disorder in young children or youth with limited verbal skills. Where this is a hypothesized mechanism, transition times and new or very stimulating situations can lead to significant stress and difficult behaviours. Strategies such as warning regarding transitions, visual cues, a calming, supportive tone of voice, and relaxation techniques taught to caregivers and ultimately to the individual, are often effective in reducing the perceptions of stress, leading to more enjoyable and positive experiences. It is important to be aware of some of the subtle signs that an individual is becoming anxious, and to intervene early with such tactics as distraction and redirection. Cognitive behavioural therapy is emerging as an effective therapy for older children and adolescents with anxiety and OCD (Barrett, 1998), but it is unclear how applicable this therapy may be for individuals with a dual diagnosis. There is limited information on the use of medical therapies for children with anxiety disorders, let alone with a dual diagnosis that includes anxiety (Labellarte, Ginsburg, Walkup, & Riddle, 1999). There is some preliminary evidence of medications like fluoxetine (Prozac) being helpful (Fairbanks et al., 1997). In older adolescents, the approaches found useful with adults may be worth consideration. In children who are taking other medications such as anti-seizure medications, drug-drug interactions are common, and great care must be taken when adding a new medication. As well, some anti-depressants can lower the seizure threshold, leading to a greater risk for seizures in children who have a tendency toward them.

Depression

Again, a clear diagnosis of depression in young children is extremely difficult. Attempting to provide the child with a supportive, success oriented environment, and facilitating positive family development will prevent the occurrence of reactive depression, but this can still occur related to loss, stress, or disruption outside the family's control. When there are concerns a child may be depressed due to environmental factors, dealing with and removing stress, providing positive support and opportunities for clearly positive social experiences often will be effective. There is, again, limited information on the use of medical interventions in children and young adolescents with depression (Masi, Favilla, & Mucci, 1998). It is unclear if anti-depressant medication is effective in children and young teenagers.

Aggressive behaviour

Aggressive behaviour is often the issue that leads to high levels of concern and requests for assistance. The tolerance for this behaviour is very low in society, particularly in schools, and the occurrence will lead to requests for urgent intervention. There may be a tendency to use restraint as a way of controlling young children's aggression, but this often cannot be done safely in older children and adolescents. Restraint may aggravate the behaviour, and should only be done under careful supervision where safety is a concern. This chapter has emphasized considering behaviour as a form of communication, and thus it is essential to give careful consideration to the multiple issues when developing intervention strategies.

There are some medications such as the newer anti-psychotic medications respiridone and olanzapine that can reduce aggressive behaviour in specific instances. They may also have side effects such as weight gain. There is little information about their long-term use. With prolonged use of the medication, there is a risk of development of long-term difficulties with motor co-ordination, a problem called tardive dyskinesia.

Adolescents and transitional age young adults

The spectrum of emotional disorders changes in and after pubertal development to a pattern consistent with adults. Educational programmes and expectations shift to an emphasis on community, employment and life skills, and are more consistent. Anxiety and depression become more common, and thought disorders and schizophrenia begin to emerge. Bipolar disorder can be more easily defined as patterns of behaviour change can be tracked. The interventions for bipolar disorder are very similar to those for adults. Personality styles and traits have been observed over time, so that significant deterioration associated with the emergence of a significant emotional disorder will be clearer.

Care in children is usually delivered with parents being the major informants and decision makers. Adolescents increasingly acquire this responsibility. It is important to include the adolescent when making decisions about treatment, and to respect their decision about participation, if they are able to provide this information. In Ontario, the primary mandate for children's mental health services rests with the Ministry of Community and Social Services (MCSS); whereas, in adults, there is a blend between the Ministry of Health Mental Health system and MCSS support services. This requires families to learn to negotiate a whole new set of services and systems of care delivery when their children reach the age of 16-18 years. Additional support to the families and assistance with linkage to new resources and systems during this transition is often required.

Summary

Issues related to dual diagnosis in children and youth change over time, and there is a need to consider the expectations of the child's environment. Emotional and behavioural problems are common. The development of an understanding of the mechanisms leading to problems will lead to the most appropriate interventions. Certain conditions are diagnosed in children, where others may emerge in adolescence and early adult life. Knowledge of the biological contributions to behavioural and emotional problems will also support the prioritization of intervention strategies.

Do You Know?

1. What factors may lead to aggressive behaviour in young children?
2. Name two biological entities and name a behaviour that may be an expression of the problem.
3. What are treatments for Attention Deficit Hyperactivity Disorder?
4. Name two types of Pervasive Developmental Disorder.

Resources

Angelman Syndrome http://rigel.phys.ualberta.ca/cass
Autism/Pervasive Developmental Disorders
     http://www.autismsociety.on.ca/main.html
Down Syndrome http://www.cdss.ca/
Fetal Alcohol Syndrome http://www.ccsa.ca/fasdir.htm
Fragile X Syndrome http://www.fragile-x.ca/
Klinefelter Syndrome http://www.genetic.org/ks/index.html
Prader Willi Syndrome http://www.pwsausa.org/
Williams Syndrome http://www.bmts.com/~williams/
Tuberous Sclerosis
     http://epilepsyontario.org/links/condlinks/ts.html

References

AACAP. (1998). Practice parameters for the assessment and treatment of children and adolescents with obsessive-compulsive disorder. *Journal of the American Academy of Child and Adolescent Psychiatry, 37(10),* Suppl, 27S-45S.

American Psychiatric Association (1994). *Diagnostic and statistical manual of mental disorders (4th ed.).* Washington, DC: Author.

August, G.J, Realmuto, G.M, MacDonald, A.W., Nugent, S. M., & Crosby, R. (1996). Prevalence of ADHD and co-morbid disorders among elementary school children screened for disruptive behavior. *Journal of Abnormal Child Psychology, 24(5),* 571-595.

Barrett, P.M. (1998). Evaluation of cognitive-behavioral group treatments for childhood anxiety disorders. *Journal of Clinical Child Psychology, 27(4),* 459-468.

Cadman, D., Boyle, M., Szatmari, P., & Offord, D.R. (1987). Chronic illness, disability, and mental and social well-being: Findings of the Ontario Child Health Study. *Pediatrics*, 79(5), 805-813.

Cunningham, C.E., Bremner, R., & Boyle, M. (1995). Large group community-based parenting programmes for families of preschoolers at risk for disruptive behaviour disorders: Utilization, cost effectiveness, and outcome. *Journal of Child Psychology and Psychiatry, 36(7)*, 1141-1159.

Einfeld, S.L, & Tonge, B.J. (1996). Population prevalence of psychopathology in children and adolescents with intellectual disability: II. Epidemiological findings. *Journal of Intellectual Disability Research, 40(4) (Pt 2)*, 99-109.

Fairbanks, J.M., Pine, D.S., Tancer, N.K., Dummitt, D.S. 3rd., Ketngen, L.M., Martin, J., Asche, B.K., & Klein, R.G. (1997). Open fluoxetine treatment of mixed anxiety disorders in children and adolescents. *Journal of Child and Adolescent Psychopharmacology, 7(10)*, 17-29.

King, G.A, Rosenbaum, P.L, & King, S.M. (1996). Evaluating family-centred service using a measure of parents' perceptions. *Child Care Health and Development, 23(1)*, 47-62.

Labellarte, M.J., Ginsburg, G.S., Walkup, J.T., & Riddle, M.A. (1999). The treatment of anxiety disorders in children and adolescents. *Biological Psychiatry, 46(11)*, 1567-1578.

Landgren, M., Pettersson, R., Kjellman, B., & Gillberg, C. (1996). ADHD, DAMP and other neurodevelopmental/ psychiatric disorders in 6-year-old children: Epidemiology and co-morbidity. *Developmental Medicine and Child Neurology, 38(10)*, 891-906.

Lord, C. (1995). Follow-up of two-year-olds referred for possible autism. *Journal of Child Psychology and Psychiatry, 36(8)*, 1365-1382.

Masi, G., Favilla, L., & Mucci, M. (1998). Depressive disorder in children and adolescents. *Europ J. Paediatr Neurol, 2(6)*, 287-289.

Wolraich, M.L., Hannah, J.N., Baumgaertel, A, & Feurer, I.D. (1998). Examination of DSM-IV criteria for attention deficit/hyperactivity disorder in a county-wide sample. *Journal of Developmental and Behavioral Pediatrics, 19(3)*, 162-168.

Wolraich, M.L., Hannah, J.N., Pinnock, T.Y., Baumgaertel, A., & Brown, J. (1996). Comparison of diagnostic criteria for attention-deficit hyperactivity disorder in a county-wide sample. *Journal of the American Academy of Child and Adolescent Psychiatry, 35(3)*, 319-324.

Chapter 16

Aging and Dual Diagnosis

Keith Fidler and Bruce McCreary

Learning Objectives

Readers will be able to:

1. Identify the nature of the health problems experienced by persons with developmental disabilities as they grow older.
2. Describe the main features of various mental disorders in older persons with developmental disabilities.
3. Explain how aging has been conceptualised as a biomedical phenomenon.

Introduction

"Aging is a collective term for all those progressive deteriorative changes that occur in mature individuals and lead to a reduced expectation of life with increasing age" (Wright & Whalley, 1984).

This chapter reviews various disorders associated with aging in a context of universal experiences also associated with age. In daily practice it is important to examine the mental effects of chronic illness, sensory impairment, loss of loved ones, and residential relocation, all common in later years. For the purposes of presentation, the next section deals with general health problems, the following section with mental health disorders, and the chapter concludes with a brief comment related to various theories of aging.

General Health Problems

This section considers three sub-groups of persons with developmental disabilities. These sub-groups reveal different patterns of aging and longevity.

Those with mental retardation only are most often mildly or moderately retarded, are mobile, able to look after themselves with some supervision, and often able to do simple tasks. The aging process in these individuals follows closely that of the general population. Since many patients in this group have problems verbalizing their health complaints (Van Schrojenstein Lantman-deValk et al., 1997) screening techniques to detect conditions associated with aging are advisable and perhaps even more important than in the general population.

The Case of Fred

Fred had a moderate degree of intellectual impairment. The cause of this impairment was not known. While he could understand what he heard, his ability to speak clearly was severely limited. He chose to be by himself, could do menial tasks such as picking up litter, and he had few health problems until he reached his seventies. At that time, he developed cataracts, had an occasional bout of pneumonia, and died of a myocardial infarction at age eighty-four years.

A second sub-group has mental retardation with neurologic signs and/or epilepsy. Aging in this group involves consideration of their mental retardation, associated medical problems (such as epilepsy), secondary medical problems (such as a predisposition to aspiration) and, for many, genetic predispositions that may contribute to deteriorative changes.

The Case of Betty

Betty was a profoundly intellectually impaired woman with tuberous sclerosis who died of pneumonia at age thirty-three. She had experienced several episodes of spontaneous pneumothorax. She was non-ambulatory because of spasticity and had a seizure disorder.

Betty showed the mental retardation, the genetic predisposition, and associated features of tuberous sclerosis. It is possible that aspiration, a secondary process, contributed to her pneumonia and early death. Chronologically Betty was not old, but on the other hand, multiple, progressive, deteriorative processes led to her death.

Individuals with Down Syndrome represent a third subcategory. It has been known for years that persons with Down Syndrome have a unique aging profile. Martin (1977) using 21 criteria for aging found that Down Syndrome scored higher than any other syndrome. As well as the well known increased frequency of Alzheimer's dementia, there are increases in chromosomal aberrations, malignancy, premature greying or hair loss, aging pigment deposition, hypogonadism, diabetes mellitus, autoimmunity, degenerative vascular disease, cataract, and skin and adipose tissue changes (Lott & Lai, 1982; Martin, 1977; Wright & Whalley, 1984).

The Case of Beatrice

Beatrice began to walk at two years of age and said her first words at age five. She was considered to be moderately intellectually impaired. She grew to be a happy woman who liked social contact and was able to work in the laundry. Menopause occurred at age forty-three. She developed cataracts and had a cataract extraction and lens implant at age forty-seven. Hypothyroidism began at age forty-nine, and also at this time, she developed tonic clonic seizures. Memory loss and other signs of dementia started in her early fifties, and she was described as "severely demented" at age fifty-seven. She died of pneumonia at age sixty years. Autopsy showed cerebral atrophy with other signs of Alzheimer's disease.

The mental adjustment of older persons, regardless of their particular sub-group, can be affected by sensory impairments or discomfort related to such problems as gastroesophageal reflux, urinary retention and osteoporosis. Maintaining mobility and fitness has many benefits for physical and emotional health (Frizzell, 1997). It is an important factor in preventing osteoporosis. The goal should be to accumulate thirty minutes of moderate intensity physical activity most days of the week (Frizzell, 1997).

The occurrence of cancer increases logarithmically with age (Wright & Whalley, 1984). Cancer prevalence in adults with mental retardation aged sixty - ninety years was found to be comparable to that of the aging Dutch population (Kapell et al., 1998). There are two apparent exceptions. There is an increased incidence of chronic myeloid leukemia in Down Syndrome (Wright & Whalley, 1984), and esophageal adenocarcinoma is higher in the mentally retarded group, possibly due to the increased prevalence of gastroesophageal reflux (Evenhuis, 1997a).

Cardiovascular problems appear to occur more frequently in some syndromes associated with mental retardation. For instance, in both Down Syndrome and fragile x syndrome individuals there is an increased risk of mitral valve prolapse (Goldhaber, Brown, & Sutton, 1987; Loehr, Synhorst, Wolfe, & Hagerman, 1986). There is some question whether the rate of hypertension among adults with developmental disability is the same as, or less than, the general population. In an unpublished study comparing 220 adults with developmental disabilities to 80 adults without developmental disability in Southeastern Ontario, Ouellette-Kuntz and Craig (1999) found the rate of hypertension in the developmentally disabled group to be 13.6 percent compared to 15 percent in the non-developmentally disabled group. Evenhuis (1997a) reported a lower prevalence of hypertension in those with intellectual disability aged sixty-five years and older than has been reported in the general Dutch population (Evenhuis, 1997a).

There is a perception that health care for the developmentally disabled is often not what it should be (Turner & Moss, 1996). If this is so, it is unlikely that the aging person with this condition will receive any better care than younger patients. Improving health care may require training programmes for family physicians and other primary care professionals (Turner & Moss, 1996). Because of communication difficulties, even those with mild intellectual impairment cannot be counted on to express their symptoms adequately (Turner & Moss, 1996). Changes in behaviour may be the only way that they can communicate a medical problem.

Mental Health Disorders

This section reviews the mental disorders that occur in older persons with developmental disabilities and the management of these disorders in relation to universal experiences of growing old. The difficulties involved in the differential diagnosis of mental disorders in persons with developmental disabilities (King, De Antonia, McCracken, Forness, & Ackerland, 1994; Verhoeven & Tuinier, 1997) are no less in older individuals. Of the various disorders, dementia is obviously one that commences in later years. This contrasts with other disorders that begin early and are variably persistent over many years. "Behaviour problems" tend to be less prevalent in older persons (Day, 1994), affective disorders and dementia more prevalent, and other disorders unchanged. (Van Schrojenstien, Lantman-deValk et al., 1997)) In managing individual referrals, clinicians must carefully assess the impact of recent or current stressors along with the features of any identifiable mental disorder.

Behaviour Problems

The Case of Sally

This sixty year old woman has a mild degree of intellectual impairment. She grew up in a lower socio-economic environment in northern Ontario, and was committed to a special residential setting for delinquent females in her

> *late teens. This was characterized by severe aggression and destructiveness. She was treated with high doses of thioridazine and was often secluded because of dangerousness to others. She was transferred to a residential setting for persons with developmental disabilities at 34 and discharged to the adjacent community at 36. She performed domestic duties in a boarding home for many years, is proud of her good adjustment in the community, and now plans to retire. Unfortunately, she has recently developed failing vision because of a thioridazine-induced retinopathy.*

Sally's case illustrates the fact that many mildly intellectually impaired individuals who have major problems in early life can stabilize over time. Also illustrated, is one of the unfortunate side effects of treating disturbed behaviour with thioridazine, a special concern given that it is a popular agent in the group of neuroleptic drugs prescribed for 42% of older persons with developmental disabilities (Pary, 1993). There are alternative medications for aggression (Fava, 1997) and neuroleptics should be used ideally only for those with psychotic symptoms.

Behaviour problems tend to be more persistent in those with severe intellectual impairment who reside in residential centres. Reid, Ballinger, Heather, & Melvin (1984) note that "hostile irritability," stereotypy, overactivity, self injury and social withdrawal continued over a six year interval in a British follow-up study. In Arkansas, Bihm, Poindexter, and Warren (1998) observed that 11% of a residential population were seriously aggressive; they were more often diagnosed as "psychotic" or described as being "demanding and needy", prompting a wise recommendation: "Aggression should not be viewed in isolation, but seen as part of a complex set of factors, including related behavioural disturbances, psychiatric disorders and environmental determinants."

Since behaviour problems decrease in prevalence over time in those who have mild intellectual impairment, and persist in those more severely impaired, the development of behaviour problems for the first time in later years in any individual with a developmental disability should alert the clinician to consider dementia, an affective disorder, or an adjustment disorder.

Schizophrenia

The Case of Gerald

Gerald was adopted at three and raised on a farm in Southeastern Ontario. A poor student, in his late teens Gerald became "easily led" and involved in a variety of delinquent behaviours. At 19 he stole a truck and was referred to a psychiatric hospital when the police observed symptoms suggestive of a mental disorder. On examination, Gerald had a severe thought disorder, reported auditory hallucinations, and simply laughed about his delinquent activities. Now 50, and living under supervision in a group home for the past three years, his psychotic symptoms have yielded only partially to treatment with various antipsychotic medications. A recent tendency to depressive moods, and in particular to attempts at bodily self harm (pierces his skin with sharp objects, swallows foreign objects) has prompted the addition of an antidepressive medication. Gerald is fortunately free of side effects associated with long term use of psychotic medications.

The diagnosis of schizophrenia can be made in the usual way in those with mild intellectual impairment. Referred to in the past as "pfropfschizophrenie," a recent study of 39 cases revealed more negative symptoms, episodic memory deficits, and chromosomal variants than in a control population (Doody, Johnstone, Sanderson, Cunningham-Owens, & Muir, 1998). As illustrated by Gerald's case, psychotic symptoms are variably present over many years and current practice, at least in cases where the patient may be dangerous to themselves or others, is "relapse prevention" with antipsychotic drugs (Kissling, 1992). Although Gerald has been free of worrisome side effects, clinicians should carefully monitor those on long-term therapy. Polydipsia and water intoxication occur in a small number of cases receiving extended treatment (Bremner & Regan, 1991); worsening of behaviour as the day proceeds and the development of confusion or seizures are often observed. Polydipsia and water intoxication are reported to be less likely when clozapine or risperidone are prescribed (Canadian Clinical Practice Guidelines for the Treatment of Schizophrenia, 1998). Much more prevalent, 34% of 53 individuals reviewed by Sachdev (1992), and potentially very disabling is tardive dyskinesia. Neither level of mental retardation nor indices of "brain damage" were shown to be associated with risk but increasing age, and especially "total neuroleptic load" (i.e., dose level and years of administration) are risk factors. Sachdev reported little difficulty in distinguishing various stereotypic movements in their patient population from the features of tardive dyskinesia. The dyskinetic movements were mainly seen in the lingual, perioral and other facial muscles; the disorder was rated as mild in 75% of those affected, and in only 2 individuals (12.5%) judged to produce any degree of incapacity. Vitamin E, 400 IU twice daily has been reported useful in the treatment of tardive dyskinesia

(Elkashef, Ruskin, Bacher, & Barrett, 1990).

Dementia

The Case of Joan

Joan, a lady with Down Syndrome, died at age 59. Post-mortem examination of the brain revealed severe Alz-heimer's neuropathology. Since age 7, Joan had lived in an institution. She was independent in self help skills, stubborn but friendly and affectionate, and she enjoyed sheltered employment and a variety of leisure activities. At age 50, her work skills deteriorated. By 54, she was described as apathetic and less sociable. Between 56 and her death she was supervised in the infirmary unit be-cause of aimless wandering, incontinence, and yelling at/ hitting her caregivers. The post-mortem examination, in addition to Alzheimer's neuropathology, revealed aspira-tion pneumonia.

Although the prevalence of dementia is higher in persons who are mentally retarded than in the general population (Cooper, 1997), this is especially true for those, like Joan, with Down's Syndrome. A continuing puzzle relates to observations of universal brain changes characteristic of Alzheimer's disease in those with Down's Syndrome beyond age 40 when clinical evaluation has shown much lower rates of dementia (Zigman, Schupf, Zigman, & Sliverman, 1993). The prevalence rate of dementia increases with age; the rate in the age range over which Joan demented (i.e., 50-59) is 40% (Holland, Huppest, Stevens, & Watson, 1998). Although there are case reports of much older individuals who are free of cognitive deterioration

(Chicoine & McGuire, 1997), prospective studies reveal signs of progression and the usual course of dementia seen in members of the general population with Alzheimer's disease (Oliver, Crayton, Holland, Hall, & Bradbury, 1998). Contemporary research suggests a role for alleles of the Apolipoprotein E system on chromosome 19 in determining the progress of the dementia (Alexander et al., 1997). Use of antioxidants like selegilene and vitamin E may delay functional decline, although these preparations have not been studied specifically in persons with Down Syndrome (Pary, 1997).

Dementia in persons who are mentally retarded not due to Down Syndrome appears to have similarities to the general population in terms of etiology and natural history. Evenhuis (1997b) studied 11 cases: Alzheimer's disease in 4, vascular disease in 2, mixed Alzheimer and vascular in 2, and unclear in 3 cases; and noted: "Frequent and severe physical comorbidity, especially sensory loss and mobility impairment, additionally affected the patient's level of social functioning and hampered our interpretation of their cognitive function loss." Aylward, Lai, and Dalton (1997) have proposed standardized criteria for the diagnosis of dementia in individuals with intellectual disability. They stress the desirability of "baseline" observations prior to the onset of cognitive or behavioural changes and the importance of excluding other disorders such as hypothyroidism and depression in those with Down Syndrome, folic acid abnormalities in patients on anticonvulsants and cognitive deterioration secondary to prescribed or non-prescribed medications. Gedye (1998) has documented four cases of reversible dementia associated with the use of neuroleptic medications. Clinicians will find a set of practice guidelines for the assessment and management of Alzheimer's disease and other dementias among adults with developmental disability

(Janicki, Heller, Seltzer, & Hagg, 1996) helpful in managing these challenging individuals, and in supporting their caregivers.

Affective Disorders

The Case of Wilfred

Wilfred, now 64, presented 10 years ago at the psychiatry clinic at a regional institution for persons with developmental disabilities. Since his admission there at age 13 he was described as having "behaviour difficulties" along with a mild degree of intellectual impairment. Like many residents in the institution, his behaviour difficulties had been treated with various phenothiazine tranquillizers. It became clear on careful review of the pattern of Wilfred's behaviour that he was subject to extended periods of depression characterized by agitation, weight loss, insomnia, hypochondriasis, irritability and aggressive outbursts. His antipsychotic medication was tapered and discontinued; treatment with antidepressants and electroconvulsive therapy (on two occasions since he was first assessed) has been quite successful. Between episodes of depression he is well adjusted, friendly and cooperative. His sister reports that their late mother and two maternal first cousins were subject to severe depressive episodes.

Over recent years it has become clear that persons with developmental disabilities may reveal a depressive disorder in a somewhat atypical manner (Charlot, 1998; Myers, 1998). Wilfred's case is a good example in that major behavioural features overshadowed the more classical features of depression such as lowered mood, crying, or wishing for death. The positive family history for depression also serves as an indicator of risk. Persons with developmental disabilities and affective disorders, including those in the bipolar subgroup, (King et al., 1994) can be treated in the usual manner with antidepressant drugs (Guidelines for the diagnosis and pharmacologic treatment of depressions, 1999) or with electroconvulsive therapy (Lazarus, Jaffe, & Dubin, 1990). Suicidal behaviour appears to be less common in persons with developmental disabilities although occasional case reports reflect its presence even in individuals with severe intellectual impairment (Walters, 1999).

Grief reactions represent an important differential diagnosis. Symptoms such as irritability, lethargy and hyperactivity and significant scores for depression and anxiety on the PIMRA (Psychopathology Instrument for Mentally Retarded Adults) were reported in a controlled study of bereaved adults by Hollins and Esterhuyzen (1997). A parent's death frequently leads to other stressful "life events" – for example, 39% of the subjects in the study needed to change their residence as a result of the deceased parent's final illness. In counselling those who are bereaved, clinicians may wish to use books specifically designed to support persons with developmental disabilities in their mourning process (Hollins & Sireling, 1994a; Hollins & Sireling, 1994b). As well, younger mothers and fathers should be encouraged to engage in "permanency planning" (i.e., preparing plans for living arrangements, guardianship and financial security after the parents' death) so that the developmentally disabled family member does not experience simultaneously the double blow of bereavement and residential relocation.

Although depression and anxiety frequently coexist, the detection of subjective anxiety (i.e., excessive worry, fear of a particular stimulus, or sensation of choking/palpitation) is difficult in persons with developmental disabilities; observable features of anxiety such as "hides or shields face when confronted with unfamiliar people or situations," "looks down a lot," restless, trembling, shaking, can be reliably diagnosed (Matson, Smiroldo, Hamilton, & Baglio, 1997). Stavrakaki and Mintsioulis (1997) reported that 27% of referrals to an Ottawa clinic had an anxiety disorder; only 3 persons, all females, beyond age 50 were included in this study group. A special concern in older individuals is their emotional reaction to physical disorders associated with aging. Evenhuis (1997a) in a study of mobility, internal conditions and cancer in those over 60 years of age, was struck by the absence of spontaneous complaints even in subjects with mild degrees of intellectual impairment: "Marked visual impairment, hearing loss, chest pain, dyspnea, dyspepsia and micturition problems were just tolerated or experienced atypically as irritability, inactivity, loss of appetite or sleep problems." In meeting the clinical challenge implied in these observations, Evenhuis notes that diagnosis and intervention for these conditions require: (i) knowledge of specific risk factors and atypical presentation of symptoms, (ii) close observations by carers and (iii) regular routine diagnostic screenings. The deficiencies in health care provision observed by Cooper (1997) in Britain and Edgerton, Gaston, Kelly, and Ward (1994) in the USA would suggest that these requirements are unlikely to be met unless much more support is made available to older persons with developmental disabilities.

Autism and Autism Spectrum Disorders

The Case of Jack

Jack, now 54, developed normally until age 2 ½ when he stopped relating to others, no longer used words, and was content to swing or rock. Born to wealthy Canadian parents, he spent 3 years in a New York residential treatment program and another 2 years in a similar program in Boston. His autistic features persisted in spite of treatment, and he was placed in a group home for persons with mental retardation in southeastern Ontario. At times restless and self-injurious, he seemed most content in the company of a mildly retarded teenage girl. He developed grand mal seizures at 16. At 20, when the teenager left the group home, he became very self-abusive and was admitted to a psychiatric hospital. Trials on various medications (haloperidol, fenfluramine, Vitamin B6 and sertraline) were not successful, and he continues only on carbamazepine for seizure control. Two years ago, he was placed in a group home. While he makes some eye contact he remains aloof, makes only grunting sounds, and requires assistance with daily living skills. He is rarely self-abusive now.

Jack's history is typical of autism, although in many instances the disorder appears to be present from birth rather than commencing after a brief period of apparently normal development. Gillberg (1995) refers to autism and "autistic spectrum disorders (including childhood schizophrenia)" as "disorders of empathy." There are significant challenges in establishing the adult prognosis in childhood although severe intellectual impairment and the absence of socially useful language predict the poor adult prognosis illustrated in Jack's history. Since many with less severe symptoms present for the first time in adulthood with depression or antisocial behaviours, clinicians need to search for the characteristic early features if the correct diagnosis is to be made. This is especially true of those with Asperger's syndrome and "high functioning autism" who may remain undiagnosed until well into adulthood or receive diagnoses such as schizoid or schizotypal personality disorder, type II schizophrenia, atypical depression, paranoid disorder or obsessive compulsive disorder (Gillberg, 1998). Gillberg (1995) reports that 30 to 40% of those with autism develop seizures before 30 years of age. Aman, Van Bourgondien, Wolford, and Sarphare (1995) surveyed medication use in those with autism: more than 50% of the sample was taking some psychotropic, anti-epileptic, vitamin or "medical" agent; caregivers were most satisfied with anticonvulsants, antidepressants, and stimulants. Although there was a wide age range in the study (1-82 years), and the likelihood of receiving some form of medication increased by 3.2% for each year of age, the mean age of 16 years for the sample suggests that the survey was predominantly concerned with younger individuals than Jack. An independent study of the reported benefits of the use of high doses of vitamin B6 was recommended. Recent observations on the use of risperidone suggest that this preparation may be particularly useful in treating autistic symptoms (McDougle, Holmes, Carlson, Pelton, Cohen, & Price, 1998).

Diogenes Syndrome (Senile breakdown, senile squalor syndrome)

The Case of Albert

Albert, aged 55, appeared at the clinic only because he wished a mental assessment relevant to having his motor vehicle operator's license reinstated. He reported that he had grown up in an institution for the mentally retarded and had worked on a farm between age 20 and the farmer's death 22 years later. He acknowledged a severe drinking problem on the farm, but abstinence over the past 12 years. He lives alone. He receives a disability pension. He is socially isolated and travels about the city on a bicycle. There are numerous bags attached to his bicycle full of junk or garbage that he collects and hoards. He is poorly groomed, dirty and foul smelling. There were no indicators of psychosis. His concreteness and limited fund of general knowledge suggested a mild degree of intellectual impairment. Satisfied that a letter reporting his assessment would be sent to the license bureau, he rejected any further "help" or follow-up.

Although the Diogenes syndrome was first described over 30 years ago (MacMillan & Shaw, 1996), only recently have cases with mental retardation been reported (Williams, Clarke, Fashola, & Holt, 1998). The literature is obviously biased in terms of various selection factors, like Albert who only came forward because of his license situation, and only half of the individuals reported to date have a recognizable mental disorder. Albert's extreme self neglect, social withdrawal and hoarding are typical; although his living conditions were not observed one can assume, given the balance of his appearance and demeanor, that there was domestic squalor and a lack of concern about living conditions (Cooney & Hamid, 1995). His case appears to support the hypothesis that the Diogenes syndrome may occur in persons with developmental disabilities as a manifestation of "intellectual disability (e.g., poor social and adaptive functioning) coupled with inadequate support" (Williams et al., 1998, p. 318).   Albert was reported to have functioned more normally, his abuse of alcohol notwithstanding, as long as the farmer who employed him survived. The need to balance "individual rights and wishes of patients, and the need to attend to their health needs" (Cooney & Hamid, 1995) in intervening with those with Diogenes syndrome, is no less in those cases where a degree of intellectual impairment co-exists.   In Albert's case, his only known "support" is the director of a programme concerned with helping those who wish to overcome drinking problems, a programme that he appeared to have used to advantage.

Comment

Centuries ago Aristotle believed that a living organism started life with an innate latent heat which gradually dissipated over time and eventually disappeared (Roy, 1987).   Selye (1980) felt that persons were born with only so much energy or ability to adapt and that stresses of various kinds caused a gradual reduction of this energy leading to aging and eventual death (Selye & Prioreschi, 1960). More recent theories have assumed a "biological clock" that ticks away within the brain, controlling not only the daily, monthly and yearly biological cycles of our lives, but the greater cycle that takes us through infancy, childhood, adolescence, adulthood and old age. Hayflick (1965) has demonstrated that mammalian diploid cells from certain tissues, when cultured in vitro, have a finite life span, and that embryonic cells double more times than mature cells. Clearly, a factor within the cells changes over time finally leading to loss of vitality in the cell. A worn out telomere may be the aging factor that causes the cell to eventually self-destruct (Shiels et al., 1999). As well, cellular aging may be the result of ongoing damage to the biomolecules of cells from reactive oxygen species which are continuously formed from the oxidative metabolism of glucose. This damage leads to a decline in the ability of cells to function and duplicate, leading to deterioration of function of the entire organism (Mann, 1997). It is interesting and perhaps evidence for this mechanism of aging that Trisomy 21 individuals (Down Syndrome) have an extra copy of the superoxide-dismutase gene. This may accelerate the aging process seen in this syndrome (Dickinson & Singh, 1993).

Developmentally disabled persons make up a diverse group with over three hundred etiologies identified as contributing to mental retardation. We may assume that many of the syndromes associated with mental retardation, as appears to be the case with Down Syndrome, have their own peculiarities in the aging process. Indeed, evaluation of how persons with developmental disability age may answer some of the broader questions of aging that are front and centre as we enter the 21st century.

Do You Know?

1. Why those with multiple disabilities have higher death rates than persons with intellectual impairment alone?
2. Why persons with Down Syndrome are thought to have a unique aging profile?
3. Which categories of mental disorder increase in prevalence with age?
4. Two disorders that may be easily confused with Alzheimer's disease in older persons with Down Syndrome?
5. What is entailed in permanency planning?
6. What characterizes Diogenes Syndrome?

References

Alexander, G., Saunders, A., Szczepanik, J., Strassburger, T., Pietrini, P., Dani, A., Furly, M., Mentis, M., Roses, A., Rapaport, S., & Schapiro, M. (1997) Relation of age and lipoprotein E to cognitive function in Down Syndrome adults. *Neuro Report; 8*, 1835-1840.

Aman, M., Van Bourgondien, M., Wolford, P., & Sarphare, B. (1995). Psychotropic and anticonvulsant drugs in subjects with autism: Prevalence and patterns of use. *Journal of American Academy of Child and Adolescent Psychiatry, 34 (12),*1672-1681.

Aylward, E., Burt, D., Thorpe, L., Lai, F., & Dalton, A. (1997). Diagnosis of dementia in individuals with intellectual disability. *Journal of Intellectual Deficiency Research, 41(2)*, 152-164.

Bihm, E., Poindexter, A., & Warren, E. (1998). Aggression

and psychopathology in persons with severe or profound mental retardation. *Research in Developmental Disabilities, 19(5)*, 423-438.

Bremner, A. & Regan, A. (1991). Intoxicated by water: polydipsia and water intoxication in a mental handicap hospital. *British Journal of Psychiatry 158*, 244-250.

Canadian clinical practice guidelines for the treatment of schizophrenia (1998). *Canadian Journal of Psychiatry, 43 (52)*, 255-405.

Canadian Network for Mood and Anxiety Treatment (1999). *Guidelines for the diagnosis and pharmacologic treatment of depression*. Toronto, ON: Author

Charlot, L.R. (1998). Developmental effects on mental health disorders in persons with developmental disabilities. *Mental Health Aspects of Developmental Disabilities, 1(2)*, 29-38.

Chicoine, B. & McGuire, D. (1997). Longevity of a woman with Down Syndrome: A case study. *Mental Retardation, 35(5)*, 477-479.

Cooney, C. & Hamid, W. (1995). Review: Diogenes Syndrome. *Age and Aging, 24*, 451-453.

Cooper, S. (1997a). High prevalence of dementia among people with learning disabilities not attributable to Downs Syndrome. *Psychological Medicine, 27*, 609-616.

Cooper, S. (1997b). Deficient health and social services for elderly people with learning disabilities. *Journal of Intellectual Deficiency Research, 41(4)*, 331-338.

Day, K.& Jancar, J. (1994). Mental and physical health in aging in mental handicap: A review. *Journal of Intellectual Deficiency Research, 38*, 241-256.

Dickinson, M. & Singh, I. (1993). Down Syndrome, dementia and superoxide dismutase. *British Journal of Psychiatry, 162(8)*, 11-17.

Doody, G., Johnstone, E., Sanderson, T., Cunningham-Owens, D., & Muir, W. (1998). Pfropfschizophrenie revisited: Schizophrenia in people with mild learning disability. British *Journal of Psychiatry, 173*, 145-153.

Edgerton, R., Gaston, M., Kelly, H., & Ward, T. (1994). Health care for aging people with mental retardation. *Mental Retardation, 32(2),* 146-150.

Elkashef, A., Ruskin, P., Bacher, N., & Barrett, B. (1990). Vitamin E in the treatment of tardive dyskinesia. *American Journal of Psychiatry, 147*, 505-506.

Evenhuis, H. (1997a). Medical aspects of aging in a population with intellectual disability: III Mobility, internal conditions and cancer. *Journal of Intellectual Deficiency Research, 41(1)*, 8-18.

Evenhuis, H. (1997b). The natural history of dementia in aging people with intellectual disability. *Journal of Intellectual Deficiency Research, 14(1)*, 92-96.

Fava, M. (1997). Psychopharmacologic treatment of pathologic aggression. *Psychiatry Clinics of North America, 20 (2)*, 427-451.

Frizzell, L. (1997). Fitness and exercise for older adults with developmental disabilities. *Activities, Adaptation and Ageing, 21(3),* 37-51.

Gedye, A. (1998). Neuroleptic induced dementia documented in four adults with mental retardation. *Mental Retardation, 36(3)*, 182-186.

Gillberg, C. (1995). *Clinical child neuropsychiatry.* Cambridge, UK: Cambridge University Press.

Gillberg, C. (1998). Asperger syndrome and high functioning autism. *British Journal of Psychiatry, 172*, 200-209.

Goldhaber, S., Brown, W., & Sutton, M. (1987). High frequency of mitral valve prolapse and aortic regurgitation among asymptomatic adults with Down Syndrome. *Jour-*

nal of the American Medical Association, 258 (13), 1793-1795.

Hayflick, L. (1965). The limited in vitro lifetime of human diploid cell strains. *Experimental Cell Research, 37*, 614-636.

Holland, H., Hon A., Huppest, F., Stevens, F., & Watson, P. (1998). Population-based study of the prevalence and presentation of dementia in adults with Down Syndrome. *British Journal of Psychiatry, 172*, 493-498.

Hollins, S. & Sireling, L. (1994a). *When dad died.* London, UK: St. George's Mental Health Library.

Hollins, S. & Sireling, L. (1994b). *When mom died.* London, UK: St. George's Mental Health Library.

Hollins, S. & Esterhuyzen, A. (1997). Bereavement and grief in adults with learning disabilities. *British Journal of Psychiatry, 170*, 497-501.

Janicki, M. Hellcr, T., Seltzer, G., & Hagg, J. (1996). Practice guidelines for the clinical assessment and care management of Alzheimer disease and other dementias among adults with developmental disabilities. *Journal of Intellectual Deficiency Research, 40(4)*, 374-382.

Kapell, D., Nightingale, B., Rodrigues, A., Lee, J., Zigman, W., & Schupf, N. (1998). Prevalence of chronic medical conditions in adults with mental retardation: Comparison with the general population. *Mental Retardation, 36 (4)*, 269-279.

King, B., De Antonia, C., McCracken, J., Forness, R., & Ackerland, J. (1994). Psychiatric consultation in severe and profound mental retardation. *American Journal of Psychiatry, 151*, 1802-1808.

Kissling, W. (1992). Ideal and reality of neuroleptic relapse prevention. *British Journal of Psychiatry, 161(suppl)*, 133-139.

Lazarus, A., Jaffe, R., & Dubin, W. (1990). Electroconvulsive therapy and major depression in Down Syndrome. *Journal of Clinical Psychiatry, 51,* 422-425.

Loehr, J., Synhorst, B., Wolfe, R., & Hagerman, R. (1986). Aortic root dilatation and mitral valve prolapse in the fragile X syndrome. *American Journal of Medical Genetics, 23 (1-2),* 189-194.

Lott, I. & Lai, F. (1982). Dementia in Down's syndrome: Observations from a neurology clinic. Applied Research in *Mental Retardation, 3(3),* 233-239.

MacMillan, D. & Shaw, P. (1996). Senile breakdown in standards of personal and environmental cleanliness. *British Medical Journal, 2,* 1032-1037.

Mann, D. (1997). Molecular biology's impact on our understanding of aging. *British Medical Journal, 315,* 1078-81.

Martin, G. (1977). Cellular aging - postreplicative cells. A Review (Part II). *American Journal of Pathology, 89(2),* 513-530.

Matson, J., Smiroldo, B., Hamilton, M., & Baglio, C. (1997). Do anxiety disorders exist in persons with severe and profound mental retardation? *Research in Developmental Disabilities, 18(1),* 39-44.

McDougle, C., Holmes, J., Carlson, D., Pelton, G., Cohen, D., & Price, L. (1998). A double blind placebo-controlled study of risperidone in adults with autistic disorder and other pervasive developmental disorders. *Archives in General Psychiatry, 55(7),* 633-641.

Myers, B. (1998). Major depression in persons with moderate to profound mental retardation: Clinical presentation and case illustrations. *Mental Health Aspects of Developmental Disabilities, 1(3),* 57-68.

Oliver, C., Crayton, L., Holland, A., Hall, S., & Bradbury, J. (1998). A four year prospective study of age related cognitive change in adults with Down Syndrome. *Psychology Medicine, 28,* 1365-1377.

Pary, R. (1993). Psychoactive drugs used with adults and elderly adults who have mental retardation. *American Journal on Mental Retardation, 98(1),* 121-127.

Pary, R. (1997). Vitamin E or selegiline for Alzheimer dementia. *Habilitative Mental Healthcare Newsletter, 16(6),* 114

Reid, A.H., Ballinger, B., Heather, B., & Melvin, S. (1984). The natural history of behavioural symptoms among severely and profoundly retarded patients. *British Journal of Psychiatry, 145,* 289-293.

Roy, J. (1987). Ancient Greek myths of aging. *Geriatrics, 3 (2),* 13-15.

Sachdev, P. (1992). Drug induced movement disorders in institutionalized adults with mental retardation: Clinical characteristics and risk factors. *Australian New Zealand Journal of Psychiatry, 26,* 242-248.

Selye, H. (1980). The hypothalmus, neuroendocrine and autonomic nervous systems in aging. In J.E. Birren & R.B. Sloane (Eds.), *Handbook of mental health and aging* (pp. 100-133). Engelwood Cliffs, NJ: Prentice Hall.

Selye, H. & Prioreschi, P. (1960). Stress theory of aging. In N.W. Shock (Ed.), *Aging: Some social and biological aspects.* Washington, DC: American Association for the Advancement of Science.

Shiels, G., Kind, A., Campbell, K., Waddington, D., Wilmut, W., Colman, A., & Schnieke, A. (1999). Analysis of telomere length in cloned sheep. *Nature, 399,* 316-317.

Stavrakaki, C. & Mintsioulis, G. (1997). Implications of a clinical study of anxiety disorders in persons with mental retardation. *Psychiatric Annals, 27(3),* 182-189.

Turner, S. & Moss, S. (1996). The health needs of adults

with learning disabilities and the Health of the Nation strategy. *Journal of Intellectual Deficiency Research, 40 (5)*, 438-450.

Van Schrojenstein Lantman-de Valk, H., van den Akker, M., Maaskant, M., Haveman, M., Urlings, H., Kessels, A., & Crebolder, H. (1997). Prevalence and incidence of health problems in people with intellectual disability. *Journal of Intellectual Deficiency Research, 14(1)*, 42-51.

Verhoeven, W. & Tuinier, S. (1997). Neuropsychiatric consultation in mentally retarded patients in a clinical report. *European Psychiatry, 12*, 242-248.

Walters, R. (1999). Suicidal behaviour in severely mentally handicapped patients. *British Journal of Psychiatry, 157*, 444-447.

Williams, H., Clarke, R., Fashola, Y., & Holt, G. (1998). Diogenes syndrome in patients with intellectual disability: A rose by any other name. *Journal of Intellectual Deficiency Research, 42(4)*, 316-320.

Wright, A. & Whalley, L. (1984). Genetics, aging and dementia. *British Journal of Psychiatry, 145*, 20-38.

Zigman, W., Schupf, N., Zigman, A., & Silverman, W. (1993). Aging and Alzheimer disease in people with mental retardation. *International Review of Research in Mental Retardation, 19*, 41-70.

Chapter 17

Mental Health Issues in Clients with Severe Communication Impairments

Julie Reid, Jane Summers, Judith Adamson, Brenda Habjan, Charles Meister, and Valerie Gignac

Learning Objectives

Readers will be able to:

1. Describe how communication and sensory impairments can have a negative effect on clients' social and emotional functioning.
2. Determine conventional and non-conventional forms of communication.
3. Identify strategies to enhance clients' communication skills and how these may improve their mental health.
4. Identify changes in clients' behaviour that may indicate the need for a medical and/or mental health assessment.

Introduction

The purpose of this chapter is to discuss mental health issues in individuals with severe communication impairments. We refer specifically to clients who are primarily nonverbal (i.e., who have little or no expressive speech skills). We have chosen to focus on this particular group because it often presents the greatest challenge to health professionals and caregivers.

In contrast to the usual situation in which the client is interviewed directly as part of the evaluation process, clinicians must rely instead on information that is provided by other people (e.g., family, support workers). As a result, the clinician needs to reconcile different points of view that often arise, and must also make inferences about the client's internal state from the information that is available. On a personal level, professionals often feel uncomfortable or even inadequate in situations where they have difficulty communicating directly with a client. Moreover, many of these clients use nonverbal or behavioural means (such as aggression or self-injury) to communicate their emotional and physical needs, which may be frightening or incomprehensible to the onlooker. With training and experience, clinicians can overcome their apprehension and take on significant roles in the provision of services to this population.

We begin the chapter with a general overview of communication, followed by an outline of communication issues in clients with developmental disabilities. We then comment briefly on sensory impairments and the additional challenges they create. We also link communication and sensory impairments to mental health issues, and review strategies to enhance clients' communication skills in order to improve their social-emotional functioning. Finally, we talk about difficulties in assessing mental health problems in clients with severe communication impairments, and offer some ideas regarding how to overcome these challenges.

Before we begin, we would like to share the following principles which underlie our clinical approach to working with nonverbal clients with mental health issues:

- the ability to communicate effectively is essential for optimal mental health;
- communication and sensory impairments can have a negative impact on a client's social and emotional well-being;
- aberrant behaviour (which may be viewed as a non-conventional form of communication) is a primary reason for referrals to health professionals;
- strategies that enhance a client's ability to use conventional forms of communication can improve his/her social-emotional functioning.

Overview of Communication

What is communication?

Communication is an exchange of information and ideas between two or more people -- the message sender and the message receiver. In general, the **message sender** must determine exactly what information or idea he/she would like to exchange and send this information to the **message receiver**, who must make sense of and act on this information. A 'communication breakdown' can occur at any point in this process, leaving the message sender or receiver (or both) dissatisfied or frustrated. This process is not as clearly defined in the case of clients with severe intellectual and communication impairments (e.g., with regard to the client's communicative intent and the reciprocity or exchange of information), with the result that the client's thoughts and feelings must be inferred on the basis of behavioural indicators and other considerations.

Why do we communicate?

We communicate because exchanging information and ideas

with another person serves one or more purposes in our lives. Through communicating we are able to:

- express our wants and needs so that they can be more easily met
- share information in order to be seen as an individual
- develop social closeness in order to maintain relationships
- conform to social conventions in order to be accepted as a member of society (Beukelman & Mirenda, 1992)

How do we communicate?

All forms of communication can be divided into one of three categories -- conventional, non-conventional, and variable communication behaviours.

Figure 1- Categories of Communication Behaviours (adapted from Wyngaarden, Honeyman & Tweedie, 1996).

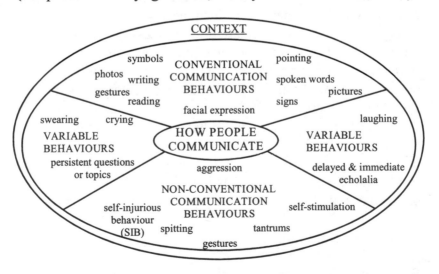

1. Conventional Communication Behaviours

These consist of verbal communication forms (speech) or augmentative and alternative communication forms (AAC). AAC is any approach that is designed to support, enhance or augment the communication of individuals who are not independent verbal communicators in all situations (Beukelman, Yorkston & Dowden, 1985). Examples of AAC approaches include written language, sign language, pictures/photos, gestures, and facial expression.

Conventional communication behaviours tend to lead to more successful communication events, and are often considered more 'acceptable' means of communication.

2. Non-Conventional Communication Behaviours

These are the forms of communication that typically are seen as 'behavioural' in nature and that cause much stress, anxiety and frustration for both the message sender and message receiver. They are also a primary reason for referral to mental health professionals (AACAP, 1999). Examples include aggression, self-injury, and noncompliance. Non-conventional communication forms tend to be more difficult to understand, are viewed as being disruptive, may pose a degree of risk to the message sender and message receiver, and are often considered to be a 'less acceptable' means of communication. They are often the focus of clinical intervention, e.g., behaviour therapy, pharmacological treatment and/or teaching conventional forms of communication to take their place.

3. Variable Communication Behaviours

These are the forms of communication that can fall into any of the above categories depending on the situation. For example, crying as a means to express sadness at a funeral would be considered to be a conventional form of communication; however, crying every time one is expected to perform a chore may be considered non-conventional and a less 'acceptable' means of communicating a message.

What factors affect communication?

Individual, interpersonal and environmental characteristics influence communication. Individual characteristics include the person's personality, skill level, sensory abilities, stress/ arousal level and internal state. Interactions between individuals are influenced by the complex interplay of these factors. Environmental factors include lighting, noise, temperature, and the number of people present.

Link Between Communication and Sensory Impairments and Mental Health Issues

A number of factors may be implicated in the development and expression of mental health problems in clients with severe communication impairments. First, a client's ability to learn and use conventional forms of communication is generally related to his/her level of intellectual functioning, such that the greater the degree of intellectual impairment, the less likely the client will independently develop speech and other symbolic means of communication. It follows, therefore, that he/she will rely primarily on non-conventional (behavioural) forms of communication when interacting with others, which, as discussed earlier, tend to be more difficult for the communication partner to understand, and less likely to produce the desired outcome for the client. As a result, the client may feel frustrated, angry, anxious or socially isolated. Conditions such as autism and pervasive developmental disorders are associated with particularly severe communication and social impairments.

Second, an increased incidence of biomedical concerns (such as neurological conditions, sensory and motor impairments) is reported among clients with more severe levels of intellectual impairment (DSM-IV, 1994). Neurological damage in and of itself may be a predisposing factor for mental health problems. As well, sensory impairments (e.g., vision and hearing disorders) may contribute to mental health problems or mimic their effects. Hearing loss, for instance, may further impair a client's language and cognitive skills, negatively affect his/her interpersonal relationships, and produce behavioural patterns that resemble psychiatric symptoms. For example, a client who has an unrecognized hearing loss and misperceives people's comments may appear to be "paranoid" to others. Consider a client with a visual impairment who shows an intense fear response in a particular situation (e.g., when required to walk down a flight of stairs). This may be viewed incorrectly as an irrational fear or phobia and treated with medication rather than ensuring that the stairs are well-lit.

> Did You Know?
>
> - compared to the general population, sensory impairments are much more common among clients with developmental disabilities (Beange, McElduff & Baker, 1995).

- vision and hearing disorders are present in approximately 10% of clients with severe intellectual impairment (McQueen, Spence, Garner, Pereira, & Winsor, 1987).
- this figure may be higher in groups with specific syndromes or disorders – e.g. sensori-neural hearing loss develops in up to 40% of individuals with Down Syndrome (Gedye & Russell, 1995).
- sensory impairments can be caused by infections during pregnancy, such as rubella
- sensory impairments may be present at birth or can develop over time.
- early detection and proper treatment are essential, yet caregivers are not always aware of risk factors and service needs (Murphy, Paquette, Ouellette-Kuntz, Stanton, & Garrett 1999).

The ability to communicate effectively is essential for a client's emotional and physical well-being. It is necessary, therefore, to look beyond basic physiological needs and consider psychological needs (e.g., affiliation, achievement, affirmation), and the impact of not having these needs met on the client's mental health (e.g., feelings of low self-worth, depression).

Interventions to Enhance Communicative
Functioning

Approaches to addressing mental health issues in clients with severe communication impairments involve providing them with a conventional means of communicating that will enhance their expressive and receptive communicative abilities, and increase the likelihood that their social-emotional needs will be met. Strategies to enhance communication are typically used in conjunction with behavioural approaches, in which conditions are arranged to promote the occurrence of "acceptable" behaviour (i.e., behaviour that enhances the client's social and personal well-being) and reduce the occurrence of "problem" behaviour (e.g., Carr & Durand, 1985).

The following steps are involved in assessment of and intervention for communication impairments:

- evaluate the client's current skills and forms of communication.
- determine the communicative function of the non-conventional behaviour.
- assess the client's symbolic level of understanding.
- use the information to develop an approach to enhance his/ her conventional forms of communication.

How to assess a client's current communication skills and forms of communication

1. Observe how the client communicates:

  - greetings (hello and good-bye)
  - wanting food/drink
  - wanting activity
  - needing help
  - needing a break
  - affirmation (yes)
  - negation (no)
  - getting attention

- about his/her physical state
- about his/her feelings
- humour
- boredom
- needing information
- sharing information

2. How s/he makes connections with people (family, staff, peers, others).

3. His/her style of interacting with others (e.g., does he/she initiate spontaneously or does he/she respond to others?).

4. His/her comprehension abilities in regard to a number of factors (e.g., familiar versus unfamiliar information, simple versus complex information, the number of directives he/she is able to follow).

5. His/her choice-making abilities (e.g., yes/no, two or more choices).

6. His/her ability to wait and to transition between activities, environments and people.

How to determine the communicative functions of behaviour

The function or reason for the non-conventional communication behaviour may be determined through direct observation, data collection (e.g., antecedent-behaviour-consequence data), manipulating conditions and determining the resulting effects on the behaviour (e.g., allowing a client to escape from a difficult task after he self-injures, and analyzing the impact on the frequency and duration of the behaviour), and/or generating hypotheses about why the behaviour is occurring (Carr et al., 1999). This type of assessment is well-suited to a joint approach by a speech-language pathologist and behaviour therapist.

How to assess a client's level of symbolic understanding

A symbol is something that stands for or represents something else. Examples of symbols include photographs, drawings, sign language and written words. Symbols may be ordered into a hierarchy that reflects their level of abstractness and the ease with which they may be learned and used (Mirenda & Locke, 1989). Generally, symbols that bear the closest resemblance to the item they represent are easiest for the individual to understand and use. An example of a concrete symbol is a cup that a client could hand to a caregiver to request a drink. At the other extreme are symbols that bear the least resemblance to the item they represent; an example of an abstract symbol is the sign for "cup".

Figure 2- Symbol hierarchy (adapted from Mirenda & Locke, 1989).

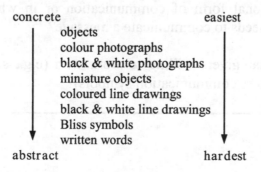

concrete   easiest

    objects
    colour photographs
    black & white photographs
    miniature objects
    coloured line drawings
    black & white line drawings
    Bliss symbols
    written words

abstract   hardest

An informal way to assess a client's level of symbolic understanding is to observe what symbols he/she may currently use
in everyday situations -- e.g., looking through magazines and
pointing to difficult or unfamiliar words, recognizing people in
photographs, understanding community signs (male/female
bathroom signs, no smoking symbols).

**Tips to Help Determine Appropriate Forms of Conven-
tional Communication for a Client**

- observe which (if any) conventional forms the client is using currently.

- consider which forms he/she has had experience with in
  the past and how successful they were.

- which symbols does the client understand?

- does the client have any functional limitations (e.g., vision,
  hearing, arm/hand, mobility) that rule out certain approaches or necessitate a different type of approach?

- what are the specific situations the client is required to use
  a conventional form of communication or in which the
  caregiver needs to communicate a message?

- what are caregivers willing to work with (e.g., sign language, picture communication symbols)?

Developing approaches to enhance conventional communication behaviour

Enhancement-based communication interventions are designed to increase clients' communicative competence and decrease their reliance on non-conventional forms of communicative behaviour (such as aggression or self-injury). It stands to reason that a client who uses more conventional forms of communication is more likely to be understood, and hence to have his/her physical and social-emotional needs met, both of which impact directly on mental health. For instance, a client who is able to signal his/her need for social interaction (which is often characterized in a negative manner as "attention-seeking behaviour") by gesturing to someone to come over rather than throwing an object will likely be perceived in a more positive manner, elicit more emotional support, and be included in more events and activities. Thus, increasing a client's communicative competence has a dramatic effect on every aspect of his/her life.

Many enhancement-based strategies make use of visual cues, which, since they are continuously available, are helpful to clients who have difficulties processing verbal information or who take longer to express themselves. In addition, they are readily understood, and enjoy widespread application and acceptance (many people could not function without their address book and daily scheduler). Visual cues may be used to:

- promote more effective expressive and receptive communication
- provide reminders about behavioural expectations
- structure an activity or a period of time
- help with acquisition of new skills (e.g., following a sequence of steps)

Examples of visual aids

Choice board

A choice board provides a means to promote choice-making by a client, and can help foster a sense of control and personal independence, both of which are important for emotional well-being. It may also be used to indicate clearly when a choice is **not** available, hopefully reducing confusion and the anxiety or frustration it may bring.

Figure 3- Example of a choice board that a client may use to indicate a preference for a particular beverage (Picture Communication Symbols ©. PCS were used with the permission of Mayer-Johnson, Inc. © Copyright 1981-2002. All rights reserved worldwide).

When-then' or 'first-then' board

This type of visual is used to make clear what has to be completed first, **before** a second activity can begin (often the first activity is a less pleasant or desirable one, such as making the bed before watching television). A **when-then** or **first-then** board can help decrease a non-conventional behaviour that is used as a means to escape from a less desirable task or activity by linking it (in a way the client can readily understand) with something that is more highly desired. In doing so, this may help motivate a client and increase his/her tolerance for delayed gratification. This type of board is a beginning step for teaching a schedule, educating the client that one activity can follow another.

Figure 4- Example of a when-then board that can be used to help a client understand that a specific task (bedmaking) has to be completed <u>before</u> the second activity (go for a swim) can begin. (Picture Communication Symbols ©. PCS were used with the permission of Mayer-Johnson, Inc. © Copyright 1981-2002. All rights reserved worldwide).

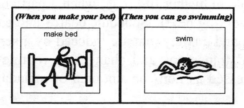

Self-help board

A self-help board is used to help clients learn new skills or activities, by depicting each step in a new task. Once each step has been mastered, the self-help board may serve as a reminder should a step in the sequence be forgotten. Self-help boards may promote independence and a sense of accomplishment. They may also reduce frustration or anger related to difficulties recalling the steps in an activity.

Figure 5- Example of a self-help board that can be used to help a client master a new task or remember the steps in a sequence. (Picture Communication Symbols ©. PCS were used with the permission of Mayer-Johnson, Inc. © Copyright 1981-2002. All rights reserved worldwide).

Schedule board/calendar

Schedule boards and calendars are used to provide structure to the client's day/life. They may help a client to see order and predictability in his/her world, prepare him/her for upcoming changes, and provide information about the activities of significant people in his/her life (e.g., when a particular staff person will be working next). Schedule boards and calendars may reduce stress and anxiety that are induced by a sense of uncertainty around transitions and changes in routine (and which may be expressed as non-conventional or maladaptive behaviours).

Figure 6-   Example of a schedule board that outlines a client's daily activities. (Picture Communication Symbols ©. PCS were used with the permission of Mayer-Johnson, Inc. © Copyright 1981-2002. All rights reserved worldwide).

Specific Activity Board

A specific activity board contains the vocabulary a client may need to use in a specific situation. For instance, ordering food at a restaurant, or playing a game of bowling. A "feelings" board contains vocabulary to enable a client to express his/her feelings.

Figure 7- Example of a feelings board that a client may use to express his/her emotions or feelings. (Picture Communication Symbols ©. PCS were used with the permission of Mayer-Johnson, Inc. © Copyright 1981-2002. All rights reserved worldwide).

Other tools

Sheila Hollins and her colleagues from Britain have created a series of stories about situations or events that can be stressful or traumatic. These stories can be used to help prepare a client for an upcoming event (such as a trip to the doctor or a move to a new home), to promote disclosure of a traumatic experience (e.g. sexual abuse), or as a means to raise difficult/

sensitive issues, and provide counseling and emotional support (e.g. after the death of a parent). Coloured pictures (alone or with accompanying text) are used to convey a story about an individual who may be experiencing a similar problem, or coping with a comparable issue.

Assessing Mental Health Problems in Clients with Severe Communication Impairments

As we discussed earlier, assessing mental health problems in non-verbal clients can be a daunting task. This statement is related to several factors:

- the lack of firsthand information regarding the client's own thoughts and feelings, and the resulting need to rely on information that comes from other sources (generally, the level of inference goes up as the client's verbal skills go down).
- the presence of other conditions (e.g. medical, sensory) and/or medication side-effects which can complicate the picture by exacerbating or mimicking symptoms of mental illness.
- the need to modify standard diagnostic criteria that require verbal disclosure or which may have limited applicability to clients with severe intellectual and communication impairments (Pyles, Muniz, Cade & Silva, 1997).
- the finding that "classic" forms of mental illness (such as depression or mania) may be more difficult to identify than aberrant behaviour patterns (Cherry, Matson, & Paclawskyj, 1997).

Several instruments have been developed to assist with the identification of mental health problems in clients with severe intellectual impairments as well as to evaluate treatment effects. These include the Aberrant Behavior Checklist (Aman & Singh, 1994), Diagnostic Assessment for the Severely Handicapped-II (Matson, 1995), Psychopathology Instrument for Mentally Retarded Adults (Matson, 1988), and Reiss Screen for Maladaptive Behavior (Reiss, 1988). These instruments are in the form of questionnaires which are completed by informants (caregivers, family members) who are familiar with the client. They may play a useful role in screening for the presence of possible mental health problems which warrant a more in-depth assessment, but should not be used as the sole means of making a clinical diagnosis.

Figure 8– BEAMS (method to outline changes in client's baseline pattern of functioning)

We have developed a simple mnemonic to assist caregivers to identify when a client may require a medical and/or mental health assessment. We use the acronym "BEAMS" to outline changes (either an increase or decrease) in the client's baseline or typical pattern of functioning. Our list of behavioural equivalents for symptoms of mental health problems is not exhaustive and is intended primarily to illustrate the diversity of issues that may arise.

B	Behaviour	e.g., client avoids particular people or places; behaves more aggressively than usual; has started to hide possessions; runs away from staff; yells or screams for no obvious reason; has lost interest in a formerly preferred activity; performs the same activity over and over.
E	Energy	e.g., client will not go for walks; motor movements are sped up; cannot sit still; moves more slowly.
A	Appetite	(and Eating Behaviours) - e.g., client refuses to eat; throws plate on the floor; will not stop eating; eats non-food items; hides food away.
M	Mood	e.g., client cries a lot; looks sad all the time; more irritable than usual; has frequent bouts of giddiness or silliness; does not show range of motions; looks anxious or worried.
S	Sleep	(and Night-Time Behaviours) - e.g. client sleeps a lot less than usual; cannot stay awake during the day; wakes up screaming at night; has difficulty falling asleep.

In general, these changes should be sustained over a period of approximately one week or longer (duration), should not occur solely within the context of a specific environment, task or person (breadth), and should be of sufficient magnitude to cause significant discomfort or dysfunction (intensity). If a caregiver has reason to suspect that a client has a medical and/or mental health problem, the steps that are listed under "How to prepare for an evaluation" in Chapter 10 may be a helpful starting point. Evaluation for underlying medical issues is extremely important since pain or discomfort may give rise to changes in behaviour (McGrath, Rosmus, Canfield, Campbell & Hennigar, 1998) and certain conditions (like hypothyroidism) can produce symptoms that resemble a mental illness. When in doubt, consult a health care professional.

Summary

In this chapter, we presented a framework for understanding and treating mental health problems in clients with severe communication impairments. We described some of the difficulties in assessing mental health problems in this population, and provided a mnemonic that may assist caregivers to identify when a client may require a medical/mental health assessment.

Do You Know?

1. How communication and sensory impairments have a negative impact on clients' social and emotional functioning?
2. What is the difference between conventional and non-conventional forms of communication?
3. Give two examples of two visual strategies?
4. What changes in a clients' behaviour indicate the need for a medical/mental health assessment?

Resources

Hodgdon, L.A. (1995). *Visual strategies for improving communication. Volume 1: Practical supports for home and school.* Troy Michigan: Quirk Roberts Publishing.

Hollins, Sheila et al. **Books Beyond Words.** Information about ordering books may be obtained from the Division of Psychiatry of Disability, Department of Mental Health Sciences, St. George's Hospital Medical School, Cranmer Terrace, London SW17 ORE, UK; Telephone 0181 725 5501 and Fax 0181 672 1070.

Picture Communication Symbols– Mayer-Johnson, Inc. P.O. Box 1579, Solana Beach, CA 92075-7579 U.S.A.
Phone: 800-588-4548 or 858-550-0084.
Fax: 858-550-0449
E-mail: mayerj@mayer-johnson.com
Website: www.mayer-johnson.com

References

Aman, M.G., & Singh, N.N. (1994). **Aberrant Behavior Checklist-Community. Supplementary manual.** E. Aurora, New York: Slosson Educational Publications.

American Psychiatric Association (1994). *Diagnostic and statistical manual of mental disorders* (4th ed.). Washington, DC: Author.

AACAP (1999). Practice parameters for the assessment and treatment of children, adolescents and adults with mental retardation and comorbid mental disorders. **Journal of the American Academy of Child and Adolescent Psychiatry,** *38* **Supplement,** 5S-31S.

Beange, H., McElduff, A., & Baker, W. (1995). Medical disorders of adults with mental retardation: A population study. **American Journal on Mental Retardation,** *99,* 595-604.

Beukelman, D.R. & Mirenda, P. (1992). **Augmentative and alternative communication: Management of severe communication disorders in children and adults.** Baltimore: Paul H. Brookes.

Beukelman, D., Yorkston, K., & Dowden, P. (1985). **Communication augmentation: A casebook of clinical management.** Austin, TX: PRO-ED.

Carr, E.G., & Durand, V.M. (1985). The social-communicative basis of severe behavior problems in children. In S. Reiss & R.R. Bootzin (Eds.)., **Theoretical issues in behavior therapy** (pp. 219-254). New York: Academic Press.

Carr, E.G., Levin, L., McConnachie, G., Carlson, J.I., Kemp, D.C., Smith, C.E. & McLaughlin, D.M. (1999). Comprehensive multisituational intervention for problem behavior in the community. **Journal of Positive Behavior Interven-**

tions, *1*, 5-25.

Cherry, K.E., Matson, J.L., & Paclawskyj, T. (1997). Psychopathology in older adults with severe and profound mental retardation. **American Journal on Mental Retardation,** *101*, 445-458.

Gedye, A., & Russell, J.E. (1995). Common concerns in Down syndrome: Initial signs and steps to take. **Habilitative Mental Healthcare** *Newsletter, 14*, 31-33.

Matson, J.L. (1988). **The psychopathology instrument for mentally retarded adults: Test manual.** Baton Rouge, LA: Scientific Publishers.

Matson, J.L. (1995). *Diagnostic Assessment for the Severely* **Handicapped-***II*. Baton Rouge, LA: Scientific.

McGrath, P.J., Rosmus, C., Canfield, C., Campbell, J.A., Hennigar, A. (1998). Behaviours caregivers use to determine pain in non-verbal, cognitively impaired individuals. *De-***velopmental Medicine and Child** *Neurology, 40,* 340-343.

McQueen, P.C., Spence, M.W., Garner, J.B., Pereira, L.H., & Winsor, E.J.T. (1987). Prevalence of major mental retardation and associated disabilities in the Canadian Maritime provinces. **American Journal of Mental** *Deficiency, 91,* 460-466.

Mirenda, P. & Locke, P. (1989). A comparison of symbol transparency in nonspeaking persons with intellectual disabilities. **Journal of Speech and Hearing** *Disorders, 54,* 131-140.

Murphy, K.E., Paquette, D.M., Ouellette-Kuntz, H., Stanton, B., & Garrett, S.A. (1999). Survey of the need for speech, language and audiology services among adults with developmental disabilities living in the community. **Journal on** *Developmental Disabilities, 6,* 1-14.

Pyles, D.A.M., Muniz, K., Cade, A., & Silva, R. (1997). A behavioral diagnostic paradigm for integrating behavior-analytic and psychopharmacological interventions for people with a dual diagnosis. **Research in** *Developmental Disabilities,* *18,* 185-214.

Reiss, S. (1988). **Reiss Screen for Maladaptive Behavior.** Worthington, OH: IDS Publishing Corporation.

Wyngaarden, P., Honeyman, S., Tweedie, G. (1996, November). Integrating behavioural and communication supports for persons with a dual diagnosis. Paper presented at the 13th Annual NADD Conference, Vancouver, BC.

Acknowledgements

We would like to acknowledge the valuable contributions of Susan Honeyman, Gary Tweedie and Peter Wyngaarden and to thank Julia Ollinger for her expert assistance with the computer graphics.

Chapter 18

Legal and Ethical Dimensions of Dual Diagnosis

Patricia Peppin

Learning Objectives

Readers will be able to:

1. Describe how law develops and changes;
2. Develop an awareness of ethical dimensions underlying laws affecting people with dual diagnoses;
3. Identify key legal issues arising out of a dual diagnosis; and
4. Consider how law applies to particular situations involving persons with dual diagnoses

Introduction

This chapter introduces you to a range of legal and ethical issues that can arise when an individual is diagnosed with a psychiatric disorder and a developmental disability. The first section provides a brief discussion of the way law develops, to provide a context for the following discussion. In the second section, the values that underlie the law are examined. The concept of equality is used as a lens to examine the disadvantaged position of dually diagnosed individuals in society. The third section considers how to construct an understanding of dual diagnosis, through examining theories of discrimination.

The final section analyses specific legal consequences particularly applicable to persons with dual diagnosis. The chapter has been designed to give you a general sense of these legal issues. Because law changes, and because any specific situation may raise other issues, legal advice should be sought to deal with specific cases.

Interpreting Law

Law comes from a variety of sources in Canadian society. It is important to understand the sources of law to appreciate how law changes over time, and how law reform is achieved in a legitimate way. This is particularly important for the study of the law's application to people with dual diagnoses because their needs and problems have the potential to bring them into closer contact with law than many others in society.

Laws result from authoritative decision-making by legitimate actors within the three branches of government - the legislative branch, the judiciary, and the executive. Judge-made law is referred to as "common law". Law has the potential to restrain activities, as it does when criminal activities are successfully deterred. This role of law in setting boundaries for action rests on the authoritative nature of law, and on the mechanisms for enforcing its prohibitions. Law's second role is to enable activities. The certainty of law and its enforceability make it possible for people to arrange their affairs.

Values, Law and Dual Diagnosis

1. Values

Law is based on values, and we need to determine what those

values are if we are to understand the law. Certain values are reflected in laws, while other values lie outside the range of particular laws.

Writers in the field of bioethics have identified four ethical principles of importance to decision-making in this field. They are: *autonomy, benefeasance (creating benefit), non-malfeasance (not doing harm), and justice.* (Beauchamp & Walters, 1989). Similar values are sometimes given different names, and somewhat different meanings, in different areas of the law, such as tort law, criminal law and the Canadian Charter of Rights and Freedoms. These similar terms are indicated in the following list:

- autonomy/liberty/freedom of conscience and religion
- benefeasance/best interests/protection
- non-malfeasance/avoiding harm/physical inviolability/ security of the person
- equality/substantive justice/formal justice

Some of the values listed above are fundamental human rights. Human rights apply to everyone in society, and can be seen as an expression of the rights and freedoms that exist because of our basic humanity. Each is based on the idea that every individual is entitled to certain basic rights and freedoms, and that these rights and freedoms should be protected through law. Some rights are also collective or group rights. Rights are expressed and protected through the Canadian Charter of Rights and Freedoms in the Canadian constitution, through human rights legislation, and through applicable international law and the Universal Declaration of Human Rights, proclaimed by the United Nations in 1948.

The values listed above also form the basis for legal protections through other types of law. Tort law provides a means for people whose interests have been violated through wrongful acts to seek compensation. Tort law is also intended to deter wrongdoing. For example, if a person intentionally touches another person without consent, that is considered a battery. The fact that a lawsuit can be brought means that the person whose bodily integrity was infringed can be compensated. As well, we hope that such wrongful behaviour will be deterred by the possibility of a legal action.

Conflicts about values may arise in many health and social services areas, and these conflicts are familiar to people working in these areas. One such conflict occurs when care providers' attempts to protect individuals come into conflict with that individual's right to autonomy and physical inviolability. Preventing and deterring harm to third parties, which is a purpose underlying the criminal justice system as well as the tort system, is a value that may well conflict with the individual's fundamental freedoms, including the Charter section 7 right to "life, liberty and security of the person", and the right not to be deprived thereof, "except in accordance with the principles of fundamental justice". All Charter rights are also subject to limitation since government may justify the rights limitation as being reasonable in a free and democratic society. Achieving one value may be impossible without diminishing another value.

2. Equality

The equality section of the Charter provides that every individual has the right to equality without discrimination on the basis of mental or physical disability, and other grounds. Each of the two conditions making up a dual diagnosis - psychiatric and developmental disability – could be found to come within the category of mental disability. The cases that have been decided under the equality section of the Charter indicate that inequality may be found in conditions of disadvantage, which are indicated by historic disadvantage, stereotyping, and prejudice.

Equality is defined broadly in Canadian law so that it deals with the effects of action and not only the intent. Formal equality protects procedural rights such as the right to be treated equally before and under the law. Equality of effects means that the result of the behaviour should itself not be unequal. For instance, individuals in wheelchairs who could enter a theatre only by means of stairs would have equal opportunity in a formal sense, but would not have achieved equality in terms of effects until they could reach the top of the stairs. Adverse effects interpretation provides greater protection for substantive rights. Anti-discrimination legislation and the Charter both provide vital support for the respect and dignity to which all people are entitled, and for the right to be free from discrimination (Rioux & Frazee, 1999).

If we use the "lens" of equality to look at the situation of persons with a dual diagnosis, we find many signs of inequality.

Mental incompetence

Until recently in most Canadian provinces, a judicial declaration that a person was mentally incompetent had far-reaching consequences. This was a global and all-embracing determination. The mentally incompetent person was placed in the custody of a guardian, and lost the right to make key personal and/or financial decisions. Essentially, the individual lost the status of an adult in law. As a result of changes in legislation in some provinces, including Ontario, persons with limitations of mental capacity in some areas of their lives can be declared incompetent for these tasks, but may be considered to remain competent for other tasks. For example, persons with capacity in one area of personal care may continue to make those decisions while having decisions about another area, where they are incapable, made by a substitute decision-maker. The parens patriae (literally, parent of the fatherland) jurisdiction arises in the court on the declaration on mental incompetency. It has epitomized paternalism, containing the elements of custody and control along with the elements of responsibility and caring. The parens patriae jurisdiction has important benefits for individuals lacking mental capacity, but it is only recently that it has been tempered by respect for the individuals' rights, and an acknowledgement that its application must be limited to appropriate areas. The changes in the Ontario Health Care Consent Act and Substitute Decisions Act resulted from a lengthy process that included much consideration of the rights of people with mental disabilities.

Institutionalization

Institutionalization was similarly two-edged, providing the opportunity for benefits in the care and support unavailable elsewhere, while also creating the significant disadvantages inherent in a closed environment. Recognition of the potential for abuse in a closed environment (Dykeman, 1999) and increasing awareness of the detrimental effects of isolation from communities' patterns of life (Wolfensberger, 1972; Radford & Park, 1999), has led to downsizing of institutions and massive movements of developmentally disabled individuals from large and medium-sized institutions into group homes, smaller institutions and family settings. The deinstitutionalization and normalization movement has been an attempt to create a living environment in the community that would enhance opportunities for normalization and development of their individual potential.

Persons with developmental disabilities who have left large institutions in Ontario to move to forms of community residence have had considerably better residential options than persons leaving psychiatric facilities, where a laissez-faire attitude has prevailed (Simmons, 1990; Drassinower & Levine, 1995). Those who have both conditions should, in theory, have options available in either system, but their history is more likely to illustrate the gaps in the social service system for members of this population, an inability to provide service to deal with all aspects of the condition, and the way mental health and developmental disability services have been organized from a bureaucratic standpoint.

Reproduction and sexuality

Controls on reproductive and sexual life were most clearly indicated by the eugenics legislation in force in Alberta and British Columbia, enacted in 1928 and 1933 and in force until 1972 and 1973 respectively. In the 44 years during which the Alberta statute provided authority for eugenic sterilization, authorization was given for 2,822 people to be sterilized, and many of these people had not yet reached puberty (Robertson, Appendix to Muir v. Alberta, 1996). The Alberta legislation distinguished after 1933 between psychotic persons whose consent to sterilization was required, and "mentally defective" persons whose consent was not required. Women who were considered mentally disabled were targetted by the legislation, since they were seen as the source of feeblemindedness

(Goundry, 1994; Simmons, 1982). Other groups considered socially undesirable were also targeted, including poor people and immigrants from minority cultural groups (Robertson, Muir Appendix, 1996). The case of Muir v. Alberta led to compensation for her forced sterilization, a decision that had been based on faulty grounds, and one that had failed to apply the statute or follow government procedures. Leilani Muir's case, although not typical of those situations where decisions about people were made in accordance with the statute, led the way for others who had been sterilized to secure compensation.

The Eve decision by the Supreme Court of Canada declared that the Court would not use the parens patriae jurisdiction to authorize a non-therapeutic sterilization for contraceptive reasons for a person mentally incapable of deciding to have such a procedure herself (Peppin, 1989 - 1990). The Court was conscious of the history of control of persons with mental disabilities through control of reproduction, and in particular the atrocities committed by the Nazis. The Court made its decision not to authorize contraceptive sterilization on the basis of her rights, and disapproved of limiting the bodily integrity of the mentally incapable woman, of limiting the right to procreate, and of using a procedure that was intrusive, irreversible and non-therapeutic, to which she could not consent herself. Although the decision has been praised for its stance on behalf of the rights of mentally disabled individuals, it has also been soundly criticized for fundamental failures, including its failure to take sufficient account of her best interests, as involving the possible desirability of contraceptive sterilization, as required under the parens patriae jurisdiction (Re F, 1987, H.L.; Shone, 1987; Peppin, 1989 - 1990; Olesen, 1995). The Ontario legislation on consent to treatment leaves this decision intact by stating that the legislation does not apply to an authorization of sterilization that is not medically necessary. With a long-term contraceptive option available now, in the form of Depo Provera, the precise legal issues faced in the Eve case have become less pressing clinically, although the criteria used by the Supreme Court of Canada are still relevant to "non-therapeutic" procedures in general. The equality section of the Charter, which was not applied to the Eve case because the equality section was not in force when the case began, would presumably be available for consideration in any subsequent litigation in this area.

Sexuality and sexual violence

Research indicates that the level of violence, including sexual violence, against women with disabilities is high (Goundry, 1994). Sexuality is subject to control, and becomes a matter of some concern in institutional settings, particularly where non-consensual behaviour constituting battery or abuse may take place (McSherry & Somerville, 1998; Mossman, Perlin & Dorfman, 1997). Such non-consensual activity may be perpetrated by residents or by care providers. McCreary and Thompson have outlined the close relationship between being abused and becoming a perpetrator of a sexual offence (1999). The prevalence of childhood sexual abuse among women psychiatric patients is a significant related issue (Dykeman, 1999).

Stereotyping

Stereotyping and stigma are still conditions of life for persons with developmental disabilities. The trial judge in the Muir case stated that the damage of being sterilized was aggravated by her wrongful stigmatization as a moron or high-grade mental defective, which led to humiliation on a daily basis in her relations with family, friends and employers. Interestingly, the stigmatization was wrongful in her case because the province had failed to follow its own statutory requirement, practices and procedures when it institutionalized her and sterilized her. Such stigma continues today for those who are perceived to have a disability, and a current example can be found easily in the conversations of some children, teenagers and adults who use terms for mental disabilities as casual indicators of low regard.

Constructing an understanding of dual diagnosis

The academic literature on disability distinguishes between the physical impairment and the social construction of disability. Impairment does not necessarily produce powerlessness, stereotyping, prejudice, and a condition of disadvantage. Disability is seen as a concept with multiple dimensions expressed bodily, personally and socially (Bickenbach, 1993). The context within which a person with a disability experiences his/her life includes the social construction of disability - that is, the way members of the culture view a person with a disability, including that person herself or himself. As we seek to understand the situation of people with dual disabilities, hearing their experiences and voices is vital. As Goundry (1994) has noted, "women with disabilities have identified a number of broad social issues as particularly relevant to their lives and have described the systemic barriers which undermine their equality aspirations. Violence, self-image, reproduction, parenting, employment, poverty, and sexuality are among those issues which have a particular meaning(s) for many women with disabilities – meaning(s) that are just beginning to be articulated in the literature" (Goundry, 1994, p. 1).

In a biological context, attempts are being made to develop an understanding of dual diagnosis within an ethical framework that is increasingly affected by developments in our understanding of biology. As genetic innovations increase our understanding of the human body and its development, it seems that society needs to be reminded of the limitations of scientific understanding. Reducing human behaviour to genes, and expecting genes to provide answers to human difference are two "worrying" aspects of this process (Lippman, 1993). Although genetics and biochemistry are contributing to our understanding of disabilities, genes are not solely determinative of the person's life.

In a social context, a response to an individual's need based simply on consideration of his/her best interests is insufficient if it fails to consider the social order that produces the condition of disadvantage experienced by the individual. If a legal or psychiatric theory focuses on individual behaviour while excluding the social context within which the behaviour has developed, it can be considered deficient. The capacity of an individual to engage in autonomous decision-making needs to be seen in the context of society, including its structure of political inequality (Edelman, 1980; Weinberg, 1988; Minow, 1990; Sherwin, 1992).

The social structures themselves need to be challenged, and the power and rights that characterize human relationships should be the focus (Minow, 1990; Duclos (now Iyer), 1993; Razack, 1994). For example, Sherene Razack (1994) has analyzed sexual violence against girls and women with developmental disabilities. She has argued that the relations need to be seen as social arrangements that constitute groups differently as dominant and subordinate, and that these constructions interact across social dimensions of gender, disability and age.

In a psychological context, when more than one condition of inequality and disadvantage is present, such as developmental disability and mental illness, the interplay may occur in complex ways. The disabilities may reinforce one another, may lead in different directions, or may simply be added together to make the effect greater. When considering the nature of inequality and discrimination, it is important to take this analytical step of considering how the conditions interact. When an individual has a dual diagnosis, the other reinforcing or alleviating conditions, such as his/her gender, race, age, sexual orientation, may have an effect on his/her social and legal situation. Any one of these factors may reduce or enhance the power of an individual in relation to other individuals with similar conditions (Razack, 1994).

Legal issues affecting people with dual diagnoses

Specific legal issues may arise as a consequence of a person with a developmental disability also having a diagnosis of psychiatric disorder. The range of issues that might arise for any individual includes: *access to services; right to decide about treatment and substitute decision-making for persons mentally incapable of making a decision; exposure to violence and abuse; violence committed by the individual directed at him/ herself or others; involuntary commitment; restraints; and participation in experimentation and research.* This is not an all-inclusive list, and the focus is particularly on key issues in the areas of personal care and social service.

1. Access to services

The problem of inadequate service is experienced by dually diagnosed individuals who have difficulty obtaining treatment suitable to both conditions. This may occur when they "fall between" two service systems, such as those of the Ministries of Health and Long Term Care and Community and Social Services. Similarly, an individual who has come into conflict with the law may be incarcerated in a provincial or federal institution, where specialist care may or may not be available.

Negligence law requires that individuals who owe a duty of care to another person meet a standard of care. Failure to meet the standard of care for a treatment amounts to negligence and this leads to liability when harm of a foreseeable type has been caused by the negligence. This raises the question of how the standard of care is to be determined, and how it is to be maintained in service settings. This is a particularly complex question because the dual diagnosis area has few practitioners, and because multiple caregivers are often involved. One American study examined the treatment and social support services provided to persons with dual diagnoses, and found the level of service delivery insufficient, citing evidence of excessive drug therapy, including drug therapy where the diagnosis did not warrant it (Thomas, 1994). Similar areas of concern have been identified across Ontario. Increased awareness of these issues by professionals and caregivers will hopefully improve their conditions under which persons with developmental disability are treated in the mental health sector.

In the recent case of Eldridge v. British Columbia (1997), the Supreme Court of Canada decided that an authority's decision not to fund sign language interpreters in hospitals constituted discrimination on the basis of disability because deaf persons were unable to benefit equally from the health care services available to everyone, and that this constituted a denial of plaintiffs' equality rights under the Charter. This decision on access to services is likely to be of considerable significance to people with disabilities.

2. Right to decide about treatment

The Health Care Consent Act and Substitute Decisions Act govern health care treatment decision-making in Ontario. Treatment is defined broadly in the Act, and the kinds of health practitioners who may provide treatment are also broadly determined, based principally on a selection of those professions currently regulated under the health professions regulatory legislation in Ontario. A valid treatment decision is one that is informed, voluntary, made by a capable person or their substitute decision-maker, and one made without fraud or misrepresentation. People are presumed to be capable, and it is only when there are reasonable grounds to believe otherwise that capacity is assessed. The determinative factor of mental capacity is assessed on the basis of the ability to understand the information relevant to the decision, and the ability to appreciate the reasonably foreseeable consequences of a decision or lack of decision. Both cognitive abilities must be present for an individual to be considered mentally capable. Capacity is assessed at a particular time with respect to a particular decision.

Guardians may be appointed by a court to act for individuals who are mentally incapable with respect to personal care matters or financial matters or both. A guardian may be appointed for one or more areas of personal care decision-making in which the individual has been found incapable, while that person retains authority to make decisions over all the other areas. Court-appointed guardians are required to act in accordance with principles outlined in the legislation.

Persons with developmental disabilities who are incapable of making treatment decisions are able to have substitute decision-makers make treatment decisions for them. Substitute decision-makers (SDMs) are listed in rank order in the legislation and generally the highest person on the list who is available, willing, old enough and mentally capable is the substitute decision-maker for that treatment decision. A guardian authorized to make treatment decisions is at the top of the list, followed by an attorney for personal care authorized to make treatment decisions under a power of attorney for personal care, and then a representative appointed by the Consent and Capacity Board, a spouse or partner, a parent or 16+ child, access parent in the situation where one parent has custody, a sibling, and finally another relative (by blood, marriage or adoption). If there is no person available and willing to act as substitute decision-maker, the Public Guardian and Trustee, a public official, must be the substitute decision-maker. This is an important provision for long-institutionalized and older persons with disabilities, ensuring that they will not be without services even though no one associated with them is available to act as substitute decision-maker. The Public Guardian and Trustee must also act as decision-maker if equally entitled substitute decision-makers fail to reach an agreement on a decision.

The decision made by the substitute decision-maker must be made in accordance with the principles set out in the Health Care Consent Act. The substitute decision-maker must decide on the basis of a wish made by the person when capable of doing so and when at least 16 years of age. This prior capable 16+ wish must be followed by the SDM as long as it is not impossible to carry out. If there is no such prior capable 16+ wish, then the SDM must decide on the basis of the best interests of the mentally incapable person. In determining the best interests, the Act requires that the SDM consider the following: (i) the values and beliefs the individual held when capable, on the basis of which he/she would make this decision; (ii) his/her incapable wishes; (iii) risk-benefit factors including likely improvement with the proposed treatment, prevention or slowing of deterioration; and whether a less restrictive or intrusive treatment would be as beneficial, and the risk-benefit calculation. The basic principle for substitute decision-making may be expressed as: wishes, or if none, then best interests. Requiring the decision to be made on the basis of the individual's wish, and outlining best interests criteria that incorporate aspects of the individual's values and context are important protections for the individual's autonomy.

Another way in which autonomy is protected is through recognition of the power of attorney for personal care. Individuals who are capable of doing so may make out a power of attorney for personal care, naming their own substitute decision-makers in the event of subsequent incapacity. Wishes may also be expressed in this formal document, if the person is capable of making that particular decision.

Procedural rights are also found in the legislation, including rights of appeal to the Consent and Capacity Board, and from it to the courts. Rights advice is an important part of any system affecting individual rights, such as the mental health system of involuntary commitment and community treatment orders, and the health care decision-making scheme. Unless people subject to the law are made aware of their rights, the rights are meaningless. Similarly, substitute decision-makers acting on behalf of individuals with a mental incapacity must also be made aware of their responsibilities. Without this knowledge, they may unwittingly fail to respect the autonomy or best interests of the individual. *"Advocacy, protection, and representation of people with dual diagnoses require heightened understanding of this population and their rights because such people experience difficulty in understanding the legal mechanisms available to assert their rights"* (Bersoff, Glass & Blain, 1994, p. 60). Rights advisers are provided in psychiatric facilities in Ontario, including public hospitals with psychiatric wards. Health practitioners proposing treatments have obligations to inform individuals of their rights under the health care consent legislation, in accordance with norms set by their professions, and also have an obligation to inform substitute decision-makers of their responsibilities and the bases (outlined above) on which they are legally required to make substitute decisions (A.M. v. Benes, 1999, Ont. C.A.). The Canadian Charter of Rights and Freedoms applies to statutes.

3. Crisis situations

Violence by others toward a person with developmental disability, self-injurious behaviour and violence to others by these persons, are all serious occurrences that have legal dimensions. Emergency situations, requiring quick treatment to prevent serious bodily harm or severe suffering, are dealt with under specific sections of the Health Care Consent Act.

Violence and abuse directed towards vulnerable adults, such as the dually diagnosed, was one concern of government that led to the changes in the legislation governing consent to treatment and substitute decision-making. The <u>Substitute Decisions Act</u> contains an important provision that applies when it is suspected that an apparently incapable individual is being abused or neglected. When an allegation is made that a person is or may be suffering "serious adverse effects", possibly because of mental incapacity, the Public Guardian and Trustee (PGT) is required to investigate. Serious adverse effects are defined for this part of the Act as serious illness or injury, or deprivation of liberty or personal security. Such an investigation may lead to an order of temporary guardianship, naming the PGT as temporary guardian, and could involve apprehending and removing the person.

This mechanism has been designed to bring to the attention of a public official those situations of abuse, neglect and self-injurious behaviour to which mental incapacity is contributing. In these instances, the PGT is given a right of entry, subject to certain conditions, in order to determine whether the person is incapable, and to assess the situation in which adverse effects may be taking place. Only in these limited circumstances is it permissible to intervene.

In considering the appropriate course of action in a crisis situation, the question of whether a common law duty of care exists must be answered. Institutions have been held to have a duty of care to the individual, a duty to make the environment safe for other patients (<u>Stewart v. Extendicare Ltd.</u>), and a duty to control and supervise psychiatric patients so as to prevent harm to third parties in the hospital (<u>Lawson v. Wellesley Hospital</u>), or to third parties outside the institution who have a sufficient relationship of proximity, and are "exposed to a risk of danger because of the nature of the patient" (<u>Wenden v. Trikha, 1991</u>, p. 157). Health professionals who have established a relationship with the person will owe him or her a duty of care (Picard & Robertson, 1996). Other care providers may also owe duties. The responsibility of a physician is to use the reasonable degree of skill, care and knowledge ordinarily possessed by professionals in that context. Specialists, such as psychiatrists, are held to the standard of specialists, as are non-specialists who hold themselves out as having that degree of expertise. A court may find that the standard of care should be higher than the professional standard in situations "fraught with obvious risk" (ter Neuzen v. Korn, 1995).

The above-mentioned situations constitute crises. In a crisis situation, an assessment by a treating psychiatrist would include consideration of the potential for harmful behaviour and ways to manage it. If steps are proposed to limit the behaviour of an individual engaging in conduct dangerous to others – such as fire-setting or sexually aggressive behaviour - it is important to ask what steps have been taken to reduce the danger, including those taken to prevent any precipitating events to such violence. If there is reason to believe that the risk is not under control, it would be appropriate to ask the nature of the obligations owed to the individual by the psychiatrist and any institution, and what duty and standard of care applies in relation to members of the community where the person lives.

In considering the elements of risk to others and to the individual, it is important to give weight to the individual's own perspective, including his/her understanding of the situation, and whether he/she would be willing to warn others as a means of minimizing risk. In some circumstances, a court may find that a duty to warn others is required of the treating professional. When engaging in long-term planning, it would be important to consider the effect of any alternatives on the person's opportunity to participate in making a community living experience work. The area of crisis management is one where it is particularly important to obtain legal advice.

The duty to control another person arises in tort law as an aspect of the duty of care. When a duty of care exists, or when a special relationship gives rise to this duty to protect or control, then a court will require that a certain standard of care be met, in order to prevent harm from arising to the individual or to another person. For example, innkeepers are required not to keep serving alcohol to patrons past a certain point of inebriation, in order to prevent the customers from harming themselves or third parties such as other drivers. A common law duty to restrain or confine a person when immediate action is needed to prevent serious bodily harm to them or others is not affected by the Health Care Consent Act.

Duties to restrain or control come into conflict with rights to physical inviolability and security of the person, in addition to individuals' autonomy rights, all of which receive protection in tort law and under the Canadian Charter of Rights and Freedoms. Such steps to confine or restrain a person must be reasonable and legally authorized (Conway v. Fleming, 1999).

Section 12 of the Charter prohibits "cruel and unusual treatment or punishment". This section, it has been argued, might apply to the legislation permitting decisions authorizing intrusive measures such as electro convulsive therapy, contingent electric shock, and other such aversive therapies (Kaiser, 1986; Weagant & Griffiths, 1988) Statutes and institutional guidelines also reflect this interplay of rights. For example, any government guidelines on behaviour modification, physical or chemical restraint, would have important implications for the range of actions permissible or required. Further considerations are whether such an intrusive measure meets the standard of care of the profession, and whether an informed decision has been made.

Whether intrusive procedures can be seen as therapeutic is a controversial issue. Weagant and Griffiths (1988) have asked if the particular aversive conditioning measure known as contingent electric shock can be a treatment when it is a punishment used in a crisis situation. On this basis, the authors suggest that the limitation on non-therapeutic procedures directed to mentally incapable persons stated by the Supreme Court of Canada in the Eve case would apply to contingent electric shock, so that it would be available only on the consent of the individual. Further, they suggest that sections 12 and 7 of the Charter provide strong bases for preventing contingent electric shock from being used on a non-consenting person.

A new Ontario statute is intended to reduce the use of physical and chemical restraints and monitoring devices used to prevent serious bodily harm. The *Patient Restraints Minimization Law* (2001) was introduced as a private member's bill by former Health Minister, Frances Lankin, who had found that her 88 year-old mother had been placed in restraints in hospital, even though the family had stated that they wished no restraints to be used (Priest, 2001). Researchers interviewed by the Toronto *Globe and Mail* indicated that Canada is among the highest users of restraints and that restraints can be misused when they are used to solve staffing problems or when other alternatives exist or when they themselves cause injuries (Priest, 2001).

The stated purposes of the Act are to minimize the use of restraints and to encourage hospitals and facilities to use alternative less controlling methods whenever possible when they find it necessary to use restraints to prevent serious bodily harm to a patient or others. Regulations to the new Act will provide the details necessary to implement the legislation. To "restrain" means "to place the person under control by the minimal use of such force, mechanical means or chemicals as is reasonable having regard to the person's physical and mental condition". The Act also governs the use of monitoring devices to prevent serious bodily harm to the person or others. It applies to public and licensed private hospitals and to facilities and organizations set out in the regulations, although it doesn't apply where the Mental Health Act applies to the use of restraints on patients or other people in psychiatric facilities.

Only physicians and others specified in the regulations may order restraint, confinement or monitoring devices. The use of restraints, confinement or monitoring devices by a hospital or facility must meet the criteria in the Act or come within the common law duty of a caregiver to confine or restrain when immediate action is necessary to prevent serious bodily harm to the person or others. The statutory criteria that authorize the use fall into two categories – enhancing freedom/giving greater enjoyment of life or preventing serious bodily harm. In either case, its use must be necessary to prevent serious bodily harm to the person or another and any regulatory criteria must have been met. In the case of enhancing freedom or life enjoyment, the restraints much achieve this purpose and a plan of treatment to which consent has been given must authorize its use. Hospitals and facilities have duties to establish and comply with policies, including policies to encourage less controlling alternatives, to monitor patients and to provide staff training.

In an examination of dually diagnosed individuals and "forcible administration of psychoactive medication to involuntarily committed and voluntarily admitted mental patients outside of the criminal justice system", it was found that American courts examining the issue gave weight to the safety of state hospitals, particularly when the patient was incapable (Bersoff, Glass & Blain, 1994). The authors recommended that psychological treatments that are less intrusive, such as group therapies and token economies, should, in order to avoid judicial scrutiny under the U.S. constitution, be used for treatment and for the safety of those staff and patients in the institution, and that they not be used for punitive motives.

Psychiatric treatment and community treatment orders

The provincial Government has enacted revisions to the Mental Health Act (in force, Dec. 1, 2000) that have been described as an attempt to balance individual and social needs, rights and responsibilities (Witmer, 2000). Health Minister Elizabeth Witmer has also drawn on the deinstitutionalization movement as a rationale for creating community treatment orders.

The Mental Health Act criteria for application for psychiatric assessment and involuntary admission have been relaxed by removing the requirement that the threatened danger be "imminent". The Mental Health Act criteria for a physician's application for a psychiatric assessment require that a physician's examination produce reasonable cause to believe one of threatened or attempted bodily harm to the self, violent behaviour or causing fear of bodily harm to another, or lack of competence to care for the self, plus apparent mental disorder likely to result in serious bodily harm to the person or such harm to another or serious physical impairment of the person.

Involuntary commitment requires determination of the mental disorder plus one of the resulting predictions unless the person is in the custody of a psychiatric facility, and that the person not be suitable as an informal or voluntary patient. The amended legislation makes it easier to send an individual to a psychiatric facility for a psychiatric examination. Involuntary commitment has become mandatory if the criteria are met, rather than permissible. This means that physicians no longer possess discretion at this point. It is possible to have a person psychiatrically assessed and involuntarily committed if he/she has been treated in the past for an illness likely to cause serious effects if untreated, if the following other factors exist: a) clinical improvement has resulted, b) the mental disorder is the same, c) serious effects (serious bodily harm, deterioration or impairment) are likely to be caused by his/her condition, d) he/she is mentally incapable of consenting to treatment in a psychiatric facility and his/her substitute decision-maker consents, and e) in the case of commitment, informal or voluntary admission is not suitable.

In these circumstances, a physician may make a "community treatment order" (CTO), provided that a number of additional criteria are met. These criteria are: the need for continuing treatment or care and supervision in the community; past commitment within a certain period or a CTO; an examination within the past 72 hours, on the basis of which the criteria for an application for psychiatric assessment have been met; serious bodily effects predicted to result from an absence of such treatment/care and supervision; the ability to comply with the CTO; a plan; and consultation. The individual or his/her substitute decision-maker must have consented to the CTO, and rights advice must have been provided or refused. The Act states that the individual must comply with the order and attend appointments with the physician.

The Health Care Consent Act applies to community treatment orders in addition to treatments generally. Prior *expressed* capable adult wishes will still prevail when they are clear, but the individual with no expressed prior capable wishes will be subject to the best interests determination of the substitute decision-maker. There are several areas in this Act that may be challenged by counsel using the protections of rights of the Charter. These include: a) preference for treatment, b) application of duress in the form of required compliance with treatment c) the threat of re-commitment to a psychiatric facility, and d) its relaxation of the standard for involuntary psychiatric assessment. The difficult questions related to implementation of this policy change have yet to be addressed, including provision of sufficient community resources to carry it out.

Experimentation and research

Research on human subjects in Canada is governed by a network of laws and guidelines. The common law requires that researchers meet the "full and frank disclosure" standard, while negligence law applies to the design, authorization and conduct of such research. The Tri-Council Policy Statement was adopted by the three federally funded research councils to apply to research funded by them. The TCPS, which has the status only of a statement and not the status of law, is interpreted and applied by Research Ethics Boards in the institutions, which are responsible for the review of research protocols in accordance with legal and ethical standards. One deficiency of this system is the lack of accreditation of REBs. Under a new federal regulation, the federal government has authority to inspect clinical trials of prescription drugs to ensure the protection of human subjects and compliance with established standards. As well, the role of REBs is recognized. The TCPS states that persons should not be prevented, purely on the basis of mental capacity, from participating in research that is potentially beneficial to them or to their group. This statement marks the change from a view of research as potentially harmful to a recognition of the research participation as having benefits, including early access to experimental drugs.

Conclusion

In this chapter, the legal and ethical aspects of dual diagnosis have been considered. The issue of equality has been examined in particular detail, with some discussion of how equality is to be determined when two conditions of mental disability coincide. This intersection affects their position in the constitutional sphere and in Canadian society, since both conditions have a history of social stigma, physical invasions, and lack of power. Following this, an overview was given of specific legal consequences of dual diagnosis.

Future professionals in the fields of health and social services have a need to understand the law applying to their professional service and to the situations of clients. Success in implementing any law depends on whether health care practitioners understand the law and apply it. We also need to hear more from people with such diagnoses so that we can all learn more about the effects of law on their lives.

Do You Know?

1. What situations could be changed so that people with dual diagnoses can achieve greater equality?
2. In what situations involving people with dual diagnoses do fundamental rights come into conflict?
3. Describe three situations in which a dually diagnosed person would be affected by the law. Outline how the law would apply to those situations.

Resources

Brown, I. & Percy, M. (Eds.). (1999). *Developmental disabilities in Ontario*. Toronto: Front Porch Publishing.

Downie, J. & Caulfield, T. (Eds.). (1999). *Canadian health law and policy*. Toronto: Butterworths.

Gordon, R. M. & Verdun-Jones, S. N. (1992). *Adult guardianship law*. Toronto: Carswell.

Picard, E.I. & Robertson, G. B. (1996). *Legal liability of doctors and hospitals in Canada*. (3rd Ed). Toronto: Carswell.

Sneiderman, B., Irvine, J. C., & Osborne, P. H. (1995) *Canadian medical law*. (2nd Ed). Toronto: Carswell.

Robertson, G.B. (1987). *Mental disability and the law in Canada*. Toronto: Carswell.

Some useful websites are:

www.attorneygeneral.jus.gov.on.ca/html/LEGIS/legis.htm
    Ontario legislation
www.attorneygeneral.jus.gov.on.ca/html/PGT/pgthome.htm
    Office of the Public Guardian and Trustee

www.acjnet.org/
Access to Justice network

References

Appelbaum, P. (1994). *Almost a revolution: Mental health law and the limits of change.* Oxford, UK : Oxford University Press.

Arboleda-Florez, J. (1996). *Mental illness and violence: proof or stereotype*? Ottawa: Health Canada.

Bay, M. (1993). Implementing competency legislation for health care. *Health Law in Canada, 14,* 35.

Beauchamp, T.L. & Walters, L. (Eds). (1989). *Contemporary Issues in Bioethics.* (3rd Ed.) Belmont, CA: Wadsworth Publishing Company.

Bersoff, D., Glass, D., & Blain, N. (1994). Legal issues in the assessment and treatment of individuals with dual diagnoses. *Journal of Consulting and Clinical Psychology, 62,* 55-62.

Bickenbach, J. (1993). *Physical disability and social policy.* Toronto: University of Toronto Press.

Brown, I. & Percy, M. (Eds.). (1999). *Developmental disabilities in Ontario.* Toronto: Front Porch Publishing.

Drassinower, M. & Levine, S. (1995). More sinned against than sinning: housing, mental illness and disability. *Windsor Review of Legal & Social Issues, 5,* 91-156.

Dykeman, M.J. (1999-00). Addressing systemic issues in women's mental health: An inquest into the death of Cinderella Allalouf. *Journal of Women's Health and Law, 1,* 15-30.

Duclos, N. (1993). Disappearing women: Racial minority women in human rights cases. *Canadian Journal of Women and the Law, 6,* 25.

Edelman, M. (1980). Law and psychiatry as political symbolism. *International Journal of Law and Psychiatry, 3*, 235-244.

Field, M.A. & Sanchez, V.A. (1999). *Equal treatment for people with mental retardation: having and raising children.* Cambridge, UK: Harvard University Press.

Goundry, S.A. (1994). *Women, disability and the law: Identifying barriers to equality in the law of non-consensual sterilization, child welfare and sexual assault.* Canadian Disability Rights Council: Winnipeg, Man.

Johnston, S.J. & Hoalstead, S. (2000). Forensic issues in intellectual disability. *Current Opinion in Psychiatry, 13*, 475-480.

Kaiser, H.A. (1986). Electroconvulsive therapy as "cruel and unusual treatment or punishment". *Health Law in Canada, 7*, 35-51.

Lippman, A. (1993). Worrying – and worrying about – the geneticization of reproduction and health. In G. Basen, M. Eichler & A. Lippman (Eds.), *Misconceptions.* (pp. 39-65). Hull, P.Q.: Voyageur Publishing.

McCreary, B.D. & Thompson, J. (1999). Psychiatric aspects of sexual abuse involving persons with developmental disabilities. *Canadian Journal of Psychiatry, 44*, 350-355.

McSherry, B. & Somerville, M. (1998). Sexual activity among institutionalized persons in need of special care. *Windsor Yearbook of Access to Justice , 16*, 90.

Minow, M. (1990). *Making all the difference.* Ithaca, NY: Cornell University Press.

Mossman, D., Perlin, M. & Dorfman, D. (1997). Sex on the wards: Conundra for clinicians. *Journal of the American Academy of Psychiatry and the Law, 25*, 441.

Olesen, C.M. (1994). Eve and the forbidden fruit: Reflections on a feminist methodology. *Dalhousie Journal of Legal*

Studies, 3, 231-240.

Peppin, P. (1989-90). Justice and care: mental disability and sterilization decisions. *Canadian Human Rights Yearbook* 65-112.

Peppin, P. (1994). Power and disadvantage in medical relationships. *Texas Journal of Women and the Law, 3,* 221-263.

Peppin, P. & Baker, D. (1999). Entitlements in four areas of law. In I. Brown & M. Percy (Eds.), *Developmental disabilities in Ontario* (pp. 67-82). Toronto, ON: Front Porch Publishing,

Priest, L. (2001, July 28). When patients turn into prisoners. *Globe and Mail,* p. A2.

Radford, J.P. & Park, D.C. (1999). Historical overview of developmental disabilities in Ontario. In I. Brown & M. Percy (Eds.). *Developmental disabilities in Ontario.* (pp. 1-16). Toronto: Front Porch Publishing,

Razack, S. (1994). From consent to responsibility, from pity to respect: Subtexts in cases of sexual violence involving girls and women with developmental disabilities. *Law & Social Inquiry, 19 ,* 891-922.

Rioux, M.H. & Frazee, C.L. (1999). Rights and freedoms. In I. Brown, & M. Percy (Eds.), *Developmental disabilities in Ontario* (pp. 59-66). Toronto: Front Porch Publishing.

Robertson, G.B. (1996). Appendix to Muir v. Alberta. (1996), 36 Alta. L. R. (3d) 30s (Q.B.)

Sherwin, S. (1992) *No longer patient.* Philadelphia: Temple University Press.

Shone, M.A. (1987). Mental health – sterilization of mentally retarded persons – parens patriae power: Re Eve. *Canadian Bar Review, 66,* 635.

Simmons, H.G. (1982). *From asylum to welfare.* Downsview, Ont.: National Institute on Mental Retardation.

Simmons, H.G. (1990). Mental-health policy in Ontario compared to policy for persons with developmental handicaps. *Canadian Journal of Community Mental Health, 9 ,*163-176.

Thomas, J. R. (1994). Quality care for individuals with dual diagnosis: The legal and ethical imperative to provide qualified staff. *Mental Retardation, 32,* 356-361.

Weagant, B. & Griffiths, D.M. (1988). Legal advocacy and the use of aversives. In G. Allan Roeher Institute (Ed.), *The language of pain: Perspectives on behaviour management* (pp. 115-130). Toronto, ON: G. Allan Roeher Institute.

Weinberg, J.K. (1988). Autonomy as a different voice: Women, disabilities, and decisions. In M. Fine & A. Asch (Eds.), *Women with disabilities: Essays in psychology, culture, and politics* (pp. 269-296). Philadelphia: Temple University Press.

Witmer, E. (Hon.) (2000). Speech to the XXVth *Congress of the International Academy of Law and Mental Health,* July 12, 2000, Siena, Italy (notes on file with the author).

Wolfensberger, W. (1972). *The principle of normalization in human services.* Downsview, Ont.: National Institute on Mental Retardation.

Cases:

A.M. v. Benes (1999), 46 O.R. (3d) 271 (C.A.).

Abela v. Rajan, [1992] O.J. No. 1590 (Gen. Div.).

Clark v. Clark (1983), 40 O.R. (2d) 383 (Co. Ct.).

Conway v. Fleming (1999), 43 O.R. (3d) (Div. Ct.).

Crocker v. Sundance Northwest Resorts Ltd. (1988), 44

C.C.L.T 225 (S.C.C.).

Eldridge v. British Columbia (Attorney General), [1997] S.C.J. No. 86.

Eve v. Mrs. E., [1986] 2 S.C.R. 388.

Fleming v. Reid (1991) 4 O.R. (3d) 74 (C.A.).

Lawson v. Wellesley Hospital (1975) 61 D.L.R. (3d) 445 (Ont. C.A.), aff'd [1978] 1 S.C.R. 893.

Morgentaler v. The Queen, [1988] S.C.J. No. 1.

Muir v. Alberta (1996), 36 Alta. L.R. (3d) 305 (Q.B.).

Re F., [1989] 2 W.L.R. 1063 (H.L.).

Rodriguez v. British Columbia (Attorney General), [1963] S.C.J. No. 94.

Stewart v. Extendicare Ltd., [1986] 4 W.W.R. 559 (Sask. Q.B.).

ter Neuzen v. Korn (1995), 127 D.L.R. (4th) 577 (S.C.C.).

Wenden v. Trikha, [1991] 8 C.C.L.T. 2d 138 (Alta. Q.B.), aff'd (1993), 14 C.C.L.T. (2d) 225 (Alta. C.A.).

Statutes:

Canadian Charter of Rights and Freedoms, Part I of the Constitution Act, 1982, being Schedule B to the Canada Act 1982 (U.K.), 1982, c. 11.

Health Care Consent Act, S.O. 1996, c. 2 (Sch. A), as am.
Mental Health Act, R.S.O. 1990, c. M.7, as am.

Patient Restraints Minimization Law, S.O. 2001, c. 16.

Substitute Decisions Act, S.O. 1992, c. 30, as am.

Acknowledgements

I would like to express my thanks to Sara Guild and Litza Anderson for their excellent research assistance. Portions of this paper were presented to the XXIVth Congress of the International Academy of Law and Mental Health, Toronto, Ontario, July 1999, in a joint session that included papers presented by Dr. Bruce McCreary and Phil Burge. I am grateful to them and to my colleagues Sheila Noonan, Rosemary King and Stan Corbett for discussions about these issues.

Appendix A

Syndromes and Diagnostic Features
Jane Summers, Chrissoula Stavrakaki, Dorothy M. Griffiths, and Thomas Cheetham

Syndromes/ Genetic Causes	Diagnostic Features	Behavioural Phenotype	Medical/Psychiatric and Medication Vulnerabilities	Psychological Vulnerabilities	Social Implications/ Vulnerabilities
Autism	Delayed patterns of social, affective, and communication development speech delay impaired social interaction restricted activities	Hyperactivity Short attention span Impulsivity Aggressivity Self-injurious behaviour Abnormal eating/ sleep patterns Sensitivity to sounds	EEG abnormalities/ seizure disorders Coexistence with other neurological medical conditions (soft neurological signs) No specific medication available Medication addresses symptoms (i.e. ,amphetamines for ADHD, antipsychotics for aggressivity, SSRI's for behavioural/anxiety depressive disorders	Period of normal development (1-2 years) Low IQ in 75% (developmental disability) Language comprehension lower than vocabulary Extremely high abilities in certain areas (music, math, reading)	Social withdrawal/ isolation Inflexibility to routines or rituals Insistence on sameness Distress to changes of routine Stereotypic body movements Abnormal focus of interest
Rett's Syndrome	Deterioration from apparently normal development in infancy or early childhood Slow down of head growth Lack of interest in the environment Loss of hand use/ stereotypic hand movements	Anxiety in response to external situations Brief and consistent screaming Hyperventilation Self-inflicting behaviour Frightened expressions and general distress Low mood/crying spells Biting of fingers and hands	Hypoplastic cold blue feet Scoliosis Changed sensitivity to pain Intensive eye communication EEG abnormalities Breath holding Bloating Bruxism Night laughing No specific medication available; only treatment of symptoms and problem areas	Severe to profound degree of developmental disability Motor and language impairment Similarities with autism and difficult to differentiate at an early age	Behavioral issues tend to be misunderstood Inability to self help skills can be easily mistaken Wetting, soiling present causes social issues Laughter and screaming can be misdiagnosed or behaviors Inability to speak is socially isolating and causes frustration

Syndromes/ Genetic Causes	Diagnostic Features	Behavioural Phenotype	Medical/Psychiatric and Medication Vulnerabilities	Psychological Vulnerabilities	Social Implications/ Vulnerabilities
Down Syndrome	Chromosomal disorder Trisomy 21 occurs in 94% of Down Syndrome Trisomy 21 occurs in 4% of all pregnancies 25-40 genes have currently been identified with chromosome 21 Translocation: part of chromosome transferred to another location (f. 21:13)	Appears more passive Less reactivity Lower adaptability Require more stimulation Less persistent More inflexible and resistive to change Require more attention Conduct problems	Brain weight in children less Brain abnormalities Seizure disorders (1:3 ratio) Early memory and cognitive skills loss before the age of 50 years Eye problems; keratoConus, strabismus, blepharitis Oral problems: maxilla and mandible are smaller Heart defects Lungs are smaller Gastrointestinal anomalies Skin problems Medication— treating symptoms and/or physical problems	Failure to develop normal language Central auditory processing abnormalities Expressive language difficulties is a hallmark of this syndrome Reduced short-term memory and distractibility	Social withdrawal/ passivity in some Diminished social competence in some Difficulty learning reference cues Difficulty transferring goal-directed play skills (from a joint group to individual play situations) Greater inflexibility to routines or rituals
Gilles De La Tourette Familial with genetic vulnerability Basal ganglia development is abnormal Possibly an autoimmune disorder	Chronic motor and verbal tics/ they may appear together or separately More males/females 6-8 males/1000 4-5 females/1000	Destructibility Academic/social problems Conduct problems Anxiety with rigidity of thinking and compulsion Anxiety disorder	Comorbitiy of OCD Comorbidity of ADHD Learning disorders Conduct disorders Medication neuroleptics Haldol, Pimozide, and Clonidine SSRI's stimulants for ADHD and vocal tics	Academic/learning problems Developmental delays Specific reading/math disabilities	Social impairment Behavioural problems Difficulties settling in a given task or performance Tic disorders are "stress-sensitive"

Syndromes/ Genetic Causes	Diagnostic Features	Behavioural Phenotype	Medical/Psychiatric and Medication Vulnerabilities	Psychological Vulnerabilities	Social Implications/ Vulnerabilities
Williams Syndrome Deletion of chromosome 7 q11.23 Multisystem disease	Dysmorphic facial features Cardiovascular disease Delayed development	Attention problems Excessive worrying Talking too much Not eating well Overfriendly to strangers Oversensitivity to sounds Negative mood	Hyperopia/strabismus Chronic otitis media Voice low pitched & coarse Aortic narrowing Hypertension UI: chronic abdominal pain/ constipation Kidney/urinary problems Hyperextendible joints Hypercalcemia and failure to thrive Hypotonic initially– hypertonic later diabetes	Grammar is somewhat delayed Vocabulary is of relative strength, although developmental delays are common Onset of language delayed Auditory role memory is a strength Visual-spatial construction drawing low block design low	Performance on socialization is high/ overfriendliness/ advanced interpersonal skills Performance on communication and on daily living skills lower than other domains Anxiety disorders quite common Many can achieve independent living with regular employment Treatment of physical problems and anxiety are required
Prader Willi Syndrome	Caused by genetic alteration of the 15 chromosome (Del 15 q11-13) 1 in/15 000 Lack of paternal contribution by the specific chromosomal region	Often severe problems Temper tantrums Stubbornness Oppositionality Rigidity Crying Stealing, especially with regards to food Obsessions Underactivity Excessive sleep Anxiety	Hypotonia Obesity Hypogonadism Facial features distinct Short stature Viscous saliva High pain threshold Skin picking Osteoporosis	IQ usually around 70 Range from average to profound disability Impaired adaptive functioning Low adaptive performance with significant behavioural dysfunction and a persistent drive to eat Language development delayed	Persistent drive to eat is associated with increased weight behaviour difficulties family stress Language and coping skill delays increase risk of maladaptive behaviours Psychiatric disorders such as OCD, anxiety, and depressive disorder

Syndromes/ Genetic Causes	Diagnostic Features	Behavioural Phenotype	Medical/Psychiatric and Medication Vulnerabilities	Psychological Vulnerabilities	Social Implications/ Vulnerabilities
Fragile X Syndrome Mutation in fragile X gene (DNA testing identifies carriers in addition to individuals who are also affected) Most common cause of developmental disability 30% or all X-linked forms of DD	Language delay Motor delay Hypotonia Hyperactivity	Short attention span Impulsivity Hyperactivity Hypersensitivity to sounds Hyperarousal Tactile defensiveness Tantrums daily Aggressivity Transition can be very difficult Perseveration Autistic-like features	Prominent ears Long face Hyperextensibility of joints Flat feet Soft skin Cleft palate Macroorchidism Higher growth in early years Social anxiety Personality disorder Seizures (20%) Chronic otitis media Medications stimulants Clonidine Folic Acid (helpful to 50%) mood stabilizers are useful (Tegretol, Epival)	Males developmental disability sensory integration problems motor coordination impaired hyperarousal/ disinhibition Females mild degree of DD learning disabilities organizational problems math difficulties tangential speech mood lability	Hyperarousal Sensitivity to sounds and other stimuli Avoidance of crowds Social isolation Behaviour and personal- ity difficulties Poor eye contact Easily misdiagnosed as Autism
Phenylke- tonuria Autosomal recessive Inherited from both parents Affect both males and females in equal numbers	If untreated: phenylalanine toxicity dopamine reduction developmental disability eczema seizures ataxia motor deficits behavioural problems	Newborn screening prevents the disorder If missed: developmental delay delayed milestones When treated even later, many symptoms disappear ADHD OCD Autistic like features	Treatment phenylalanine restricted diet (special formula) diet discontinuation before 10 yrs of age creates delays in development discontinuation after 10 yrs. may be tolerated, but subtle psychological consequences exist Personality and temperament disturbance Medication stimulants not very good	Visual-motor deficits are prevalent Fine motor speed is diminished Problems in mental processing Executive functioning (ability to retain informa- tion and use it later for problem-solving) is diminished When "cognitive load" is increased, children be- come confused	Factors influencing outcome: age at initial treatment lifetime level of metabolic control current dietary status Psychiatric and learning comorbidity causes social problems and behavioural issues Agoraphobia/depression common in adolescence/ adulthood

Syndromes/ Genetic Causes	Diagnostic Features	Behavioural Phenotype	Medical/Psychiatric and Medication Vulnerabilities	Psychological Vulnerabilities	Social Implications/ Vulnerabilities
Seizure Disorder Due to inherited or acquired neurodevelopmental abnormalities Sudden discharge of electrical activity in the brain that results in alteration of sensation, behaviour, or consciousness	Epilepsy is condition of recurrent seizures Epileptic syndrome is characterized by a recurrence of consistent symptoms and behavioural manifestations	Impairment of attention/ concentration Ability to learn and remember material is impaired Decreased reaction time and decreased psychomotor speed Impairment and exaggeration of sensory input	Sensory misperceptions/ hallucinations Objects are perceived as smaller (micropsia) Visual misperceptions (auras) usually olfactory or gustatory Abdominal and epigastric sensations Cephalgic auras and as sharp pain on the head easily misdiagnosed as migraines The above features are experienced by these persons as dissociations and not as real events Medication antiepileptics anticonvulsants	Disturbances of executive functions Sensory systems are affected Motor systems are affected Language skills and reading acquisitions are affected Dysnomia and anomia are linked to complex partial seizures and are easily misdiagnosed as memory problems Hypergraphia is common Circumstantiality of written and spoken language is evident	Specific personality characteristics have been associated with various forms of seizure disorders hyperactivity/inattention rigidity obsessive compulsive features developmental delay specific learning disabilities All of the above features can be misinterpreted as laziness, stubbornness, and eccentricities

Appendix B

Common Psychiatric Conditions Associated with Developmental Disabilities

Jane Summers, Chrissoula Stavrakaki, Dorothy Griffiths, and Thomas Cheetham

Common Psychiatric Conditions Associated with DD	Behavioural Profile	Medical/ medication Vulnerability	Psychological Vulnerabilities Associated with Psychiatric Condition	Social Implications/ Vulnerabilities

Attention deficit/ hyperactivity Disorder
 • *3-5% of school age children*
 • *Genetic cause, possibly a single dopamine transported gene and a variation in the dopamine (D4) receptor gene*
 • *Exposure to various toxins in utero, such as alcohol, cocaine, lead and vapour abuse can lead to this syndrome*
	• *Impulsivity*
	 • *Inattention*
	 • *Hyperactivity*
	 • *Difficult temperament*
	 • *Low frustration threshold*
	 • *High intensity of response*
	 • *70% develop school problems*
	 • *Speech and language problems*
		• *ADHD is associated with many other genetic/ chromosomal disorders:*
		   Fragile X
		   Turner Syndrome
		   Tourette
		   neurofibromatosis
		   glucose-6-deficiency
		   sickle cell anemia
		   phynylketonuria
		   Noonan's Syndrome
		   Williams Syndrome
		 • *Dysfunction of multiple control systems, including:*
		   vocal, sensory, social, associative, appetite, motor, behavioural, communicative, and affective control systems
		 • *Medication*
		   amphetamines
		   SSRI's
		   Clonidine
		   antipsychotics
		   mood stabilizers
			• *Tasks with deficits that are found in ADHD are:*
			   perceptual tasks
			   logical search task
			   memory tasks
			   motor control tasks
			   perceptual tasks
				• *Within school settings appear to be hampered by their temperaments and learning deficits*
				 • *They are isolated and are not chosen by their peers as friends*
				 • *They experience either high incidence-low impact problems/ poor social acceptability*
				 • *Low incidence/ high impact problem/ social rejection*

(table continues)

Common Psychiatric Conditions Associated with DD	Behavioural Profile	Medical/ medication Vulnerability	Psychological Vulnerabilities Associated with Psychiatric Condition	Social Implications/ Vulnerabilities
Anxiety Disorders •Genetics are commonly linked with panic disorder but less in other types of anxiety •They seem to be related to genetics of the mood disorders •Developmental disabilities are frequently associated with anxiety disorders as a result of genetic and environmental factors	•Fears •Panic attacks •Feelings of impeding doom •Excessive worries •Obsessions •Compulsions •Specific social phobias	•SSRI's (antidepressants) •TCA (antidepressants) •Antianxiety medication Benzodiazepine Beta-Blockers •Behavioural techniques •Cognitive behavioural therapy •Family therapy •Psychodynamic therapy	•May burden the already limited cognition of the person with DD •Symptoms of fears and/or worries become identifiable as an anxiety disorder when: the worry/fear impairs functioning; presence of autonomic symptoms	•Anxieties and fears can become so incapacitating that they interfere with the person's life •Social or specific phobias are very common in the person with DD •OCD is very frequent in these persons •Social isolation/ withdrawal •Behavioural problems such as tantrums, S/B, aggressivity, common
Learning Disabilities •Most prevalent group of neurobehavioural disorders affecting children and adults •Strong genetic component •Extremely heterogeneous group of learning problems with diverse characteristics - genetic - environmental insults of the brain - environmental lack of stimulation	•Severe LD 1-5% •Mild 4-5% •Reading disabilities- dyslexia •Math deficits •Graphomotor production •When combined math and reading disabilities is the manifestation of a single pattern of neurocognitive deficit (26% due to genetic factors)	•Comorbidity with ADHD •Major social emotional manifestation in small subgroup of LD •Comorbidity with specific syndromes, e.g., Turner, Klinefelter, Fragile- X, Tourette, neurofibromatosis •Comorbidity with sex chromosomal observations •Comorbidity with other neurocognitive disorders •Medication is only used for the comorbid disorders •Psychoeducational and behavioural program	•Boder (1973) described 3 groups: dysphonetic type (lacks word analysis) dyseidetic type (impairment in visual memory) mixed type •Bakker (1979) described: L-type read quickly– make errors of omission P- type (read slowly– make time consuming errors)	•Attention deficits •Social isolation •Behavioural disorders •Anxiety disorders •Depressive disorders •Disruptive disorders •Adolescent years of a person with LD can be very tumultuous

Glossary of Terms

Adverse effects

Noxious, undesirable effects that occur at doses normally used for treatment. The term side effect could be desirable or undesirable effects of medication, which are not necessarily noxious. However, these terms are used interchangeably in this book. We focus on the side effects that are significant, either due to their frequency or their potential dangers.

Akathisia

Inability to sit still or an intense subjective sense of restlessness.

Alzheimer Disease

Noninfectious progressive brain amyloidosis associated with dementia and eventual death.

Amnesia

Loss of memory, due to injury of the brain or severe emotional trauma. There are several kinds of amnesia including: *anterograde amnesia, retrograde amnesia,* and *transient global amnesia.*

Analgesics

Pain-relieving substance (e.g., aspirin, acetominophen).

Anorexia

Lack or loss of appetite for food.

Antabuse

Trade name for disulfiriam, drug used in the treatment of alcoholism. Reactions can be severe and life-threatening if a patient on this drug ingests alcohol.

Anticonvulsant medications

Any drug used to counteract seizures.

Antihypertensive medications
> Drug treatment to lower blood pressure

Antipsychotic
> Drugs used to treat a psychosis.

Antisocial
> Conduct indicating indifference to another's person or property; criminal behavior, dishonesty, or abuse are examples. IN DSM-IV, childhood or adolescent antisocial behavior and adult antisocial behavior are included as "other conditions that may be a focus of clinical attention."

Anxiety disorder
> In DSM-IV, this category includes panic disorder without agoraphobia, panic disorder with agoraphobia, agoraphobia without history of panic disorder, specific (simple) phobia, social phobia (social anxiety disorder), obsessive compulsive disorder, post traumatic stress disorder, acute stress disorder, generalized anxiety disorder (includes overanxious disorder of childhood), anxiety disorder due to a general medical condition, and substance induced anxiety disorder.

Asperger's Syndrome
> One of the PDDs, characterized by eccentric and obsessive interests, social skill deficits, and impaired social interactions, gross motor clumsiness, and speech and language difficulties.

Ataxia
> Result of failure of muscular coordination or irregularity of muscle action; one can see that the patient has abnormal manner of walking.

Attention Deficit Hyperactivity Disorder (ADHD)
> A child whose inattention and hyperactivity- impulsivity cause problems may have this disorder. Symptoms appear

before the age of 7 years and are inconsistent with the subject's developmental level, and are severe enough to impair social or academic functioning. In the predominantly inattentive type, characteristic symptoms include distractibility, difficulty in sustaining attention or following through on instructions in the absence of close supervision, avoidance of tasks that require sustained mental effort, failure to pay close attention to details in schoolwork or other activities, difficulties in organizing activities, not listening to what is being said to him or her, loss of things that are necessary for assignments, and forgetfulness in daily activities. In the predominantly hyperactive-impulsive type, characteristic symptoms are that the person inappropriately leaves his or her seat in classroom or runs about, fidgets or squirms, has difficulty engaging in leisure activities quietly, has difficulty awaiting turn in games, and blurts out answers to questions before they are completed.

The two types may be combined.

Audiologist

One who studies hearing, especially of impaired hearing that cannot be corrected by drugs or surgery. Audiologists can train people to overcome problems related to hearing loss, but cannot treat infection or disease.

Augmentation

Addition of another medication to improve the initial partial therapeutic response to a medication.

Autistic disorder

In DSM-IV, this disorder is described as the presence of markedly abnormal or impaired development in social interaction and communication and a markedly restricted repertoire of activity and interests.

Benzodiazepine

Class of psychoactive drugs; included are the tranquilizers

diazepam (Valium) and chlordiazepoxide (Librium) and the sedative-hypnotic fluazepam (Dalmane). Tolerance and dependence can occur with prolonged use of benzodiazepines.

Bioethics
The ethics of medical and biological research and practice.

Biopsychosocial Model
Case formulation approach that includes consideration of the possible effects of multiple biomedical and psychosocial factors on occurrence and recurrence of challenging behaviours.

Bipolar disorder
Mental disorder characterized by episodes of *mania* and *depression.* One or the other phase may be dominant at a given time; the phases may alternate; or aspects of both phases may be present at the same time. Treatment is by psychotherapy and by the use of antidepressants and tranquilizers. Also called *manic-depressive psychosis.*

Buspirone (Buspar)
Medication used in the treatment of anxiety disorders and for short-term relief of symptoms of anxiety.

Canadian Charter of Rights and Freedom
Laws regulating Human rights and freedoms.

Cardiologist
A specialist in heart function.

Case Formulation
Developing an understanding of the instigating, vulnerability and maintaining conditions pertinent to the challenging behaviour of concern.

Cerebral Palsy
loss or deficiency of muscle control due to permanent, nonprogressive brain damage occurring before or at the time of birth. Symptoms include difficulty in walking, poor coordination of the limbs, lack of balance, speech or

other sense organ difficulties, and sometimes developmental disability.

Chronological Age

Age of a person expressed as the period of time (e.g., months, years) that has elapsed since birth.

Chromosomal Abnormalities/Aberrations

Any change in the normal structure or number of chromosomes, often causing physical and mental abnormalities.

Clonidine

Antihypertensive (trade name Catapres) that may be administered either orally or via transdermal patches; has also been used in heroin and alcohol withdrawal with variable success. Adverse effects include drowsiness, dry mouth, and, rarely, sexual dysfunction.

Communication disorders

In DSM-IV, this group includes expressive language disorder, mixed receptive/expressive language disorder, phonological disorder, and stuttering. In developmental expressive language disorder, scores on tests measuring expressive language development are below those on tests of nonverbal intelligence and those on tests measuring receptive language. Symptoms may include limited vocabulary, speaking only in the present tense, errors in recalling words, and developmentally inappropriate sentence length. Mixed receptive/expressive language disorder is characterized by testing performance on both receptive and expressive language development batteries that is substantially below performance on nonverbal intellectual batteries. The typical manifestation is an inability to understand words or sentences.

In DSM-IV, this group includes expressive language disorder, mixed receptive/expressive language disorder, *phonological disorder*, and *stuttering*.

Comorbidity

The simultaneous appearance of two or more illnesses, such as the co-occurrence of schizophrenia and substance abuse or of alcohol dependence and depression. The association may reflect a causal relationship between one disorder and another or an underlying vulnerability to both disorders. Also, the appearance of the illnesses may be unrelated to any common etiology or vulnerability.

Congenital Heart Disease

Structural defect of the heart or great vessels or both, and is present at birth. Any number of defects may occur, singly or in combination. They result from improper development of the heart and blood vessels during the prenatal period. Congenital heart defects occur in about 8 to 10 of every 1000 live-born children in the U.S.A.

Contributing stimulus events/conditions

Establishing operations or setting events. When present, a specific behaviour is more likely to occur when the person is exposed to the triggering event for that behaviour.

Craniotomy

surgical opening into the skull, performed to control bleeding, remove tumors, or relieve pressures inside the cranium.

Criminal Code of Canada

Laws adopted by Canada against criminal activity.

Cryptorchidism

Undescended testes in men.

Deinstitutionalization Movement

movement to move individuals who have intellectual disabilities into the community.

Delirium

State, usually brief, of incoherent excitement, confused speech, restlessness, and hallucinations. It may occur in high fever, ingestion of certain toxic substances and drugs, nutritional deficiencies, endocrine imbalance, or severe stress (e.g., postoperative) or mental illness. Treatment includes bed rest, quiet, the use of drugs to quiet the patient, and treatment of the underlying causes.

Dementia

Progressive state of mental decline, especially of memory function and judgment, often accompanied by disorientation, stupor, and disintegration of the personality. It may be caused by certain metabolic diseases, drug intoxication, or injury, in which cases it is often reversible once the underlying cause is treated. If, however, it is caused by a disease such as Alzheimer's disease, by brain injury, or by degeneration brought about by aging, the changes that occur are irreversible.

Dependence on psychoactive substances

Cluster of behavioural, psychological, and physical symptoms which indicate that the person has lost control over the use of substance, and continues to use it despite experiencing its adverse consequences.

Depo Provera

Injection derived from the female hormone, progesterone used as birth control for women. Provera may be given if a female's menstrual periods have stopped or a female hormonal imbalance is causing the uterus to bleed abnormally. Provera may also be prescribed to treat endometriosis, menopausal symptoms, premenstrual tension, sexual aggressive behaviour in men, and sleep apnea

Depression

Psychiatric illness sometimes known as unipolar disorder.

Developmental Disability

Disorder characterized by a significant subaverage intellectual functioning with onset before age 18 years, and concurrent deficits or impairments in adaptive functioning.

Dexedrine

Trade name for a central nervous system stimulant (dextoamphetamine sulphate) used in the treatment of narcolepsy and some attention deficit disorders in children; it was formerly used to reduce appetite in the treatment of obesity. Adverse effects include restlessness, increased blood pressure, and other signs of central nervous system excitation, as well as nausea and loss of appetite. It must be used with caution by persons with hypertension, cardiovascular disease, and many other disorders. It is potentially addictive.

Dissociative disorder

In DSM-IV, this disorder is described as a disruption in the usually integrated functions of consciousness, memory, identity, or perception.

Down Syndrome

Most common form of developmental disability, occurring as a result of a chromosomal abnormality.

DSM-IV

Diagnostic and Statistical Manual of Mental Disorders (DSM-IV). The American Psychiatric Association's official classification of mental disorders. The fourth edition was published in 1994.

Dual Diagnosis

When one has both a developmental disability and a mental illness. For example a person with Down Syndrome who also is depressed.

Dysarthria

Impairment of speech articulation due to disturbances of muscular control resulting from central or peripheral nervous system damage.

Dysmennorhea

Painful menstruation; primary dysmennorhea, intrinsic to the process of menstruation and not the result of any other disease or condition is very common. Typically cramp-like pain in the lower abdomen, sometimes accompanied by nausea, vomiting, intestinal cramps, and other discomfort begins just before or with the onset of menstrual flow. Secondary dysmennorhea, caused by a specific disorder (e. g., uterine tumor, pelvic infection), is usually marked by pain that lasts longer and is often accompanied by bladder or bowel discomfort; treatment depends on the underlying cause.

Dysphoric Mood

Unhappy and unsettled mood.

Dysrhythmia

Disturbance of rhythm.

Eating Disorder

Marked disturbance in eating behavior. In DSM-IV, this category includes anorexia nervosa, bulimia nervosa, and eating disorder not otherwise specified.

Echolalia

Automatic, meaningless repetition of another's words, sometimes occurring in schizophrenia, autism, and other neurological and mental disorders.

Encopresis

An elimination disorder in a child who is at least 4 years of age, consisting of repeated passage of feces into inappropriate places (clothes, floor, etc.) and not due to a general medical condition.

Enuresis

An elimination disorder in a child who is at least 5 years of age, consisting of repeated voiding of urine into bed or clothing, and not due to any general medical condition.

Epilepsy
   Neurological disorder characterized by recurrent episodes
   (ranging from several times a day to once in several years)
   of convulsive seizures, impaired consciousness, abnormal
   behavior, and other disturbances produced by uncontrolled
   electrical discharges from nerve cells in the brain. Trauma
   to the head, brain tumor, chemical imbalances, and other
   factors may be associated with epilepsy, but in most cases
   the cause is unknown. Common types of epilepsy are
   grand mal and *petit mal.*

Erotophobia
   Fear of being loved or in love.

Extroversion
   Directing of feelings and interests toward external things
   and the outside world rather than toward oneself.

Facilitation
   Makes a situation easier.

Feeding Disorder
   Persistent failure to eat adequately, with loss of weight or
   failure to gain weight, and not due to an associated gastrointestinal or other general medical condition. In DSM-IV,
   feeding disorders include pica and rumination disorder.

Fragile x syndrome
   The most common form of inherited mental retardation,
   due to unusual X-linked pattern related to trinucleotide repeat expansion.

Functional Behavioral Analysis
   Generated assessment of problematic behaviour(s) so that
   the root cause can be addressed.

Galactorrhea
   Excessive flow of milk; secretion of milk not associated
   with breast-feeding, sometimes a sign of a pituitary gland
   disorder.

Gastrointestinal Disorders
Pertaining to the stomach and the intestines.
Geneticist
Medical specialist for genetic conditions.
Geriatrician/ Geriatrics
Medical specialty that deals with the problems of aging and the diagnosis and treatment of diseases affecting the aged.
Global Assessment of Functioning Scale (GAF)
Assessment for an individual's overall functioning level, according to DSM-IV (APA, 1994).
Grand-Mal
Type of seizure during which the patient becomes unconscious, may develop bluish discoloration (cyanosis) of the skin and lips due to oxygen lack, and experiences convulsions involving the entire body; also called a generalized seizure. Type of epilepsy characterized by recurrent grand mal seizures.
Gynecomastia
Enlargement of the breasts.
Hyperpyrexia
Excessive high blood temperature.
Hypertension
Persistently high arterial blood pressure; it may have no known cause or be associated with other diseases.
Hypogonadism
Small testes, small penis, inadequate testosterone production
Hypomania
A mild form of mania.
Hypothyrodism
Underproduction of thyroid hormones by an underactive thyroid gland. About 1 percent of the adult population suf-

fer from hypothyrodism. It is most common in elderly
women, although it occurs at all ages and in both sexes.
Treatment consists of replacement therapy with the thyroid
hormone thyroxine; in most cases hormone therapy must
be continued for life.

Hypotonia
Loss of muscle tone.

Iatrogenic
Pertaining to condition caused by medical diagnostic procedures, or exposure to medical treatment, facilities, and
personnel (e.g., corticosteroid-induced *Cushing's syndrome*).

Idiosyncratic language
Characteristic or manner unique to an individual or group;
peculiar or unusual variation, as in an unusual reaction to a
drug or a particular food.

Impairment/Disability/Handicap
Injury, disability, functional loss, or weakened state (e.g.,
hearing impairment).

Infantilization
Condition in which childhood characteristics (mental and/
or physical) continue into adulthood.

Introversion
Tendency to turn one's interests inward toward the self.

Instigating factors
Stimulus events that signal occurrence of challenging behaviours. Instigating stimulus conditions represent two
subclasses of event: triggering and contributing. Terms
such as cue, prompt, discriminative stimuli, primary instigating event, setting events, establishing operations, secondary instigating event, priming event, and triggering event
are used by various authors to refer to antecedent instigating factors, but with different technical or descriptive

meanings.

Integrated Biopsychosocial model

Case formulation model that identifies that specific roles assumed by each modality of influence (bio-psycho-social), and the manner in which these may interact in influencing the occurrence, severity, variability, and recurrence of challenging behaviours. The model facilitates maximum integration of biomedical and psychosocial treatments designed to influence the multiple conditions producing the behavioural challenges.

Intelligence Quotient (I.Q.)

A numerical rating determined through psychological testing that indicates the approximate relationship of a person's mental age (MA) to chronological age (CA).

Interdisciplinary

Members of two or more disciplines using a systematic and intergrated approach based on their respective body of knowledge working together to achieve common goals.

Klinefelter Syndrome

Genetic disorder , occurring only in males, where individuals are tall and thin with relatively long legs. Individuals appear physically normal until puberty, when signs of hypogonadism become evident.

Learned helplessness

A condition in which a person attempts to establish and maintain contact with another by adopting a helpless, powerless stance.

Luteinizing hormones

Hormone produced by the *anterior pituitary gland* that stimulates the secretion of sex hormones by the testes and ovaries and is involved in the production of mature spermatozoa and ova.

Maintaining factors

Reinforcing events or consequences that follow behaviours and increase the likelihood that those behaviours will occur again on future exposure to the instigating conditions.

Mental Illness

Conceptualized as a clinically significant behavioral or psychological syndrome or pattern that occurs in an individual, and that is associated with present distress or disability, or with a significantly increased risk of suffering death, pain, disability, or an important loss of freedom.

Multidisciplinary

A number of disciplines dealing with the same issue.

Myoclonus

Produced by shock-like contractions of a muscle or group of muscles.

Negative Reinforcement

Occurs when an unpleasant or aversive event is removed following behaviour. This contingent removal increases the likelihood that the behaviour will be repeated.

Nephrogenic Diabetes Insipidus

Excessive urine excretion due to failure of the kidney to reabsorb water.

Neuroleptic

Drug that produces neurolepsis (altered state of consciousness marked by indifference to the surroundings; quiescence).

Neurological disorder

A disorder that affects the nervous system.

Neuropathy

Any disturbance in the peripheral nervous system.

Neurologist

A physician with postgraduate training and experience in the field of organic disease of the nervous system whose professional work focuses primarily on this area. Neurologists also receive training in psychiatry.

Noonan Syndrome

Genetic disorder associated with congenital cardiac defects and short stature.

Obsessive Compulsive Disorder

An anxiety disorder characterized by obsessions, compulsions, or both, that are time-consuming and interfere significantly with normal, routine, occupational functioning, usual social activities, or relationships with others.

Occupational therapy/therapist

An adjunct therapy that utilizes purposeful activities as a means of altering the course of illness. The patient's relationship to staff and to other patients in the occupational setting is often more therapeutic than the activity itself.

Oppositional Defiant Disorder

A pattern of negativistic and hostile behavior in a child that lasts at least six months. Symptoms may include losing one's temper; arguing with adults or actively refusing their requests; deliberately annoying others; being easily annoyed, angry, and resentful; and being spiteful and vindictive.

Optic chiasm

Pertaining to the eye or to the sight. X shaped structure; the crossing of two lines or tracts, crossed fibers of the optic nerve.

Orthopedist

One who studies the branch of surgery concerned with disorders of the bones and joints and their associated muscles, tendons, and ligaments. Orthopedic surgeons perform many tasks, including setting broken bones and putting on casts; treating joint conditions such as dislocations, slipped disks, arthritis, and back problems; treating bone tumors and birth defects of the skeleton; and surgically repairing or replacing hip, knee, or finger joints.

Orthostatic hypotension

Abnormally low blood pressure with a fall in blood pressure upon standing.

Ovarian Dysgenesis

Defective embryonic development.

Paraphilia

One of the major groups of sexual disorders; in DSM-IV, this group includes exhibitionism, fetishism, frotteurism, pedophilia, sexual masochism, sexual sadism, voyeurism, and transvestic fetishism. The paraphilias are recurrent, intense sexual urges and sexually arousing fantasies that involve nonhuman objects, children, or other nonconsenting persons, or the suffering or humiliation of oneself or the sexual partner.

Pedophilia

One of the paraphilias, characterized by marked distress over, or acting on, urges involving sexual activity with a prepubescent child who, more often than not, is of the same sex.

Pervasive Developmental Disorder (PDD)

Characterized by severe and pervasive impairment in several areas of development: reciprocal social interaction skills, communication skills, or the presence of stereotyped behaviour, interests, and activities.

Phenotype

Observable characteristics of an organism that are the result of a genetic makeup and environmental factors.

Phenylketonuria (PKU)

Genetic disorder in which the absence of, or a deficiency in, the enzyme necessary for conversion of the amino acid phenylalanine into tyrosine causes the accumulation of

phenylalanine and its metabolites in the body and in the
urine. Symptoms include eczema, an unusual odor to the
urine, and progressive mental retardation. Treatment includes a diet low in phenylalanine. The test is referred to
as the PKU test.

Phonology
The phonemes or sounds of a language.

Physiotherapist
Uses techniques to prevent or reduce joint stiffness and to
restore muscle strength in the treatment of arthritis or after
a fracture has healed. Methods of treatment used by
physiotherapists include exercises, which may be active or
passive, massage, heat treatment, cold, water and electrical
currents. Physiotherapists help treat severe respiratory diseases and care for the respiratory needs of patients who are
on ventilators or recovering from major operations.

Polyembolokoilamania
Insertion of foreign objects into bodily orifices.

Positive reinforcement
Occurs when a pleasant or desired event follows the behaviour. As a result, the likelihood is increased that that behaviour will be repeated.

Post Traumatic Stress Disorder (PTSD)
An anxiety disorder in which exposure to an exceptional
mental or physical stressor is followed, sometimes immediately and sometimes not until three months or more after
the stress, by persistent re-experiencing of the event,
avoidance of stimuli associated with the trauma or numb-
ing of general responsiveness, and manifestations of increased arousal. The trauma typically includes experiencing, witnessing, or confronting an event that involves ac-
tual or threatened death or injury, or a threat to the physical
integrity of oneself or others; with an immediate reaction

of intense fear, helplessness, or horror.

Prader-Willi Syndrome

Genetic disorder due to deletion on paternal chromosome 15. This affects both males and females and all races. The major characteristics include hypotonia, hypogonadism, hyperphagia, cognitive impairment and difficult behaviors. One major medical concern is morbid obesity.

Priapism

Prolonged, painful erection.

PRN's

Prescriptions, abbreviation for *pro re nata,* meaning as needed.

Prozac

Medication prescribed for the treatment of depression. Prozac may also be prescribed to treat Obsessive Compulsive Disorder. It has also been used to treat obesity and eating disorders.

Psychiatrist

Physician who specializes in psychiatry; the branch of medicine concerned with the study of prevention and treatment of mental illness and emotional and behavioural problems.

Psychologist

One who specializes in the study of mental activity, especially as it relates to behaviour. Psychologists make an important contribution to the diagnosis and treatment of mental and emotional problems. They play a major part in the use of behaviour therapy, counseling, and in the treatment of behaviour disorders affecting people with a mental handicap.

Psychopathology

Study of the causes and manifestations of mental disorders.

Psychotherapy
> Treatment of mental disorders by psychological, not physical techniques. There are many approached to psychotherapy including *behavior modification, psychoanalysis,* and *group therapy.*

Psychotropic Medication
> Any drug prescribed to stabilize or improve mood, mental status, or behaviour.

Reciprocal relationships
> Relationships in which both parties benefit.

Recovery
> Coping with the reality of who you are and moving on to live a satisfying life.

Resilience
> The capacity to withstand problems and rebound from them with minimal negative impact, adaptability, durability, stamina.

Rett Sydrome
> Genetic disorder virtually always diagnosed in females, thought to be caused by an X-linked dominant gene that is lethal to male offspring who inherit it. Characterized by stereotypical hand movements, impaired expressive and receptive language, and psychomotor delay.

Risperidone/Risperdal
> Medication prescribed to treat mental illnesses, such as schizophrenia.

Ritalin
> Trade name for the central nervous stimulant methylphenidate, used in the treatment of attention deficit disorders in children.

Rubinstein-Taybi Syndrome
> A genetic disorder due to deletions on the short arm of chromosome 16.

Savant Syndrome

Very high intellectual ability in certain areas, such as math, music, etc.

Schizoid

Personality disorder described in the DSM-IV. Character-ized by detachment from social relationships and restricted emotional range in interpersonal settings. Some examples are that the person neither desires nor enjoys close relation-ships, prefers solitary activities, appears indifferent to praise or criticism, has no (or only one) close friend or confidants, and is emotionally cold or detached.

Schizophrenia

Group of idiopathic psychotic disorders characterized by both positive and negative symptoms associated with dis-turbance in one or more major areas of functioning such as work, academic development or achievement, interper-sonal relations, and self-care. Positive symptoms may in-clude delusions, which may be bizarre in nature; hallucina-tions, especially auditory; disorganized speech; inappropri-ate affect; and disorganized behavior. Negative symptoms include flat affect, *avolition, alogia,* and *anhedonia.* Dura-tion is variable: DSM-IV requires a minimum of six months.

Schizotypal

Characterized by a combination of discomfort with and re-duced capacity for close relationships, and cognitive or perceptual distortions and eccentricities of behavior. Pos-sible manifestations include odd beliefs or *magical think-ing* inconsistent with cultural norms; unusual perceptual experiences including bodily *illusions;* odd thinking and speech; no (or only one) close friends because of lack of desire, discomfort, with others, or eccentricities; and per-sisting, excessive social *anxiety* that tend to be associated with paranoid fears rather than negative judgments about oneself.

Sedation

Induced state of reduced activity and excitability; a state of calm and quiet, sometimes with sleep.

Seizure

Convulsion or sudden attack cue to various causes, including epilepsy.

Sign

Any objective evidence (i.e. perceptible to the examining health care worker) of a disease or of a patient's condition.

Sleep Apnea

Temporary failure to breathe while sleeping.

Smith-Magenis Syndrome

Genetic syndrome due to deletion on chromosome 17. This syndrome is associated with speech delay, psychomotor and growth retardation and behavioural problems.

Social support

Positive or helpful interpersonal transactions or exchanges that occur between people.

Somatoform Disorders

Group of disorders with symptoms suggesting physical disorders, but without demonstrable organic findings to explain the symptoms. There is positive evidence, or a strong presumption, that the symptoms are linked to psychological factors or conflicts. In DSM-IV, this category includes *somatization disorder, conversion disorder, hypochondriasis, body dysmorphic disorder, and pain disorder.* Included as a somatoform disorder not otherwise specified is *pseudocyesis.*

Speech Language Pathologist

A specialist dealing with speech and language

Statutes
    Laws
Sterilization
    Surgical procedure in which a man or woman is rendered
    incapable of reproducing; in males the procedure is vasec-
    tomy; in females a form of tubal ligation.
Stimulants
    Agent, such as a drug, that activates or increases the activ-
    ity of a body part or system. Amphetamines and caffeine
    are central nervous system stimulants.
Stimulus complex
    Certain behaviours occur only when several instigating
    conditions combine to trigger the challenging behaviour.
    A particular stimulus event on its own may be insufficient
    to trigger the challenging behaviour and become effective
    only when included in a stimulus complex, that is, when
    combined with other instigating conditions.
Substitute Decisions Act
    Act referring to the rights of a substitute decision maker to
    give consent.
Symptom
    Any subjective evidence (i.e. perceived by the patient) of a
    disease or of a patient's condition.
Symptomatic Behavior
    Exhibiting the symptoms of a particular disorder.
Tachycardia
    Abnormally rapid heart rate.
Tardive Dyskinesia
    Difficulty, distortion or impairment of movement (facial
    and or extremities) produced by long-term administration
    of antipsychotic drugs.
Tolerance
    Decrease in susceptibility to the effects of a drug due to its

continued administration; in other words, it takes an increased amount of the medication in order to produce the same effects.

Tourette's Syndrome

Tic disorder consisting of multiple motor and vocal tics that occur in bouts, either concurrently or separately, mostly every day or intermittently over a period of twelve months.

Triggering stimulus

Events/conditions are called discriminative stimuli or antecedents. The challenging behaviour does not occur unless the triggering events are present. A number of different events may serve a triggering event role for any specific challenging behaviour.

Turner Syndrome

Genetic disorder specific to females, consisting of sexual infantilism, short stature, and webbed neck.

Williams Syndrome

Genetic syndrome associated with a distinct behavioural phenotype, caused by an abnormality on chromosome 7.

World Health Organization (WHO)

Established in 1948 as an agency of the United Nations with responsibilities for international health matters and public health. Its headquarters are in Geneva, Switzerland. Its other functions include sponsoring medical research programs, organizing a network of collaborating national laboratories, and providing expert advice to its 160 member states on matters such as health service organizations, family health, and mental health.

Index

Page numbers in italics are terms located within case examples